VOLCANO
IN
PARADISE

VOLCANO
IN
PARADISE

Phil Davison

Methuen

Published by Methuen 2003

1 2 3 4 5 6 7 8 9 10

Copyright © 2003 by Phil Davison

The right of Phil Davison to be identified as the author of
this work has been asserted in accordance with the Copyright,
Designs and Patents Act 1988.

First published in 2003 by Methuen Publishing Ltd
215 Vauxhall Bridge Road, London SW1V 1EJ
www.methuen.co.uk

A CIP catalogue record for this book is available
from the British Library.

Methuen Publishing Reg. No. 35643167

0 413 77184 9

Printed and bound in Great Britain by
Creative Print and Design (Ebbw Vale), Wales

Contents

For Arlette

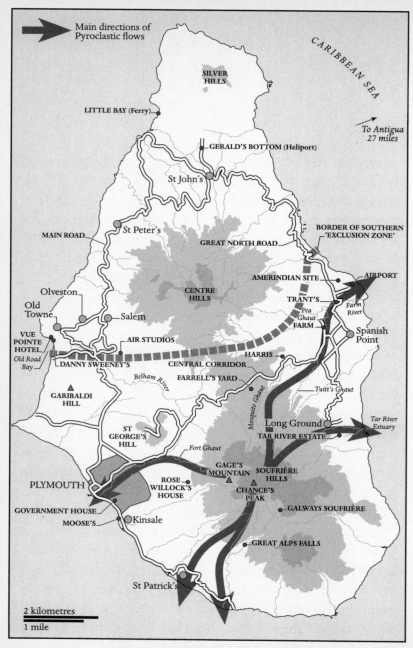

Montserrat, September 2002

Preface

In 1979 the American pop singer Jimmy Buffett, aglow from his first big hit, '(Wastin' away again in) Margaritaville', sat astride a warm mountaintop rock on the British island of Montserrat in the Caribbean. He was between recording sessions at the island's Air Studios, newly built by the former Beatles producer George Martin, so he and his backing musicians had hiked up to one of the island's tourist attractions, Galways Soufrière, for a picnic.

Martin had decided Montserrat (both 't's are pronounced and the accent is on the final syllable) was the perfect hide-away where pop artists like Buffett, the Rolling Stones, Paul McCartney, Eric Clapton, Elton John, Dire Straits and The Police could record, then walk down the streets without attracting a second glance. Or even a first. To the mostly black, laid-back locals, fame counted for nothing. They were also among the friendliest folks Martin had ever come across. He took to the place so much he bought a mansion as a holiday home.

Jimmy Buffett loved the Caribbean too, and he wanted a catchy song with a calypso flavour for his new album. He gazed down from the lush green mountain, towering over the picturesque village of St Patrick's, towards his anchored 50-foot ketch, *Euphoria II*. In the air was the smell of sulphur from the fumaroles, or steam vents, that gave this ring of mountains their name, the Soufrière (Sulphur Spring)

Hills. The sulphur was sweetened by the aroma of strong
Caribbean ganja being passed around the musicians.
Buffett didn't call his group the Coral Reefer Band for
nothing. Inspired by the steaming vents, and perhaps the
spliffs, he scribbled down some lyrics:

> Now I don't know, I don't know,
> I don't know where I'm a-gonna go
> When the volcano blow.
> Ground she movin' under me,
> Tidal waves out on the sea . . .

When local backing musicians helped his band record it at
Martin's studios below, they had a good laugh. 'Jimmy,
man, de mountain no blow. De mountain she dead, man.'

'The Mountain', as locals collectively called Galways,
Chance's Peak and the rest of the jagged ring that made up
the Soufrière Hills, was looked on by the islanders as a
gentle green giant. It had lush jungle-clad slopes, waterfalls,
panoramic views towards Antigua or Guadeloupe, and rare
flora and fauna that brought visitors to an island so small
that it was left off most maps. Geologically, The Mountain
may have been made up of volcanic rock, but that was
ancient history. It was, the islanders assumed, extinct. It
hadn't erupted in recorded history and never featured on
any list of world volcanoes.

The year after Buffett's calypso-style song came out on
the album to which it gave its name, *Volcano*, Mount St
Helens in the US state of Washington erupted, killing 57
people and laying waste to a massive area of natural
beauty. It was a disaster that brought the danger of volcanoes home to the developed world. This wasn't ancient

history. This wasn't Vesuvius. This was the unstoppable power of Nature in our own backyard, in our own era.

Mount St Helens changed the way the experts looked at volcanoes. They took closer interest in volcanic mountains in Japan. They looked at them in Indonesia, they studied them in Hawaii, Colombia, Mexico, the Philippines. But few thought to look at the islands of rum and reggae, of cricket, coral and calypso. Down in the Caribbean, it was assumed, nothing could stop the carnival.

In 1995, 16 years after Jimmy Buffett scribbled his song on its slopes, the gentle green giant awoke. In terms of world news, Montserrat's mountain put the little island on the map. Then, quite literally, it attempted to wipe it off again.

As a foreign correspondent, I covered events in Montserrat from 1995, when life on the idyllic island abruptly changed. What follows is a true story, based on interviews with islanders and others, eyewitness accounts, including my own, and government and scientific reports. The islanders did their utmost to share their recollections with me. I only hope I have done them justice.

This is a story of brave, God-fearing folks whose ancestors were brought to the Caribbean islands in chains but who refused to flee when a force more ruthless than the old colonial masters, mighty Nature itself, challenged their resilience and faith anew. May their paradise be not lost, but merely interrupted.

P. D.
Twickenham, England
September 2002

I

The black and the green

It started off like just another day in paradise. Already at dawn, a warm breeze rippled through the coconut palms. Shimmering waves reshuffled sands of silky volcanic black. But the 11,000 souls who inhabited the island officially known as Montserrat, British West Indies, and nicknamed 'The Rock', knew this particular day would just keep getting better. Today would be party time in paradise.

The date was Friday 17 March, St Patrick's Day 1995. The islanders of Montserrat may have been a long way from Tipperary, their skin as black as the island's ebony sands, but they celebrated this day as much as anyone in Ireland or beyond. Referring to its lush green mountains and its early Irish settlers, Montserrat billed itself justifiably to tourists as 'The Emerald Isle of the Caribbean'. It was the only country in the world outside Ireland itself, including the United States, where St Patrick's Day was a public holiday. On this Caribbean island, St Pat's Day celebrations started a week in advance to allow the party to build up steam. That made it second only to Christmas. Montserratians loved Jesus so much they stretched out his birthday celebrations for a month.

The little British colony was formally governed by Her Majesty the Queen through her representative, His Excellency the Governor, a British civil servant who still dusted off his white colonial uniform, swan-feathered pith helmet and sword on ceremonial occasions. His friends and staff just called him 'H.E.' Montserrat had remained, by pragmatic choice in the Sixties, a Crown colony while bigger islands like Jamaica and Antigua grabbed their independence from their former masters.

On the few maps where it appeared, Montserrat resembled a teardrop, as though shed by neighbouring Antigua 27 miles to its windward north-east. Perhaps, according to local folklore, that was because of the pain these islands had suffered through centuries of annual hurricanes. To passing aircraft at night, the little island sparkled like a wayward diamond, dangling a little loose from the necklace of islands known as the Lesser Antilles. From Antigua, on a clear day, it looked like a three-spined iguana, its landscape marked by three highland ranges rising in height from north to south. They were the craggy Silver Hills in the narrow north, the rolling Centre Hills and the lush green ring of jagged Soufrière Hills in the south, at the base of the teardrop. The latter, topped by Chance's Peak, towered 3,000 feet over the port and capital, Plymouth, and over the most populated villages, the most fertile farmland and the leading tourist sites.

This was also the only place in the world, Ireland included, which had a government-organised official Pub Crawl as part of the St Patrick's Day celebrations. It had started the night before, 16 March, with coachloads of drinkers starting in a coordinated tour. They were less coordinated as they straggled into the village of St Patrick's, focal point of the celebrations, for the day's first event, 'dawn on the lawn', a hangover-postponing breakfast washed down by the islanders' beloved Guinness.

Local radio broadcaster Rose Willock, known as 'The Voice of Montserrat', had had to skip the Pub Crawl. She had the dawn shift at the island's only radio station, Radio Montserrat, more often referred to by its callsign ZJB, but she needed no alarm clock. In Montserrat, dawn didn't break, it erupted. The all-night symphony of beeping tree frogs, crickets and grasshoppers gave way to a cacophony of cocks, donkeys, howling stray dogs, the ripping growl of the island's unique 'mountain chicken' (a giant frog), the swish of rabbit-like agoutis through the bush, and the waking song of shoreline egrets, frigate birds and the rare, magnificent national treasure, the Montserrat oriole. And that was before the reggae, calypso, 'soca' or gospel music kicked in from every loudspeaker in every household. Waking up was not a problem. Staying in bed was.

Rose drove her Suzuki hatchback down from the two-storey villa she had built two years earlier at Upper Amersham, on the slopes below Chance's Peak. The moon had just paled to make way for dawn as she rolled down her car window to taste the air perfumed by hibiscus and oleander, salted by a light sea breeze. Pearly-eyed thrasher birds played their usual game of chicken in front of her wheels. On the car radio was the voice of her fellow islander Alphonsus Cassell, known to the music world as 'The Mighty Arrow', singing his best-known hit, '(Feelin') Hot, hot, hot'. Rose smiled. She remembered the baby-faced Alphonsus as a schoolboy in Plymouth, scribbling satirical calypso songs about his teachers, and later honing his vocal skills with the local gospel and folk group, the Emerald Community Singers.

Arrow had made his first dollars importing and selling overcoats to Montserratians emigrating to cold, foggy

England. He started with a clothing store in Plymouth. Now he was known worldwide as King of Soca, the up-tempo soul-calypso beat. But between world tours he came back to live quietly on the island, run his Plymouth clothing store, Arrow's Man Shop, and frolic in the arrow-shaped swimming pool at his luxury villa.

This St Patrick's Day morning, Rose Willock was swathed in one of her trademark rainbow outfits of African influence, but with extra emphasis on green. Rose was in her forties, with the powerful good looks and physical presence of a Winnie Mandela, but with warm rather than intimidating eyes behind her giant-framed spectacles. She was an experienced broadcaster, trained at the BBC's World Service headquarters at Bush House in London and at Deutsche Welle in Germany. On the air, she had something of the broadcasting delivery of Oprah Winfrey, one of the women she admired most. She had once been dubbed 'the Caribbean Oprah', but to most islanders she was simply the Rose of Montserrat.

Below her as she drove, she saw the twinkling lights of the pastel toytown capital, Plymouth, proud of its reputation as 'the cleanest town in the Caribbean'. Further south, dappled reflections from the ocean etched out the clifftop village of St Patrick's, in the area where she had gone to nursery and primary school. Off shore, she could see the billowing white square sails of a magnificent tall ship. Its nightlights were still twinkling as it eased towards Old Road Bay to drop anchor. Must be the windjammer MV *Fantôme* or its sister ship the *Mandalay*, she thought, coming in from Florida. It would be bringing in a load of sunburnt cruise tourists for a day of windsurfing or coral reef scuba diving. Some would simply sink into hammocks strung between mango trees and sip golden rum on the beach. The thought made Rose smile. She had not forgotten the recent lean years when tourism had ground to a halt and the cruise ships stayed away. That was down to the deadly Hurricane Hugo in 1989.

Rose could imagine the cruise-line tourists stepping on to Old Road Bay's beach. They'd see the fine black sand, remove their shoes, then discover the hard way that black sand retained far more heat than the golden version. She could picture them now, hopping painfully towards the shade of the palms. Poor souls, she thought, then laughed at the unintended pun.

Rose was headed for the ZJB studios below Lovers' Lane in Plymouth to open the show 'Good Morning, Montserrat'. But by mid-afternoon she and almost everyone else on the island would be jammed into the narrow streets of St Patrick's, a village of only 50 or so scattered houses, or several hundred people, for the big party later in the day. It was not so much for the love of Ireland or its patron saint. On Montserrat, the celebration had a double meaning. It was at least as much a celebration of being black as of being green. She would remind her listeners of that when she went on the air to encourage them to join the party.

Christopher Columbus spotted Montserrat on 11 November 1493, on his second voyage to what he thought were the Indies. Its serrated peaks reminded him of a mountain range near Barcelona, so he named it after a monastery there, Santa Maria de Monserrate, believed by some to be the site of the legendary Holy Grail. He claimed the little island for Spain in passing but was told by his 'Indian' guides, rightly or wrongly, that there were

5

neither riches nor people on what they called *Alliouagana,* the 'Isle of Thorns'. He was also anxious to ride the trade winds on to the new colony of Hispaniola, so neither he nor his men went ashore. Had they done so, Montserrat might have become a Spanish-speaking cousin of Cuba, Puerto Rico or the Dominican Republic.

As it happened, the island lay untouched for almost 140 more years. It was in 1632 that the first European settlers arrived, a group of some 800, mostly Irish Catholics, who had been forced off the nearby island of St Kitts by its English rulers. It was a convenient way for the Protestant English to quarantine the unwanted Catholics. Irish men and women who sailed to the West Indies fleeing Protestant persecution back home had run into it again in a tropical setting.

Within a year, as word spread that a little island called Montserrat had become a safe haven for Catholics, more sailed down from the new North American settlement in Virginia to escape Protestant persecution up there. It was little more than a decade after the Pilgrim Fathers had set sail from the original Plymouth, bigotry among their baggage. Hundreds more Irish, as well as Scottish Covenanters, were shipped to Montserrat in chains after Oliver Cromwell's successes in Ireland and Scotland in the mid-seventeenth century.

The Irish Catholics were shipped out to the new English colonies manacled together on lower decks, in conditions little better than those of the African slaves who followed them in the second half of the seventeenth century. Historians estimate that more than 100,000 Irish men and women, from all walks of life, were shipped out in the 1650s alone, branded as 'dangerous rogues, rebels or vagabonds'.

Tens of thousands of children were taken from their Catholic parents and shipped out as slaves, to be converted to Protestantism. Those who tried to flee had the letters FT – fugitive traitor – branded on their foreheads.

Other Irish Catholics, without work or food at home, sailed out voluntarily, in return for the cost of the voyage and their keep, as unpaid indentured servants. Although Montserrat was run by the English Crown, by English or wealthy Irish Protestants, and was nominally Anglican by faith, Irish Catholics were soon the majority, albeit a powerless one.

The ruling class built up Plymouth as the capital and port. The Catholics built up their own settlements on the white cliffs below the western slopes of the Soufrière Hills and gave their villages names such as Kinsale and St Patrick's. For many years they had to worship in secret. Priests came to them from other islands, disguised as fishermen or merchants, and held secret Mass among the elephant ear plants, heliconia and thick ferns of The Mountain, on Chance's Peak or in the lush, deep gorge beyond. Thus began Montserrat's unique Irish legacy – black folks with Irish surnames, Irish place names, Irish-influenced jigs and music. And the celebration of St Patrick's Day among coconut palms and mango trees, so far in every way from the original Emerald Isle.

Rose Willock, director of ZJB Radio, was black, like almost all Montserratians, descendants of African slaves brought in after the Irish to cut sugar cane. By the time of emancipation in the nineteenth century, the Africans' descendants had become the vast majority on the island. The black slaves had arrived with no surnames, so when they were eventually emancipated in the nineteenth century they took on the names of their former masters or Irish workers. That's what turned Montserrat into a fantasy island of black folks called Riley, Roache, Blake, Daley, Galway, O'Garra, Farrell or Sweeney. Many slaves opted for the surname 'Irish' itself. Most retained a touch of Irish brogue and a smattering of words and phrases from the original Emerald Isle. The lighter skin and facial features of some islanders showed they had mixed Irish-African blood.

As always, Rose Willock had helped organise this St Patrick's Day's activities and had designed costumes for the traditional re-enactments of the island's history. Like all her compatriots, she hoped the day would prove a symbol of the island's rebirth. Montserrat had been virtually flattened by Hurricane Hugo in 1989, suffering damage to 95 per cent of its homes and tourist installations. A banking scandal the same year, with the closure of a couple of hundred 'brass-plate' banks for suspected money-laundering, had shaken investors. Only now, six years on in 1995, was the island feeling back on its feet. The buildings were repaired, the tourists had returned and honest dollars were flowing in. The calypso was back and so were the smiles. Rose tapped her fingers on the steering wheel instinctively as Arrow sang:

> O-lay, o-lay, o-lay, o-lay,
> Feelin' hot, hot, hot,
> Me mind on fire, me soul on fire,
> Feelin' hot, hot, hot . . .

Pushing 6 a.m., the sun had already seeped over the horizon and was waking the nearby islands of Antigua and

Guadeloupe. Rose couldn't yet see it. The green peaks of the Soufrière Hills were still projecting serrated shadows over Plymouth and the village of St Patrick's on the island's western shores. 'The Mountain' was more than just the high point of the island's scenery and the biggest tourist draw. It was a reassuring presence, protecting most island homes from the Atlantic trade winds. With its swirling mists and ever-changing shades of green, it seemed like a living, breathing being, with the hint of a benign smile when tickled by the sun, but occasionally it went into a huff, burying its head in dark clouds. Whatever its mood, it was visible from most of the island. Its green slopes and deep ghauts (pronounced 'guts', the local name for ravines) snaked down like scratch marks directly to Plymouth, St Patrick's and the entire south. You got the impression that if you rolled a painted Easter egg from the 3,000-foot Chance's Peak it would tumble down the contours of the big ravine known as Fort Ghaut all the way to Plymouth and plop into the ocean.

Rose drove on down into Town. That's what everyone called Plymouth, just 'Town'. It was, after all, the only place arguably bigger than a village, housing just over half the island's 11,000 residents. Even at dawn on a public holiday, the broadcaster stuck to the one-way traffic system through the deserted narrow streets of pastel-painted shops and businesses. She didn't have to. There were no traffic signs here. Locals learnt the hand-me-down system and moved aside with an understanding wave to tourists who inevitably drove the wrong way. Rose didn't have to run any red lights either. There were none on the island. Who needed them? Politeness was the rule of the road. Or, as islanders preferred to put it, 'Maximum respect, man.'

'The only crime here,' they were fond of saying, 'is stealin' time.'

Rose drove past the Evergreen Roundabout, the town's main intersection linking the three principal roads and serving as something of a minibus terminal. Not even six o'clock and already there were a dozen people lounging on the stone wall around the sturdy ficus tree everyone called the Evergreen. The tree was thought to date from the nineteenth century and was considered the symbolic heart of town, a small-scale Piccadilly Circus. 'Meet you at the Evergreen,' people would say.

Everyone on the island knew Rose. In fact, they all pretty much knew each other by name, or more often by nickname. Everybody had one. There was 'Never Me', 'Moose', 'Galvanised' and 'Garlic Mouth'. Then there was 'Rapier', 'Mountain Man', 'Monkey Erick' the bar owner and 'Be-Beep' the taxi driver. On the narrow, twisting roads, if two passing cars didn't hoot at each other in greeting, you knew one driver's horn must be out of order and the other had probably closed his eyes for a quick prayer between curves.

The elderly men under the Evergreen were 'limin'', what Americans would call shootin' the breeze, beneath the thick horizontal branches that became a giant parasol against the tropical sun later in the day. The shade of the tree was the town's main limin' spot, the equivalent of the Spanish plaza or the English village green. Some say the term harked back to the days when Montserrat produced some of the world's best lime juice and plantation workers used to gossip while they peeled. Bottled as 'Montserrat Lime Juice', the drink became fashionable back in Britain and the Navy found it helped prevent scurvy among sailors. That's why the sailors, and later Britons in general, were branded as 'limeys' in some of the old colonies.

The men under the tree were arguing about cricket, specifically the state of the West Indies team. That was far more important than politics or the price of a loaf. 'Ahl-right, Rose?' they called in near-unison, the standard greeting. Rose was busy admiring the tree itself, a symbol of the island's survival and resurgence after Hurricane Hugo. She and the radio station had helped lead a 'Save the Evergreen' movement after Hugo's 150-mph gusts toppled the ancient tree in 1989. Almost miraculously, the fallen trunk, though horizontal, had grown new branches. It was now far from the most aesthetic tree in the world, twisted in an odd L-shape. But it was growing again and it was green. Even the trunk was bright green today, but that was down to the emerald bunting, cardboard shamrocks and leprechauns strung around it for the party.

Rose noted that the tree had already grown back to the height of a single-storey building. She smiled. Ever green. A survivor. Just like the islanders themselves. Not even the worst Nature could throw at it – and Hugo was mean – had been able to kill that tree. And surely Nature had nothing worse to deal out than 150-mph winds.

Hurricanes were something Rose Willock knew a bit about. Her soothing voice had kept the islanders from panicking during Hugo and maintained the island's only link with the outside world. It was a scary time. Rose prayed she'd never have to go through anything like that again.

Plymouth, named after the English port from which the Pilgrim Fathers set sail in the Mayflower, had changed little during the twentieth century. It did have a brand new, $30-million port and jetty to accommodate small cruise ships, but the harbour was not deep enough for the gigantic floating-resort liners that could disgorge thousands of tourists at nearby Antigua. Montserratians (the word rhymes with 'fashions' rather than 'nations') preferred it that way. They felt they got a better class of tourist.

Four narrow streets ran roughly parallel with the ocean – Marine Drive, Strand Street, Parliament Street and Evergreen Drive. The cluster of shops and businesses within an area of some 300 by 400 yards was bordered in the south by George Street which ran down to the seafront from the lower slopes of The Mountain alongside Fort Ghaut. On Upper George Street was the Glendon Hospital, the only one on the island, where Rose and most of her compatriots had first seen the light of day. It had just been rebuilt and endowed with multi-million state-of-the-art equipment that would make it the most modern in the Caribbean. But the new building had not yet opened. (An engraved stone in an older building showed that it had been inaugurated by Princess Anne on 15 December 1973.) A brand new public library and new government and parliament buildings, as yet unused, were further signs of Plymouth's post-Hugo rebirth.

On the southern edge of town a tiny stone bridge crossed the mouth of Fort Ghaut, connecting the capital with the coast road to Kinsale, St Patrick's and villages beyond. On the other side of Plymouth, to the north, were a series of lush hillocks dotted with villas – St George's Hill, Cork Hill, Richmond Hill, Garibaldi Hill – then the Belham River valley. North of the valley was the central coastal belt, with the village of Salem and the luxury villas at Old Towne, Olveston and Woodlands, most of them flanked by swimming pools. Among them was Olveston House, George Martin's getaway mansion. Then came the winding road to the craggy, less populated north. Despite the tiny size of the island, few southerners ventured up north to the poorer hamlets of St Peter's, Carr's Bay, Sweeney's, St John's and the unfortunately-named Gerald's Bottom. They were only a few miles from Plymouth but the road was a narrow, serpentine roller-coaster. Northerners in Montserrat were looked on somewhat as highlanders are in lowland Scotland.

There were only two other 'main roads', also narrow, twisting affairs. One ran down the east coast, from the northern hamlets to the tiny seaside Blackburne airport. This was hyperbolically billed as the Great North Road. The other cut across the island from Plymouth, along the northern foothills of The Mountain, to the windward east-coast villages and the airport. They called it the Central Corridor and it was the road most tourists saw first.

The lightening sky was repainting the pastel facades of Plymouth's wooden-shuttered Georgian buildings as Rose Willock drove past. Outside the red-roofed Public Market, women were laying out a colourful tableau of breadfruit, mangoes, guavas, spiny green christophines, pineapples, soursop and pawpaw on the zig-zag green stone counters. She passed Kevin West's little Paradise photo and arts studio and postcard shop, where tourists snapped up West's fine paintings or his varied photo images of Chance's Peak, sometimes a serene green, sometimes capped in mist or cloud, always there but never the same. West had snapped that mountain from every angle, in its every mood. Or every mood it had displayed so far.

Beyond the Evergreen Tree, on Church Road outside the

island's only secondary school, the first real event of the St Patrick's Day celebrations was about to start: the dawn 'Freedom Run', a four-mile road race to St Patrick's village. Rose left her own car, climbed into the radio station's yellow Toyota mobile studio van and went on the air. Her voice, as always, was rich and mellow, its Caribbean lilt adding melody to that eloquent regional use of English that puts many in the mother country to shame.

'Good morning, Montserrat! Well, folks, a very good morning to you and listen up. As you know, today is the Big Day, St Patrick's Day, when we celebrate our Irish and African heritage. I'm down here at the Freedom Run, just about to start, the first of today's events, symbols of our ancestors' abortive efforts to gain freedom from their white colonial masters way back on March 17 in the year of 1768.' Rose hardly had to tell the islanders that the day's celebrations were about more than their part-Irish heritage. Every schoolchild knew that on St Patrick's Day 1768, while their white masters, many of them Irish, were drunk on rum and whiskey in the name of their patron saint, a group of black slave plotters attempted to take over Government House and win their freedom. Wielding sugar-cane machetes, sticks, stones and the odd musket or sword stolen from their masters, they might have succeeded and changed the course of Caribbean history had a white seamstress from Liverpool not tipped the masters off. The plot was rumbled and the nine ringleaders hanged from coconut palms on the seafront as a deterrent.

'Our ancestors tried to win their freedom against all the odds,' Rose Willock continued softly. She was black and proud. Nelson Mandela was one of her role models and her long-time ambition was to make the pilgrimage to his former cell on Robben Island. But she had no animosity towards Her Majesty's white Governor or the island's white expats. Few islanders did. They had, after all, chosen to remain a British colony, and mainly-white tourism was their livelihood. 'So let us remember today, as we celebrate St Patrick's Day in our special way, that our freedom did not come easily. It came at a price,' she told her listeners.

'We also celebrate our Irish heritage, still evident in the place names we know so well – Cork Hill, Kinsale, Galways, Farrell's – and in all those surnames which we carry – Hogan, Ryan, O'Brien, and the list goes on. Our shamrock is proudly displayed at Government House and in our passports. And, of course, less seriously, there's our tendency to flout authority.

'Yes, folks, so much to celebrate, so much to remember, so much to ponder. Let's join in all the activities planned for today – the Freedom Run, the cricket match in St Patrick's, the Slave Feast and, of course, then it will be time for the grand finale, the street jump-up where you can dance the evening away to reggae, calypso and soca.' In the Caribbean, a jump-up is a street dance. Vertical movement is as much a question of space as style. 'Get out there and enjoy yourselves,' said Rose.

Outside her ZJB studio van, Winston 'Kafu' Cabey, who ran Kafu's Auto Parts shop in Plymouth's Wapping district but was known around the Caribbean for his radio phone-in motoring show, 'Drivetime', held the starter's flag at the ready. Kafu was from St Patrick's. As a boy, he used to guide tourists up The Mountain to the picturesque Great Alps waterfall where he would earn some pocket money by carrying the frail or faint-hearted over slippery rocks to get behind the 80-foot cascade. Further up, on Galways

Soufrière, where Jimmy Buffett was inspired to write his volcano song, Kafu would show tourists how to boil an egg by lowering it in a bag into one of the steaming hot sulphur springs.

Kafu was chatting to one of the Freedom Runners, Theo Matthew, a lithe, fit young fireman known around the island as '2Pac'. 2Pac loved American rap singer Tupac Shakur and he loved his own mother, Felina. Not surprisingly, the rapper's 'Dear Mama' was his favourite song. Tattooed on his left arm, inside a heart, was '2Pac for ever'. He was one of 14 firemen on the island, usually on stand-by duty at the little Blackburne airport. It was an airstrip, really, on the eastern, windward side of The Mountain beside Trant's village and a recently-uncovered pre-Columbian Arawak Indian archaeological site.

2Pac's ambition was to be a search-and-rescue officer, but here on Montserrat, there was hardly ever anyone to search for, anyone to rescue. There was the odd airport emergency, the landing gear stuck on an incoming light aircraft, maybe a little bush fire or a rum-sodden English tourist stuck in a toilet pan. But that was about it. His mother, Felina Celestine, was from the island of Dominica but had brought him to Montserrat as a month-old baby. She helped her sister Isolyn and brother-in-law Harry Lewis work a tiered plot of tomato, carrot and pumpkin patches and a small banana plantation at Farrell's Yard on the northern slopes of the Soufrière Hills.

2Pac was taking this road race seriously. He was beginning to get a reputation as a runner-up in the mini-marathons (the island didn't have enough road to host a full marathon) and the regular round-the-island relays. Alongside him at the start on this St Patrick's morning were a fellow black islander he knew only by his nickname, 'Ghost', and a young white student.

There wasn't a racist bone in 2Pac's lean 165-pound frame, but since the Freedom Run was all about emancipation from the colonialists he didn't relish being beaten by one of the white students from the island's grandiosely-named American University of the Caribbean. It wasn't really a university. It was a private, offshore medical school for 300-odd young Americans, whose rent and purchasing dollars made up one third of the island's income. Most of all, 2Pac wanted to win for his mother. When Kafu lowered the starter's flag, the young fireman ran like the wind, with Ghost on his shoulder and the white man close behind.

They ran through Plymouth, stray dogs snapping at their heels. Passing Barclays Bank, they had a lone spectator. William Daley, a friendly homeless man known to everyone as Never Me, gave 2Pac a wave. No one knew how he got the name, just that he had returned 'a little disorientated' from a long spell in England and now slept on the seafront behind the bank. But he was well-liked and lived on donated food, cigarettes and bottles of Guinness.

The runners crossed the little stone bridge over Fort Ghaut and passed Moose's Seaquarium, a seafood restaurant built on a bougainvillea-draped jetty jutting out into the ocean at Kinsale. It was ramshackle but picturesque, getting its name from the fact that you could admire tropical stingray, picasso or parrot fish in the crystal-clear shallows while eating their less fortunate cousins. The owner, Wilford 'Moose' Meade, didn't bother staffing the bar. You helped yourself and left what you thought was fair.

2Pac was leading as the runners turned up the steep, winding road to St Patrick's, above cliffs that could have been used to shoot scenes from *Ryan's Daughter*. Dodging groups of donkeys that refused to budge, he threw a glance up at The Mountain. It now appeared black and menacing against the backdrop of the sun's white early light. The young fireman was momentarily mesmerised. He barely noticed the white student come alongside, forge ahead and cross the finishing line in St Patrick's first. 2Pac came second and Ghost was third. The young fireman congratulated the winner but he was disappointed. Second again. It was getting to be a habit. He looked back up at Chance's Peak. The first twinkling arrows of sunlight were filtering over its western slopes. It was as though The Mountain was winking.

2

The Green Flash

By mid-morning on St Patrick's Day, Plymouth's tall spindly white War Memorial, the first landmark tourists sighted from afar as they sailed towards the harbour, was throwing long shadows across the palm-lined seafront, Marine Drive. Known to locals as the Clockstand, it was a 60-foot white belltower on four lanky concrete legs, commemorating the Montserratians who fought for the colonial power in two world wars. Its upstart little clock dared to chime the same tune as London's Big Ben.

Older locals remembered watching Queen Elizabeth II, the island's Head of State, place a wreath at the memorial to great pomp and fanfare in 1966. The governor of the time, Dennis Raleigh Gibbs, was all dressed up in his fine white uniform, plumed hat and sword and the local police band did their best to stand in some sort of formation and play 'God Save the Queen' in something close to a single key. The governor, his royal boss and her entourage were rare white faces in those days before foreigners, mostly wealthy Britons and North Americans, got wise to this corner of paradise.

Today the islanders gathered alongside the monument, on the small lawn known as Artillery Park and edged by old English naval cannons, for the morning prayers and speeches that officially opened St Patrick's Day. A clutch of furry brown mongrel dogs lay around a red steel old-style English phone box, bemused by this sudden invasion of their space but too lazy to protest. That phone cabin, containing what was the first and at one time the only phone on the island, was another landmark and the favourite lounging spot for the strays. There were always chicken bones or other scraps tossed to them by the drivers at the nearby taxi rank. The forefathers of these unique and cuddly creatures, known as Montserrat Island Terriers, were first brought over by the Irish in the seventeenth century. Appropriately, most of them had green eyes.

The leader of the island's tiny local government, Chief Minister Reuben T. Meade, presided over the ceremony, accompanied by his wife, Methodist pastor Joan. The chief minister, a slim, sporty former agriculture economist who studied finance and banking at Bradford University, had gone into politics reluctantly, angered by the government's feeble response to rebuilding after Hurricane Hugo. He was 38 years old when elected in 1991. At the War Memorial on this St Patrick's Day, he led a ceremony in honour not so much of Ireland's patron saint but more of the black slave heroes of the ill-fated 1768 uprising.

Father Larry Finnegan, standing alongside the chief minister, was not black. More a mottled pink, really. But he was loved and respected as dearly as anyone else on the island. He was a giant of a man, six foot two, with a shock of white hair, and was priest at the St Patrick's Roman Catholic Church. The church was not in the village of that name but in Plymouth itself, a landmark on George Street next to Fort Ghaut. This was a big day for Father Larry. Not only had he been asked to lead prayers at the seafront ceremony, but it was also his birthday. He was born in

Dublin on St Patrick's Day, 1937. He had turned a youthful 58 today and was feeling at peace with the world.

The big priest was a long way from home but not in his thoughts. He had prayed privately earlier in the morning for peace in the troubled north of the original Emerald Isle. Back in the Northern Ireland town of Armagh, where an evangelising bishop called Patrick had built a tiny stone church 1,550 years earlier, peace was in the air on this St Patrick's Day. For the first time ever in Northern Ireland, a Protestant Boy Scout carried the flag of St Patrick, flanked by two Catholic Scouts, in a parade through the troubled town. In a province long riven by sectarian violence, that was not far short of a miracle.

The previous day, on Capitol Hill in Washington DC, President William Jefferson Clinton had taken a risk and made history by shaking the hand of Gerry Adams, leader of Sinn Fein, the political wing of the Irish Republican Army. Father Larry Finnegan hoped that handshake might augur the beginning of the end of the Troubles which had plagued his native island for a quarter of a century. Looking from the War Memorial, up the green slopes of The Mountain to Chance's Peak, he thanked God that this other Emerald Isle, his new home out in the Caribbean, was peaceful.

Having sensed an anti-colonial, though far from aggressive mood at the previous year's celebrations – his first St Patrick's Day on the island – His Excellency the British Governor Frank Savage and his wife Veronica planned to remain conspicuous by their absence at most of the day's events. Not the best day to celebrate the colonial heritage, he decided. The white ceremonial suit, plumed helmet and sword would remain in the wardrobe at Government

House, his official residence on the road south from Plymouth to St Patrick's. 'Veronica and I have a soft spot for St Patrick's village,' he told a group of visiting Irish and other journalists. 'We're both Catholics and we sometimes attend Mass in the village. But at last year's events, they acted out a pageant in which the Brits were the baddies. So I thought they might prefer to celebrate it themselves without me this year.' Diplomacy, after all, was what he was paid for.

While his colonial predecessors were being verbally bashed just up the road, the governor and his wife hosted a coffee morning for the visiting journalists and a Canadian diplomat new to the region. Government House, a green and white, mostly wooden Victorian gabled mansion built in 1908 and described in tourist guides as the most picturesque house in the Caribbean, sat overlooking Plymouth among magnificent gardens the governor and his wife had lovingly recultivated. Tourists were allowed through the gates to admire the gardens during daylight hours. To get a degree of privacy, the governor had been forced to build an office in a corner of the grounds.

In his Whitehall days, Frank Savage had been the typical, anonymous 'man in a grey suit'. Now 52 years old, he'd worn suits all his working life. Even out here in the stifling tropics he kept up the habit, although he sometimes replaced the grey with white. The suit and tie went with the job. He'd joined the Foreign Office at the bottom of the ladder at the age of 18. That meant he was wearing dark suits and carrying a briefcase and umbrella in the swinging Sixties while his contemporaries were wearing kaftans, dropping acid and going psychedelic down the King's Road to the sounds of Hendrix or the Stones.

Actually, Frank Savage was a bit of a rocker at heart. But the suit went with the job.

Savage was a working-class lad from Preston, Lancashire. His family couldn't afford to send him to university so he left school with only a handful of O-levels. That, of course, was more than enough to get him into the civil service where he found himself among upper-class former public schoolboys with plummy accents and similar qualifications. But, as a contemporary poet put it, the times they were a-changin', and the government was trying to dilute the public schoolboys with a working-class element in order to be seen to be fair. And, of course, to win votes. 'Being working-class was something I've never really been concerned about,' Frank Savage often said. 'It's what you learn on the way up that's the most important.'

How far up he'd gone depended on your point of view. But he'd certainly been around. After starting in the Passport Office in Whitehall, he'd served as a diplomat in Cairo, Washington DC, Aden, Düsseldorf, Peking and Lagos, with the usual stints back in London in between to bring him back to the reality of life without maids, chauffeurs, gardeners or a port and sherry allowance.

Aden had been no pushover. It was the only Communist Arab nation and many of the world's terrorists were being trained there at the time. Later, as consul for the whole of China from 1982 to 1986, he had helped negotiate the tricky Anglo-Chinese consular treaty and was one of the first British diplomats to venture to Lhasa in Tibet. 'They had what they called "sky burial" over there,' he told his St Patrick's Day visitors. 'That's when human vagabonds come round, take your body up a mountainside, chop you into little chunks and scatter you so that the local birds can come down and take you to heaven. I thought the relatives of missing Brits might not take too kindly to that, so I arranged a repatriation deal for British bodies instead.' Frank Savage was not a man without humour.

He was the first to admit that his posting to a tiny Caribbean island in 1993 at the age of 50 did not make him *la crème de la crème* of the diplomatic corps. 'Okay, these were never coveted posts. They are on the periphery,' he said. 'They are not the type of posts that mainstream career officers would covet. Quite frankly, the image of governors used to be one of people in those ridiculous uniforms doing fuddy-duddy jobs.' He obviously felt this was no longer the case. 'When they asked me to come here, the first thing Veronica and I did was get the world atlas out. But Montserrat wasn't on it. We had to buy a bigger atlas. The funny thing is I hate sea, sun and sand. I hate beaches. I've got an aversion to sand. I don't think I've been on the beach since I got here.'

So Frank Savage had gone up to Savile Row, world capital of conservative clothes, to get measured up for his official tropical governor's uniform. It was little different from the one the first governor, Anthony Brisket, had worn 350 years earlier, except perhaps a little more expensive at £5,000, including ceremonial sword and a pith helmet topped with plumed swan feathers of natural white and dyed red. He would only have to wear it a handful of times a year, for the Queen's official birthday, Remembrance Sunday, investitures and the like. 'Every time you put it on, you know the media are hoping the helmet will fall off,' he said. 'Every time you're in a parade, you know the cameras are on you and that bloody helmet.'

So the Savages had finally flown into little Blackburne

Airport, via neighbouring Antigua, in July 1993 on a cramped nine-seater Islander aircraft. Government House was being renovated, so they ended up staying for the first year in the famous but already disused Air Studios, built by George Martin on a ridge opposite The Mountain. Frank Savage may have had a bit of a grey image, but he had to pinch himself when he moved into the studios where Paul McCartney and Stevie Wonder had recorded 'Ebony and Ivory', where Dire Straits had made their breakthrough *Brothers in Arms* album, and where The Police had laid down their classic track 'Every Breath You Take'. Here, too, was where American Jimmy Buffett had recorded the lyrics that had come to him on top of The Mountain: 'Now I don't know, I don't know / I don't know where I'm a-gonna go / When the volcano blow . . .'

The governor and his wife slept in one of the adjoining villas built by Martin for the stars – and sometimes their wives, girlfriends, or perhaps the odd local lass – to relax between recording sessions. The studios themselves the Savages used for storing luggage and furniture from Government House during its renovation. The place had fallen into disuse after Hurricane Hugo knocked out power for months in 1989, leaving it without air-conditioning and wrecking the state-of-the-art sound equipment at a key time of year. 'There was no electricity for three months and our generator was destroyed,' Martin explained. 'Artists like to record their albums early, in the autumn, then tour in the summer, so we lost the whole season. I had twenty-five staff there and I couldn't afford to pay them for a year. That's also when people started to make records in their backyards and bathrooms.' So Martin moved his Air Studios operation to (generally) hurricane-free London.

Frank Savage, the lad from Lancashire, found himself governing a Caribbean island while trampling over engravings carved out on steps and walls by visiting popstars in past years. 'Looking For The Green Flash', James Taylor had scratched on a patio slab. Whether he was referring to the atmospheric phenomenon of green light in a Caribbean sunset or the Green Flash bar in Plymouth, no one was quite sure. Eric Clapton had carved out his initials on a step. It was here that the renowned guitarist had become friendly with the part-Montserratian studio manager and conceived a daughter, Ruth. Clapton later bought a home in nearby Antigua and built his Crossroads Centre for substance-abuse rehabilitation there. At Air Studios, too, Elton John met his future wife, Renata, a sound engineer. The studios could hardly have hosted two Englishmen as different as the flamboyant Elton John and Frank Savage, Her Majesty's man in the grey suit.

But by the time St Patrick's Day 1995 came around, the governor was well installed in historic Government House. His guests were seven Irish and two black American journalists, as well as Mrs Colleen Swords, the new Canadian High Commissioner. She was to be based in Barbados but had come to present her credentials to the government of Montserrat, part of her patch. As her Christian name suggested, Mrs Swords was of Irish origin. She had been fascinated to hear that black Caribbean islanders celebrated this day, so she'd timed her official visit deliberately. She'd also been delighted at seeing a shamrock in the entry stamp on her passport, and then passing through picturesque villages with names like Harris, Farrell's, Riley's Yard, Dyer's and Lee's on the Central

Corridor from the airport to Plymouth. The island's flag, she noted, depicted the lady Erin with a cross and a harp.

Mrs Swords was also fascinated by the strange behaviour of the governor's dog, Winston, named after the wartime leader. He was a Montserrat Island Terrier, a furry, light-brown mongrel who had been unceremoniously tossed over the garden walls of Government House the previous year as an eight-week-old puppy. Somebody wanted him to have a decent home. The Canadian diplomat watched Winston sit pertly on his haunches on the back terrace, whimpering and gazing up at The Mountain as though expecting someone up there to throw down a bone. Then he'd run around in circles, chasing his tail, but still looking up towards Chance's Peak. How odd, she thought. It looks as though the poor thing's mesmerised by that mountain.

By the early afternoon, St Patrick's, straddling a single, narrow, sloping road like thousands of villages in Ireland, was already packed. On their way from Government House, Colleen Swords and the Irish journalists passed through the village on their way to Galways Soufrière, below one of The Mountain's five peaks. The jump-up was already under way. Mrs Swords' designated driver, police officer Kelvin White, hooted his horn and gave a friendly wave to virtually everyone in the streets or other cars. He chatted to his diplomatic passenger about the ongoing O.J. Simpson trial in Los Angeles. He was, he said, not too impressed with the LA police department.

Constable White, from Trant's village by the airport, belonged to the anti-drugs task force. But he was often a designated police driver and later in the day would have yet another job, helping with crowd control in St Patrick's. Some of the locals might go too heavy on the Mount Gay rum. Some of the expats would, as always, go too heavy on the Guinness. And some of the local 'rasta men' – Rastafarian youths – were likely to be smoking ganja. To them, it was part of their religion. Literally: it was a sacred rite, essential to meditation. Constable White just hoped they wouldn't wash it down with too much Guinness. That could make things a little rowdy. His girlfriend, Michelle, was from St Patrick's. After his shift, at 10 p.m., he planned to change out of his uniform and enjoy the last of the jump-up with her.

Kelvin White, Police Constable Number 7, was also worried about his mother Linda, a well-known figure on the island for her work helping primary school children with special needs. Trained in Newcastle in England, she'd suffered cardiac arrest in January, had undergone major surgery the previous weekend and was recuperating at home in Trant's, directly beneath The Mountain's north-eastern rim.

A stone's throw from the Whites' home and farm was the tiny airport. Next to that was the pre-Columbian archaeological site recently uncovered while the little runway was being expanded. A group of archaeologists had just taken the bones of an Arawak Indian chieftain, dating from around 500 BC, back to the US for study. The dig had spooked the highly religious and superstitious locals. First, just the finding of a 2,500-year-old Indian on their island. It hadn't occurred to many islanders that somebody had been in the Caribbean before Christopher Columbus.

That Columbus 'discovered' the Americas, including the West Indies, is, of course, considered a joke, usually a sick one, by native Americans throughout the western hemisphere. There were millions of natives in the Americas, including possibly two million in the Caribbean, when the Italian adventurer first landed in what is now known as the Bahamas on 12 October 1492. How and when these natives had got there remains open to debate, but it is widely held that they came first from Asia across the Bering Strait from Siberia, then on down through North and Central America. (A few historians and archaeologists theorise that black Africans reached the Americas even before the Asians, perhaps even 100,000 years ago, either across the Bering Strait or even directly across the Atlantic. They base their argument largely on ancient artefacts showing figures they describe as having negroid features. It's a theory modern radical black nationalists like to cite, but the purported evidence is considered flimsy, even frivolous, by mainstream historians.)

Archaeological digs suggest Montserrat was populated by what we now call 'Amerindians' around 2,000 years before Columbus sailed by. First there had been the friendly Arawaks (some of them called *Tainos* by the Spaniards) and later the war-mongering Caribs. Both had sailed up from the South American mainland, from present-day Venezuela, in long dug-out canoes – the word comes from theirs, *kanowa* – sometimes equipped with sails.

It's possible there were still native Carib hunters on Montserrat, having driven out the Arawaks, when Columbus and his fleet passed by without landing on their second voyage in 1493. If so, it would have been natural for the Caribs to lie low. They would have gazed in awe at these 17 tall sailing ships riding in formation. On board were 1,200 men and beasts such as the natives had never seen – horses, cows, pigs, sheep, goats, cats and dogs – a miniature Spanish society headed for Hispaniola. They were also carrying something else that would change the face of the Caribbean – sugar cane, long the mainstay of the regional economy, which later begat the region's beloved rum.

It was not the Caribs but the Arawaks whom Columbus found first on the present-day Bahamas, and later on the island he named Hispaniola. They went mostly naked, grew cotton and tobacco brought from the South American mainland, barbecued fish, enjoyed a good smoke and slept in woven cotton hammocks. The Spaniards brought back Arawak words such as barbecue, tobacco and hammock. They did not bring back the natives' custom of self-inducing vomit with a stick to cleanse the body of impurities.

The Arawaks were surprisingly friendly to the Spaniards, They may have thought these were some kind of divine emissaries with their helmets, weapons and finery. But their friendliness backfired. The Spaniards insisted on 'sharing' the Arawaks' women. And they kidnapped hundreds of them to take back to Spain as slaves.

Within three decades, through murder, abuse and diseases to which they had no defense – mainly smallpox – some two million Arawaks had been reduced to a few thousand. Within a century, although a few of their South American cousins survived, the 'West Indian' Arawaks were extinct, leaving behind only some of their words, their artefacts and their bones. Among these were the bones of the chieftain found close to the home of PC Kelvin White at Trant's village during the extension of Montserrat's little airstrip in 1995.

After it became known that the 2,500-year-old bones had been dug up and shipped to the United States for study, some native Americans warned that this might not have been a good idea. A Seminole Indian chief in the US, James Billie, said the gods could have been angered by the removal of the bones. He asked his tribe's medicine men to chant ancient songs on behalf of Montserrat, 'to appease the gods of the Earth'.

Unlike the Arawaks, the Caribs did not lay down the red carpet for Columbus. That wasn't their style. To the Caribs, whose biggest settlements were on the islands of Martinique, Guadeloupe and nearby Dominica, making war came as easily as making babies. They had already driven the Arawaks north and westwards to the Greater Antilles – the Arawak men, that is. They kept the women on as wives. They may have been primitive but they were not stupid. They were also quite vain, using rocks or planks to flatten the foreheads of their children. Flat foreheads, it seems, were considered more beautiful. It was an early version of cosmetic surgery.

Columbus named these people *Kaniba*, later corrupted to 'Carib' but also the origin of the word 'cannibal'. The explorer had heard tales of 'men with dog's snouts who eat men. They behead him, drink his blood and cut off his genitals.' His understandable desire not to be castrated or barbecued may well have been the main reason Columbus left the Carib-occupied islands alone. The French and British eventually took control of those islands, though only after they had annihilated the Caribs towards the end of the seventeenth century. Unlike the Arawaks, a number of Caribs survived. Their descendants live on, mostly in Guatemala and on the island of Dominica. They do not like to be reminded that the word 'cannibal' was derived from their ancestors. But they do like to point out that the entire West Indies and its turquoise sea were named after them. On Montserrat, their main lasting legacy is their name and image on the island's favourite beer – Carib lager.

On the cricket pitch near St Patrick's primary school, the traditional St Patrick's Day match between the village team and the Emerald Wanderers got under way. Like everyone in the West Indies, Montserratians took their cricket seriously, to say the least. The local government used to give everyone the day off whenever the Leeward Islands team played in the Red Stripe series – sponsored by the Jamaican brewery – at picturesque Sturge Park on the northern outskirts of Plymouth. (Although the trade winds blow east to west, the Leeward Islands is the name given to the northern half of the Lesser Antilles chain and the Windward Islands to the southern stretch.)

At Sturge Park, Caribbean waves lapped almost across the boundary and on to the field. It was there, in 1990, that some superstitious cricket fanatics tried to get in touch with their African ancestors in the hope of ending the Montserrat team's losing streak. On the eve of a big match they held a 'jumbie dance', appealing to their 'jumbies', walking dead men akin to the zombies of African voodoo. To the pounding of African bongo drums, they asked the jumbies to smile on their team and bring them victory. The jumbies responded with a half-smile: the Montserrat team scraped a draw.

The St Patrick's Day match was not taken quite so seriously. The judgement calls by long-time English expat Richard Aspin were influenced by the bottles of 'green beer' – dyed St Patrick's Day versions of the local golden Carib lager – relayed to him during the match. When a batsman was out, Aspin, a former electrical engineer from the Pennines, raised his bottle. It didn't help, either, that the cricket field was built on the tiered slopes of The Mountain, directly below Galways Soufrière. Nothing in the village was flat. Fielders close to the boundary could not see the batsman. Infielders would shout 'Ball coming over' if a ball was headed for the perimeter. Outfield catches were not common.

A man of the people, Chief Minister Reuben Meade was well into the spirit of things. He and his wife joined in the Slave Feast, enjoying the staple fare of the slaves first brought here more than 300 years earlier – yams, breadfruit, local vegetables and wahoo fish. Meade smiled to himself at the thought that this survival food for African slaves was nowadays considered a quaint local delicacy by white tourists.

Island politics were forgotten for the day as Meade chatted with his leading rival, independent MP David Brandt, nicknamed 'The Heavy Roller' because of his build, his fast bowling, his black belt in karate and his political campaigning style. Both were enjoying the tasty local 'goatwater', the island's national dish, a watery stew of peppered goat distinguishable from Irish stew mostly by a powerful kick of golden rum. Young islanders in home-made costumes acted out historic dramas showing brave slaves standing up to nasty colonial masters wielding whips and cardboard swords. Hence the governor's decision to stay away to spare himself, his wife and his Queen embarrassment.

Among the revellers were passengers and crew from the MV *Mandalay*, the tall ship Rose Willock had seen sail in at dawn. The passengers, mostly American, had earlier been dispatching rum punches at the Las' Call beach bar north of Plymouth, or bathing in the nearby natural spa known as the Hot Water Pond. (Legend had it that the Hot Water Pond would cure rheumatism and other ailments if you tossed in a coin for its guardian spirit. It rarely occurred to anyone that the hot sulphuretted water was seeping from the underground plumbing of The Mountain.) The bar's owners, Lou and Shirley Spycalla, had abruptly closed, Caribbean-style, because they wanted to go to the party. But, equally in Caribbean style, they didn't dream of leaving their customers behind. They hired minibuses to take the cruise tourists up to St Patrick's.

Some of the *Mandalay*'s passengers continued beyond St Patrick's, guided by local teenagers, and hiked up to the island's most famous site, the Great Alps Falls, a narrow cascade where sunbeams filtered dramatically through mist and creeping vines. For ten dollars each, surefooted local boys carried the lady cruise tourists on their backs over the slippery rocks, through a jungle of ferns and elephant ear plants, to enjoy an invigorating power shower at the foot of the waterfall.

By late afternoon, the jump-up was going hot and heavy. Revellers danced in the streets or packed the village bars – Hub's, the Spreadeagle, and the Top o' the Cove, run by the aptly-named Will Irish. Father Larry Finnegan was enjoying his birthday. This is a long way from Dublin, he thought, or Whitechapel, in the east end of London, for that matter. He had worked there for the local Co-op store and Chiver's Jams before studying with the Divine Word Missionaries and being ordained as a priest in 1968.

Danny Sweeney, fisherman, windsurf legend and friend of some of the world's most famous rock stars, was resplendent in an emerald-green t-shirt. He was dancing with his long-time partner Margaret Wilson, a blonde Joni Mitchell lookalike from Sunderland in England and the mother of their chocolate-skinned little daughter Sarah, as well as with every other woman he could find. Danny had the shoulders and chest of a deep-sea fisherman but the legs of a dancer. 'I was jumpin' up, man. I danced them wives non-stop and sweated them off the floor,' the 47-year-old boasted.

If you were writing an Irish novel, you might well name one of your characters Danny Sweeney. But this Danny Sweeney was hardly typical. He was part African, part Irish and a convert to the Baha'i faith, which was founded in Persia and advocated the unity of mankind in one religion. If he wanted to worship with fellow members, he had to sail his fishing boat to Antigua, where there was a Baha'i temple. Although black, Danny certainly had the blarney, the light hazel mischievous eyes and the planet-lighting Irish smile. And he was not averse to blowing his top. 'They used to call me the most dangerous man on Montserrat,' he liked to say. He also had lighter skin than most islanders, more like a suntanned Mediterranean villager.

Danny was a lifelong fisherman but made most of his money in the tourist season from his beach watersports business at Old Road Bay, beside the Nest bar. The rickety, light-blue-painted Nest was the beach bar of the popular Vue Pointe hotel (pronounced View Point by the locals) in Old Towne, next to the golf course on the northern side of the Belham River valley where luxurious villas hid behind walls of oleander, hibiscus and bougainvillea. Hotel and bar were owned and run by local businessman Cedric Osborne, a handsome, white-moustached black version of American actor Howard Keel, and his sparkling Irish-American wife Carol, from Boston. Carol liked to point out to hotel guests – 'my houseplants', she called them – that she was seven eighths Irish. She was a Montserratian citizen now.

Danny Sweeney's windsurfing pupils read like a *Who's Who* of the rock business. He was the man who taught stars such as Sting to windsurf or took them deep-sea fishing during breaks in recording sessions at Air Studios. He had windsurfed to Antigua, 27 miles away. That was not for the faint-hearted. This was the Atlantic Ocean.

'Sting was good,' Danny told passengers from the *Mandalay*. 'Him and me, we used to windsurf to Redonda in the Eighties, when The Police were recording their *Synchronicity* album here.' He pointed to the little island of Redonda in the distance. 'That's fifteen miles each way, man. One time, me an' Alan Clark [of Dire Straits], we sail into the back of a whale. Got a bit of a shock. But that whale just keep on goin', man, and so did we. One time I give [Dire Straits'] Mark Knopfler a one-hour lesson but he vow never to get back on a board again. He tell me I inspired him to write the song "Walk of Life".' Sir Ian Percival, the late British MP, was also one of his pupils. 'He was sixty-three when I taught him to windsurf. "Keep your bum in, man," I used to shout at him. He got the hang of it pretty quick. That boy, he moved on to waterskiing when he was seventy-two.'

For his winning smile, the stars adopted Danny Sweeney. The Stones, Simply Red, Duran Duran, they all used to take him everywhere with them, to their favourite restaurant – a wooden shack called Andy's Village Place, serving chicken and chips – or the Agouti bar in Plymouth, named after the dark, furry, rabbit-like creature that roamed the island. Danny helped The Police shoot their 'Every Little Thing She Does is Magic' video in Salem Park, close to his home. And he loved to take the stars into the hills at night to chase mountain chicken. Danny was renowned for his imitation of the giant frog's call – 'rrrreeeeepppp, rrrreeeeepppp'. He would carry a flambeau, or kerosene lamp, dazzle them, then grab them round the waist. 'Their legs are slimy and strong, man. And they'll jump ten feet from your hand if you don't hold tight.' The big frogs, their legs alone a foot long, were a local delicacy, expensive, popular and tasty, hence the 'mountain chicken' nickname for what herpetologists call *leptodactylus fallax*. Danny told visitors you had to cut the veins from their legs before cooking them. So strong were they, he insisted, that even a severed leg would jump from the pot if you didn't. He wasn't joking.

The little streets of St Patrick's were trembling from the walls of giant speakers as Danny and the locals 'jumped up' and the expats tried self-consciously to *keep* up. On a makeshift stage on a low-loader outside the community centre, the Emerald Community Singers sang a mixture of the black and the green. They did Caribbean folk songs and gospel, then 'Molly Malone' and 'When Irish Eyes are Smiling'. Father Larry Finnegan grinned broadly as some of the children from his Catholic school danced an Irish quadrille. Irish folk singer and banjo maestro Mick Moloney, a long way from his native Limerick, jammed with local black 'string band' musicians. They mixed songs of sad departures from Ireland with songs of sad departures from Africa. And all the time there was a fiddle and a flute, the shuffle of a local maracas-like *shak-shak*, and the pounding of bongos and an Irish *bodhran*, the goatskin drum. It occurred to Mick Moloney that his own instrument, the tenor banjo, had never been more at home. As a lover and master of the instrument, he was well aware that the banjo originated in Africa and arrived in the United States in the hands of a slave.

Danny Sweeney's part-African, part-Irish eyes were smiling. For a moment, the banjo, fifes and flutes and bongos seemed to merge into one, the black with the green. For a moment, he felt as though he was in Africa and in Ireland at one and the same time. As though the old and the new continents had merged for one joyful day. The thought sat well with his Baha'i faith.

In the Spreadeagle bar, Theo '2Pac' Matthew, the road-running young fireman, recovered from the early morning Freedom Run, was sipping an ice-cold Jamaican ginger beer and chatting to the bar's owner, Peter Dyer, a lifelong fan of London's Arsenal football club. Dyer had returned to the island after living for many years in Riversdale Road, Highbury, a block from the team's London ground. Both men could feel the floor tremble from the music outside. The trembling reminded 2Pac of the stories older villagers used to tell of earthquakes below The Mountain that rocked St Patrick's in the Thirties, demolishing many buildings. With this music and vibration, 2Pac thought, there could be an earthquake and we'd never notice.

The dancers and revellers took a break and gathered at a spot they called the Grandstand to watch the sun go down, a tableau wildly different each day in the Caribbean. Chief Minister Meade and his wife were there; so were 2Pac and his girlfriend. Father Larry Finnegan was there, and Danny, Margaret and their little daughter Sarah. The passengers from the *Mandalay* were there, along with the ship's captain who was trying to get them back on board with little success. (It was close to midnight before he rounded them all up.) Constable Kelvin White was still in charge of 'crowd control' but was able to sneak a peak at the sunset. Also watching were popular local road haulage contractor Eddie Buffonge and his wife, Cathy, from Oxford. Among Eddie's claims to fame was the fact that he had bought the piano Paul McCartney and Stevie Wonder had used for the track 'Ebony and Ivory'.

The music stopped, but a single booming voice took its place. 'Repent! Repent! For it is not too late. God will wreak justice on those who do not heed his warnings. Repent!' It was Abraham White, a farmer from the eastern village of Harris, better known on the island as Brother Hammy. With a sign reading 'God's Messenger' round his neck, he was waving a large bible and spitting out its verses to make himself heard. 'Repent! Repent! For it is not too late! The sins of the people will be returned upon them,' he yelled. 'A great catastrophe will be visited on the island if you do not repent.'

The islanders were used to Brother Hammy, and his car with 'The Messenger' painted on the side. He would pop up wherever you might be, at a cricket match, on Old Road Bay beach, or limin' under the Evergreen Tree. He was always right in your face, warning of damnation, hellfire and brimstone. The islanders were mostly religious folks and they gave him the standard respect. But who wanted to think of hellfire or brimstone on their little paradise island?

They turned their heads back towards the west to watch the sun, a perfect sphere of glazed and glowing embers sinking purposefully like a luminous billiard ball. It was a perfect day, crisp and clear with no pollution and not a cloud in sight. The sort of day they hoped they might glimpse what the scientists called an 'atmospheric refractive phenomenon'. The islanders called it a gift from the heavens. As in Irish folklore, they believed it was sent as a fleeting promise of hope. Today, of all days, they hoped to see green.

The sky changed as swiftly as a sheet of pale crêpe paper stained by spilt watercolour paint. From the slopes of St Patrick's, islanders and tourists lowered their voices to a whisper as the orange ball hit the horizon, shrank to an ever-smaller glowing dome, then beamed as a solitary point of dazzling light. Silhouetted against it, a flock of white egrets winged their way home to the mangrove swamp at the Fox's Bay bird sanctuary. And then there it was, for the briefest of moments, radiating from the sun's last sinking rim in a fitting climax to this special day on the Caribbean's Emerald Isle. A dot of dazzling green, gone before they could blink.

The crowd cheered. They had witnessed the Green Flash.

None of them could know what was happening far below them, directly below St Patrick's, several miles below the surface of the ocean, the place from which, millions of years ago, The Mountain and the entire island had come. The earth below them was trembling but only the most sensitive of scientific instruments, and some of the island's animals and wildlife, could feel it.

Two tectonic plates, two pieces of the jigsaw that make up the Earth's crust, were grinding together. Through a new rift, molten rock from the Earth's hot interior was pushing upwards, upwards through the base and the innards of the Soufrière Mountain, turning the Caribbean ocean ground water to steam.

The Mountain was becoming a giant pressure cooker.

3

Black snow

Frank Hooper was a lifelong English copper who had started on the beat in West Sussex in 1966, the year the Queen found a gap in her schedule to visit her little colony of Montserrat. Hooper himself was something of a child of the colonial system. He was born in Jerusalem, where his father was serving in the Palestine police force under the old League of Nations mandate, but he grew up and went to school on the Isle of Wight.

Francis, as his wife Sheila preferred to call him, joined the police force on the mainland at the age of 21 and worked his way up to chief superintendent. That put him in charge of security for the political party conferences that came regularly to the seaside at Brighton. It was he who headed the uniformed police operation after an IRA bomb blew up the Grand Hotel, Brighton, where Prime Minister Margaret Thatcher was staying during the Conservative party conference of 1984.

Those were hard days for Frank Hooper. He hardly got to see his wife in their terraced cottage in Sussex and rarely had a chance to indulge his passion for sailing. By 1995, a fit and youthful 50 but already pushing 30 years in the force, he had at least one eye on early retirement. His plan was to use his sailing skills to deliver newly-built yachts from European manufacturers to the Caribbean. Wealthy buyers often preferred to skip the difficult part, crossing the Atlantic ocean.

In March 1995, Frank Hooper was munching on a leaky prawn sandwich in the Lewes headquarters of the Sussex police force when a job ad in the *Police Review* caught his eye. 'Commissioner of Police – Montserrat', it read. 'Where the hell is Montserrat?' Hooper thought. He dug out a world map, went home and asked 'Her Indoors' how she felt about going to the Caribbean. Sheila Hooper, a talented watercolourist, thought about the countless phone calls in the middle of the night, the interrupted weekends that go with being a policeman's wife. In her mind's eye, she could already see a fantasy island of sun, sea, sand and piña coladas. And telephones that don't work. Imagine a place where the police station can't get through to you in the middle of the night. No bombs. No danger. Peace and quiet. Paradise. 'Yeah, let's go for it, Francis,' she said. 'Let's do it.'

On St Patrick's Day 1995, while Montserrat was bedecked in green, Frank Hooper flew to Scotland for an interview at Abercrombie House, the dour grey concrete northern headquarters of the Foreign Office's Overseas Development Administration (ODA) in East Kilbride, near Glasgow. The ODA, under John Major's Conservative government, was headed by Baroness Lynda Chalker. Her department was responsible for the kind of overseas posting for which Hooper had applied.

The ODA was effectively a ministry. (It would later become one, after Labour's 1997 election victory, with the new title of Department for International Development and headed by Clare Short.) But it wasn't part of the cabinet. The department and Baroness Chalker were answerable to the Foreign Office. Being a copper, Hooper liked to see a clear-cut command structure. When he was filling in the job application forms, he had trouble working out who exactly did what in such a convoluted hierarchy – as, he was later to find out, did many of the ODA and Foreign Office's own staff.

At Abercrombie House, Hooper sat in the waiting room and weighed up the other five shortlisted candidates. He felt he had a strong chance. 'None of them had much idea where Montserrat was,' he told his wife. 'What worried me was, neither did the interviewers.' The final choice was made a couple of weeks later at the ODA's London HQ at 94 Victoria Street, close to Victoria Station. Montserrat's governor, Frank Savage, came back to cast the key vote in person. Savage knew immediately that Hooper was his man. He asked him to start in mid-July. Both men had reputations as hard workers, but on the trouble-free Caribbean island they were both looking forward to a spot of sailing and a round or two of golf.

Having locked up his terraced house in Hassocks, in the flood-prone plains of Sussex, Francis Gerald Hooper flew into Montserrat's tiny Blackburne airport from Antigua on a knee-crushing Twin Pioneer aircraft of LIAT airlines at 10.45 a.m. on Tuesday 11 July 1995. With him came his fine new title of Commissioner of Police, Royal Montserrat Police Force, British West Indies. With him, too, came Sheila. Her only title was Mrs Hooper, but you couldn't go without a nickname for long on Montserrat. She would soon become known to the islanders, to the couple's amusement, as Mistress Police.

They were, the Hoopers marvelled, treated almost like royalty. 'We were immediately taken into the VIP lounge at the airport,' Sheila Hooper wrote in her diary. 'The only difference with the rest of the little terminal was that the VIP lounge had air-conditioning. Oh, and it had a picture of the Queen over the ladies' and Prince Philip over the gents'. They put us into a car with the Union Jack on it. I felt like doing the royal wave. Every one of the island's 95 policemen seemed to be out along the route, snapping to attention and saluting Francis. The islanders came out into their gardens, or to their doors or windows, to get a glimpse of the new police couple. We were absolutely in awe of this beautiful, beautiful island. I thought, this is good, I'll have some of this.'

Frank Hooper was sweating in English clothes. His new tropical uniforms – virtually identical to those worn by his father in Palestine and later Malaya – were still being tailored in London. 'I walked into Gieves and Hawkes, in Bond Street, Mayfair, and asked for a ceremonial uniform that met colonial police dress regulations, with pith helmet, sword, boots and spurs,' he said. 'The shop assistant's face lit up. "Ooooh, marvellous, sir." It was like *Are You Being Served?* It cost five thousand pounds and I'd only wear it on five occasions a year. That uniform was going to cost British taxpayers a thousand quid every time I put the bloody thing on!'

Sheila Hooper dumped her bags in their new rented villa at Olveston, close to George Martin's Olveston House. A police driver took her to stock up on some food in Plymouth. 'I couldn't believe it,' she wrote in her diary. 'Here was this uniformed policeman pushing my supermarket trolley for me! Could you imagine that in Sussex?' It was on her way back that she first saw the Evergreen Tree, where men and women were limin' in the cool shade of its horizontal branches.

Under the tree that July morning, one man stood out with his blond wavy hair and beard. American missionary David Lea, from Ohio, and his wife Clover, a former hippie folk singer from Virginia, had fallen in love with the island at first sight in the mid-Eighties. 'Key West was getting too weird,' said Clover, who had a mane of thick blonde hair that plunged like a waterfall to the back of her thighs. 'When the jets started landing there, that was it. We decided to go where the avocados and mangoes fall off the trees. We were fruitheads, and when we came down here, our car would skid on fallen mangoes. We decided to put our *no* money where our mouth was, and we came on down.' They settled unusually far north, outside the tiny village of St Peter's.

As a non-denominational pastor, David Lea held services around the island, including in Her Majesty's Prison, a forbidding foreign legion-type fortress on Plymouth's seafront. It was still engraved with the date of its building – 1664. Clover ran a religious radio programme called 'Friends', popular throughout the Caribbean on Saturday mornings.

David Lea had been asked to come urgently to the Evergreen Tree that day by Joseph Buffonge, a 50-year-old tailor who had completed 17 years in HM Prison for murder, a rare crime on the island and one he insisted he hadn't committed. Lea had met him while preaching in the prison. He was, Lea noted, a good tailor who made uniforms for both prisoners and guards, and he had the gift of building fine model sailing ships. Buffonge had asked the American missionary to meet him under the Evergreen Tree and bring along a bible. He did not say why. But Lea immediately recalled that almost six years earlier, in

September 1989, the then prisoner had asked him to deliver a letter to the island's government. 'Gentlemen,' it began. 'If you do not give glory to God for the blessings, a great natural catastrophe will overtake this land.' Within two weeks Hurricane Hugo slammed into Montserrat, with catastrophic consequences.

As soon as David Lea arrived under the old tree, Buffonge whispered: 'It's going to happen again, David.'

'Oh, no, Joe, don't tell me there's going to be another hurricane.'

'No, man,' the ex-convict replied. He put his hand on Lea's bible and pointed up towards The Mountain. 'It de mountain, David. I had a dream, man. De mountain, she gonna blow. Montserrat will be brought to its knees by that mountain.'

Had he heard that conversation, Governor Frank Savage might have thought twice about going up The Mountain the following day, Wednesday 12 July. But he hadn't, and he and his wife Veronica went up Galways Soufrière for a picnic. They drove through St Patrick's, hiked through elfin forest, trumpet trees and elephant ear plants, then down into the lush gorge of ochre rocks at Galways to dangle their bare feet in the warm water springs. As always there was a strong smell of sulphur. 'A bit like bad eggs,' they noted. Frank Savage knew that Soufrière was French for 'sulphur spring'. The French had invaded and briefly controlled this island in 1782–3, making Montserratians subjects of Louis XVI, before the Treaty of Versailles returned it to Britain.

Almost a week later, in the wee small hours, 2Pac Matthew, the roadrunning fireman, was up on The Mountain, at

Chance's Peak. It was his girlfriend's birthday and they wanted a little privacy. Earlier, they had picnicked and looked for orchids and *cintibibi* (known elsewhere as aloe vera and used on the island to treat wounds and ailments) around Chance's Pond, close to the peak. A large sign on the way up told tourists the legend of the raven-haired mermaid of Chance's Pond, of her treasure chest and the snake that guards it. On Easter Monday, according to the legend, if you could grab her comb and get down to the ocean to wash it without the snake catching you, you could claim the treasure.

At that hour, it was almost pitch black on The Mountain. The only light came from the moon and the flicker of fireflies, the only sounds the beeping of tree frogs and the rustle of iguanas disturbing fallen leaves. The sulphur smell began to feel oppressive. The young couple felt uneasy and decided to come down from the peak. 2Pac had been climbing this mountain since he was a boy and felt he knew it inside out, but since he had joined the fire brigade he had looked on it differently. He wondered where the sulphur was coming from and why there were hot water ponds. As a kid, he used to wrap eggs in cloth, drop them into the springs and marvel at how they boiled. But what generated the heat? 2Pac took his girlfriend home, had a good night's sleep and went to work at 10.30 that morning. It was Tuesday 18 July. It was a date that would change the islanders' lives.

As 2Pac arrived for work, Sheila Hooper pulled into the driveway of Government House, the governor's gabled residence. She paused to admire the colourful gardens of bougainvillea, poinsettia, hibiscus, frangipani trees and coconut palms. Frank and Veronica Savage had personally nursed the gardens, flattened by Hurricane Hugo in 1989, back to life after they arrived in 1993. They had had a little outside help – or rather help from inside. Inmates of Her Majesty's Prison had been allowed out to work in the gardens. The prisoners got a bit of fresh air, the gardens got looked after at no extra expense to the British taxpayer. Everybody was happy.

It was a typically English ladies' coffee morning, with the clink of fine monogrammed china, linen napkins, the coffee served from an engraved silver pot by Desmond the butler and hors d'oeuvres laid out across the huge mahogany dining table. But most of the ladies were local and black – politicians, prominent citizens or the spouses thereof, invited to get to know the new 'Mistress Police'. Sheila Hooper almost had to pinch herself. A week ago, she had been in Sussex, worrying about floods. Now she was in the Caribbean, sniffing a warm, scented breeze wafting in through the open louvred windows and balcony doors.

But then the scent abruptly changed. It was 11.30 and there was a palpable sense of discomfort among the ladies. An awful odour, like rotten eggs, seeped through the old colonial mansion, replacing the sweet smell of tropical flowers. The ladies continued their conversations. Desmond offered more coffee. 'What on earth can that be?' Sheila Hooper thought. 'It must be the drains. How embarrassing for Veronica.' But she felt it would be impolite to mention it. Nobody did.

Tuesday 18 July was always going to be a big day for Danny Sweeney, the fisherman-cum-watersports maestro to the stars, and his partner, Margaret Wilson from Sunderland. They spent the morning on the jetty at Plymouth, looking at Danny's pride and joy, a brand new fishing boat, and trying to complete tedious customs formalities. Danny was getting nervous. The Atlantic hurricane season had begun. A Trinidadian cargo ship had offloaded his new 26-foot Bowen Marine fishing boat on to the jetty, where it would be a sitting duck in a tropical storm. But the customs men had taken days to process the papers, and it was costing him a fortune in wharf duties while it sat there.

Danny had grown out of his old boat, a 15-foot Boston Whaler given to him by George Martin for his help to the recording stars. He had originally christened the old boat the *Princess Margaret*. 'But old Maggie just wasn't winning any of the fishing tournaments. It needed a new name,' he said. 'It was very fast, always hitting the waves with a bump, so I changed its name to *Jumping Jack* and the next year I won the big fishing tournament.' The new boat he intended to christen *Jumping Jack Flash*, in honour of a couple of old friends of his from the Air Studios days, called Mick and Keith.

In mid-afternoon, he finally got the boat through customs. He and Margaret towed it to their home in Salem to get it ocean-ready. Danny couldn't wait to get out there and chase some tuna or the sleek, missile-shaped, blue-and-silver wahoo. 'That wahoo, man, it's the fastest fish in the sea,' he liked to say.

Back at Government House, where the coffee ladies had long since gone home, Governor Frank Savage was in his office, the one he had built in the back of the grounds, 50 yards from the mansion itself, to get away from the garden-loving tourists. It was 4 p.m. Savage was sitting below a portrait of the Queen, running through his schedule for the following day, when the phone rang. It was Juliette

Brade, the island's Disaster Relief Coordinator, a job set up to handle hurricanes. 'Governor, there's ash falling in the Kinsale area [just south of Government House on the road to St Patrick's]. People say they can hear jet engines from The Mountain.' Ash? Jet engines? Frank Savage had read how a Pan-Am Boeing 707, flying from Antigua to New York, crashed into Chance's Peak in thick mist and cloud on 17 September 1965, killing all 30 people on board. The locals were still finding pieces of debris in The Mountain's foliage to this day – cushions, food trays, occasionally a human bone. The Mountain had not always been benign.

The governor said he'd be right there, hung up and walked down to the big house. For once, Winston the dog did not run to greet him. Frank Savage walked on to the back terrace. His adopted green-eyed terrier was there, whimpering, gazing up at The Mountain, then running in circles, chasing his tail. Giving the dog a puzzled pat, the governor headed for police headquarters in Plymouth's Dagenham district. It was there that he had personally set up an Emergency Operations Centre (EOC) earlier in the year as a base to monitor and deal with hurricanes. It wasn't much: a single stone-walled room. Pretty basic. But Frank Savage was proud of it. He had personally cajoled Whitehall into giving him the funds – 'like getting blood out of a stone,' he told Veronica.

Her radio shift over that same day, Rose Willock was relaxing in her villa at Upper Amersham, below Chance's Peak. She had just been watching her favourite show, *Oprah*, when she became vaguely aware of a drumming sound outside. She assumed it was the neighbours' kids. Rose was almost another mother to her neighbours' children. Her home was an open house where kids would come in, hang out, watch TV or do their homework. So it was no surprise when Kenrick Lee, a teenage neighbour, popped through her open door. 'Rose, do you hear that sound in The Mountain?' he said.

'Now you come to mention it, yes, I've been hearing something. It must be an aeroplane.'

'No, man, it's The Mountain. She blowin' steam,' Kenrick said.

'Yeah, yeah, yeah, get out of here,' Rose laughed. She turned off the TV and went outside. The noise was still there. And it was loud. A rumble, yes, like a big jet plane, but there wasn't a plane in sight. She called the radio studio. Yes, they'd heard the reports. Yes, Rose, reports like a jet engine. There's ash falling south of Plymouth, around Moose's seaside restaurant. Rose Willock was already half-way out of the door. She grabbed some warm, comfortable clothes, a tracksuit, even a blanket and a pillow, just like she used to do during hurricanes. Her adrenalin was flowing. She'd already done one shift that day, but something told her she was going to be on the air for a while.

Frank Hooper got home early that day, at five, to make sure his wife was settling in all right at the end of their first week. After a dip in the pool, he joined her at the poolside for an ice-cold Carib beer. Ah, yes, he thought. No bomb threats. No drunk-and-disorderlies to deal with. No little old ladies complaining about their neighbours' dog poo. Then the phone rang. 'Commissioner, the volcano's erupting.'

There was a long pregnant pause before Hooper replied: 'What volcano?'

He had no idea the picturesque peaks of the Soufrière

Hills ringed an ancient volcano. 'None of us did,' he said later. 'I'd only been there a week. Nobody had told me anything about any bloody volcano.' Hooper left his beer unfinished and drove back to Plymouth and the police station, site of the Emergency Operations Centre. Soon the little EOC room was buzzing. Chief Minister Reuben Meade, who had proved himself a man of action during Hurricane Hugo, was there. Franklyn 'Frankie' Michael, an Antiguan who was a top aide to Meade and a disaster management specialist, had assumed it was a simulation exercise when he got the call. He thought the governor was testing him to see how quickly he would respond if there were a sudden hurricane alert. So he was smiling when he arrived, but not for long.

'My immediate impression was of chaos,' Frank Hooper said later. 'There was no clear layout. Everybody was talking at once. You couldn't get any sense of what was going on. Some of them were going on about there's going to be a tsunami, a tidal wave, or there are going to be earthquakes, or this, that and the other. Some of them just looked upset about being late for dinner. My training has always been that if there's something going on, you need some reconnaissance, you need some proper information.'

Hooper decided he'd go for a first-hand look at The Mountain. But night was falling. It may be a small island but he'd only been here a week. He could easily get lost. 'Arthur, grab a jeep,' he said to his right-hand man, Inspector Arthur Lewis. 'Take me for a look at this bloody volcano.' The two drove past the Evergreen Tree, south through Plymouth, and had just passed Government House when it suddenly appeared to be snowing. 'You know when you see snow in your headlights, that snow gently wafting down, these flakes glistening in your headlights.' He might have been the new boy in town but Frank Hooper knew it couldn't snow in the Caribbean. And his inspector had certainly never seen snow anywhere near these parts. 'It's ash, sir, must be from The Mountain,' said Lewis.

'By the sides of the road, we started seeing groups of people, two or three people here and there, all carrying suitcases. It was spooky,' Hooper recalled. 'These shapes just emerged out of the dark, through this black snow, like ghosts, into our headlights. They were expecting someone to come and pick them up to take them out of there. They were scared.'

'Arthur, let's go as far up The Mountain as we can, to see if we can work out where this ash is coming from.' Hooper admitted later that going up The Mountain at that time might have been 'very naïve', but Lewis was not about to contradict his new boss. They drove the little white police Suzuki jeep up a narrow track through Upper Amersham, past Rose Willock's house. Inspector Lewis pulled up in the car park below the 2,000 steep man-made steps that led through thick foliage to the Cable and Wireless antenna below Chance's Peak. He was hoping his new chief would not suggest walking up the steps in pitch blackness. Hooper didn't. 'Turn the engine off, and the lights,' the Englishman said. Lewis did and they got out of the vehicle.

It should have been eerily silent. It wasn't. 'God, Arthur, that aeroplane's noisy,' Hooper said. 'Sounds like the four engines of a jumbo jet. But it's got to be just a few hundred feet above us.' Then it hit him that there could be no planes, jumbo jets or otherwise, that close to Chance's Peak.

'That's when it occurred to me that it was The Mountain that was roaring and that volcanoes can go bang and that you don't want to be too close when they go bang.'

'Arthur,' he said. 'Maybe we shouldn't be here.'

'Sir,' responded his loyal inspector, 'I think you're right.'

The two men got into the jeep and drove downhill with a lot more urgency than they had driven up.

It occurred to Governor Savage that, out of concern about hurricanes, he had ordered a Caribbean expert to draw up a Disaster Preparedness Manual earlier that year. He and Hooper dug it out of some rusty files, dusted it off and checked its alphabetical headings. Hooper looked up V for volcanoes. Nothing. The V section was blank. The manual dealt with every other type of potential disaster, mainly hurricanes. Hooper and Savage looked at each other in disbelief. Bloody brilliant. This potential crisis was not off to a very good start.

There was a lot of noise in the EOC but there was no panic. There was, however, considerable confusion. None of them knew much, if anything about volcanoes. It had barely, if at all, occurred to them that the green peaks above Plymouth ringed the ancient crater of an active rather than an extinct volcano. Hooper had only been there a week. Savage had set up the little stone room they were standing in, but he'd had hurricanes on his mind: strong winds, not red-hot lava. And then there was the question as to who was in charge. The governor, and by extension Her Majesty's Government – HMG, as everyone called it – was responsible for foreign affairs, defence and internal security, but the local four-man government, headed by Chief Minister Meade, was in charge of the rest, including Disaster Preparedness.

There was a body called the Seismic Research Unit (SRU) down in Trinidad, whose scientists monitored the 15 volcanoes in the English-speaking Caribbean. The SRU, it turned out, had reported to Montserrat's chief minister, not the governor. And the local government, almost totally reliant on tourism and barely recovered from Hurricane Hugo, had preferred to turn a blind eye to any volcanic threat. Hurricanes were bad enough for business. A dangerous volcano on a tiny island was hardly going to pull in the tourists. They had kept their little secret pretty well hushed up, even from His Excellency the Governor.

The Seismic Research Unit was located within the rambling University of the West Indies in Trinidad, the biggest and best learning centre in the Caribbean, the 'Oxbridge' for students throughout the region. Lloyd Lynch, a 33-year-old Jamaican electronics engineer turned scientist, was getting ready to go home when the call came in from Montserrat on Tuesday 18 July: 'We're getting reports of ash falling on Plymouth.' Lynch went across the room to check the SRU's drum recorders. On the equipment that picked up signals from seismic stations on Montserrat, there was just one small 'signature', as the scientists describe the movement of a seismic drum needle, somewhat akin to that of a lie detector. Nothing convincing, Lynch thought.

'Are you sure?' he asked. He was thinking of a previous would-be emergency call from the island of Dominica, part of his patch. Having rushed to the scene, he discovered that a pair of lovers had lit a campfire on slopes of the volcano, which had melted sulphur, giving off a burst of colour and a strong smell that scared the wits out of the locals. It was a false alarm and quite an expensive trip. It had taught him caution.

Frank Hooper came on the line to describe what he had just seen – the gritty ash, the roar that sounded like a jet plane. Lynch's colleague William Ambeh, a Cameroonian working with the SRU, listened and then replied: 'Phreatic,' he told the English policeman. 'That's a phreatic event.'

'A what?' Hooper responded.

Ambeh spelled it out. 'P-H-R-E-A-T-I-C. Driven by steam.' He explained that a phreatic event – from the Greek word for 'water well' – meant that underground molten rock, known as magma, had risen and heated ground water so quickly that it had produced an explosion of steam. He and Lynch would get on the first plane to Montserrat in the morning. They packed their mountain-climbing gear, knapsacks, gasmasks, compasses, a hand-held Global Positioning System (GPS), sturdy jungle boots, a new drum recorder and some small seismometers. They weren't over-concerned. A 'phreatic event' did not necessarily mean there would be an eruption. But there could be. And it could be major.

Montserrat's mountain may not have erupted for centuries, but that was only a blink in geological time. It had just issued a reminder that it was not extinct but very much active, and active volcanoes can go pop at any time. Lynch had been up the Soufrière Hills many times. He knew that the seismicity background level, the frequency of underground earthquakes, was 'quite high', and that it had grown over the last few years.

Although originally part of the colonial system, and financed by the British government, the Seismic Research Unit had in the 1970s been taken over by the local island governments themselves, most of them by now independent. They had agreed to absorb it within the University of the West Indies. 'The trouble is,' Lynch said, 'by 1994 we were having problems with the government of Montserrat over their contributions to our services. Frankly, they were delinquent. They were a couple of years behind in their payments. When seismicity increased on the island in 1994, we told them we'd need to boost our surveillance and add some seismic stations, so they'd need to pay us what they owed. We asked for an additional one thousand US dollars a month for a telephone line but we didn't get their support for that. We had to train local Montserratians to go up The Mountain, retrieve seismic data and store it on disks. Then they had to Fed-Ex the data to us. Hardly ideal.'

Somewhat sooner than she had expected, Rose Willock was back where she belonged, in her big armchair in the studios of ZJB Radio Montserrat, below Lovers' Lane, her large-framed glasses jammed between the big headphones. Her telephones were ringing off the hook. 'Rose, de mountain explode, man. Rose, it rainin' ash.' Phone calls were coming in from overseas, too, from Montserratians worldwide. 'Listen up, folks,' Rose said on the air. 'Let me tell you, it's difficult to tell you what on earth is going on at this time, but stay tuned and as soon as this is established, you'll be the first to know. The chief minister and the governor are coming here to make a broadcast. Let me tell you, folks, there is nothing at this point to worry about. So stay calm now, folks, you all stay calm now.'

A few hours later, but several thousand miles away, British Royal Navy Commander Keith Winstanley was enjoying a quiet drink in the officers' bar of the naval base at Rosyth in Scotland. The 34-year-old from South Hams, Devon, had just handed over command of HMS *Newcastle* and was about to take command of another warship, the guided-missile destroyer HMS *Southampton*. He would fly to Florida to join his new ship, then steam south to the Caribbean in the role of what the British government called the West Indies Guardship (widely known as the WIGS, pronounced as a word rather than initials). It would be a far cry from what he called the 'crack and thump' – gun, mortar and shellfire – of Croatia and Bosnia, where he had recently served as a liaison officer between ground troops and naval vessels in the Adriatic.

Soon, Keith Winstanley would be in the place he loved best – on the bridge of a warship, cruising between Caribbean islands where Columbus had sailed half a millennium earlier. The job of the WIGS was to protect Britain's old colonies. In the old days, that meant defending them against enemy countries. Nowadays, it was more likely to involve intercepting drug-trafficking vessels headed from the Caribbean to Puerto Rico or Florida. That's where the destroyer's Lynx helicopter would come into its own. A ship like his would 'feel naked without the Lynx – the Porsche of helicopters'. He'd heard that the two navy fliers manning the Lynx on HMS *Southampton* would be Rick Anderson and Brian 'Swampy' Marsh, two of the best in the business. Drug runners beware, he thought. You wouldn't want Rick and Swampy coming after you with the kind of hardware they carried on board. You might switch off your lights or hide in a cove, but with their FLIR (Forward-Looking Infra-Red) these boys would find you. Winstanley also knew that Marsh had just done a two-year stint alongside the Special Boat Squadron to counter any terrorist attack against a British cruise ship. A useful chap to have on your team.

A fellow officer walked into the officers' bar at Rosyth, ordered a can of Tennants lager and held it high. 'Cheers, Keith, old boy. So much for your summer leave. Seems *Southampton* might have an emergency on her hands. There's some bloody volcano has just erupted in the West Indies.' Winstanley thought his friend was winding him up. He proceeded with his home leave. He had no idea that in a couple of weeks, he and his warship would be alongside a town called Plymouth – not the Plymouth of Sir Francis Drake, the one where much of Britain's Royal Navy was based, the one just down the road from his own home, but a little harbour town in the Caribbean. In a couple of weeks, he and HMS *Southampton* would be looking directly up at a fuming volcano, each well within firing range of the other.

Soon, Commander Keith Winstanley, his men and his ship would be 'mooning in the face of the tiger'.

4

A million nuclear power stations

At the time Montserrat's mountain awoke on 18 July 1995, the London headquarters of Britain's Overseas Development Administration, opposite Westminster Cathedral, had its mind on other things. Rwanda and Bosnia, mostly.

Andy Bearpark, a blunt 42-year-old northerner from Rochdale who had served as private secretary to Margaret Thatcher when she was prime minister, was head of the ODA's emergency aid department. As a self-styled 'adrenalin junkie', his calling card might well have read 'Disasters are my business'. His office was number V527, on the fifth floor, close to his boss, the minister for overseas development, Baroness Lynda Chalker. In case any civil servants got confused – which was entirely possible with this lot, Bearpark thought – offices in the ODA's Scottish HQ at Abercrombie House, where Sussex policeman Frank Hooper had gone for his first interview for the Montserrat job, were prefixed with the letter A. Those in London's Victoria Street, where Hooper finally got the nod, used the letter V.

Bearpark, still built like the rugby union player he had been as a youth – he was a staunch supporter of the Rochdale Hornets – had been Britain's front man in delivering aid to Bosnia and Rwanda. In the aftermath of massacres by Hutu tribesmen in the African nation, Bearpark and his staff had had to deal with a mass exodus into refugee camps in Goma, in the neighbouring Congo. Tension was still high in the camps in the summer of 1995 because food was not getting through. That sincerely worried Bearpark. He tried to keep his emotions out of his work but he wasn't doing too well this time. No one who'd been to the camps could easily forget the horror.

Bearpark had also been the man who got Britain's aid effort to Bosnia off the ground in the early 1990s, after he stopped working for Margaret Thatcher. He organised the first convoys of food supplies. 'On day one, I didn't have the faintest idea what an aid convoy was,' he said. 'But we had to do something and we didn't have any lorries. We drove up the M25 motorway looking for spare vehicles. We found a guy selling old Lucozade delivery lorries, bought them all up, painted them white, packed them with food and drove them to Bosnia. We could have called it Lucozaid.'

Bearpark's right-hand man, head of the ODA's five-man rapid reaction 'Disaster Unit' Peter Burton, had the office next door in the Victoria Street building, number V528. Aged 58, a veteran of 40 years in the civil service with less than two more to go until retirement, Burton was on call 24 hours a day to get British emergency aid anywhere in the world at a moment's notice, earlier if possible. His great loves were classic civil aircraft from the early days of flying and his local Baptist church football team in Tonbridge, Kent, which he coached in the Sevenoaks league. 'The other teams called us the Prayer Boys,' he said, 'but all we used to pray for was not to lose twenty-nil.' His son Robert was goalkeeper.

But most of all, Peter Burton loved getting aid to people in need. 'We're 24–7 highly responsive,' he liked to say. He knew that people like him and Andy Bearpark were often looked on as cold, heartless civil servants, pen-pushers in grey suits. But he truly cared, and the disasters he had to deal with often got to him. He knew the same went for Bearpark and that's why he enjoyed working with him. With Bearpark often in the field, in such places as Bosnia or Rwanda, Burton was left pretty much in charge of the Disaster Unit and the ODA's £12-million-a-year emergency budget.

Andy Bearpark was on holiday in Portugal when Montserrat's volcano started huffing and puffing. As it happened, he got a call that day asking him to return to London. It had nothing to do with Montserrat. (Bearpark had heard of the island but, quite frankly, had no idea where it was.) There had been horrific massacres at Srebrenica in Bosnia and the British government had called an emergency meeting in London – dubbed 'the London Conference'. Prime Minister John Major knew Bearpark's experience in the region. He had personally asked Baroness Chalker to phone Bearpark and bring him home for the conference.

At 94 Victoria Street, it was Peter Burton who took the calls and telegrams from Montserrat early on the morning of 19 July, London time, soon after the volcano started venting. Governor Frank Savage's telegrams to the Foreign Office were copied to Burton's unit but were delivered by hand. Burton winced at the fact that it took many times longer for the telegrams to get from Whitehall to Victoria Street than it did for them to make the first trip across the Atlantic.

As soon as Bearpark got back, he and Burton dusted off their giant *Times* atlas and found the little island. So *that's* where it is. A large, detailed map of the island and one of the entire Caribbean were hastily found and pinned up alongside those of the Balkans and Africa on Bearpark's office wall.

'Phone calls were flying around in all directions,' Burton recalled. First, there was the red-tape-tangled relationship between the ODA and the Foreign Office. In this case, the Foreign Office's West Indies and Atlantic Department (WIAD – usually pronounced as a word, 'Wee-add') was involved. Bearpark and his ODA colleagues tended to dismiss the WIAD staff as 'lightweights'. 'You know the sort of thing,' said Bearpark. 'When you're worried about the Middle East et cetera, you're not going to put your best people in the Caribbean department. You take some of these people you don't know what else to do with and say, "Hey, where can we put this guy where he can't do any harm? Ah-ha, got it, WIAD." '

When it came to hands-on, it was Bearpark, Burton and their small staff who had to get emergency aid rolling. If this volcano gets serious, Burton thought, the Royal Navy might have to get involved in an evacuation; might even have to send in the Royal Marines. But that would mean the usual battle over who would come up with the cash.

Burton enjoyed working with Lynda Chalker. She had been elevated to the Lords as Lady Chalker of Wallasey, and it was an open secret that her ambition was to be foreign secretary, but Burton felt her heart was in the right place. She had been visibly shaken the previous year after witnessing death at first hand among the starving refugees from Rwanda in Goma. The refugees may have included

Hutus, and it was Hutus who had perpetrated the massacres, but these people were starving to death. Hunger was hunger. To Chalker, that over-rode any other concern. To make matters worse, the refugees were threatened by a string of volcanoes that were bubbling and threatening to erupt. Goma and its camps would be directly in the path of their lava.

At the same time, the opposition leader Tony Blair was giving the Conservatives a lot of stick over Bosnia. On 19 July, the day Whitehall learnt that a volcano was erupting in a little British island in the Caribbean, Labour MP Clare Short laid into the government. On paper, Short was Labour's spokesperson on women's issues. But in the Commons that day, Bosnia was on her mind. So was overseas aid. And her targets were Baroness Chalker, the ODA, John Major and the Conservative government in general.

The government was treating Bosnia like a civil war, sending humanitarian aid to all parties, she told the House of Commons that day. In doing so, it was appeasing ethnic cleansing by the Serbs, she said. 'I believe there is a hidden strategy to accept a Greater Serbia as a way of stabilising the Balkans.' Peter Burton heard parts of her speech on the radio news. 'Feisty lady,' he said to himself. 'She's talking like a minister.'

So now Lynda Chalker and her aid managers, Andy Bearpark and Peter Burton, had not only Tony Blair but Clare Short on their backs. And a new volcano blowing off steam in a Crown colony to boot. Burton saw a lot of long days and nights ahead in Victoria Street. The ODA was badly restricted by a shrinking aid budget. It was bad enough squeezing out money for needy Africans, Burton thought. Now we've got a little island in the Caribbean to worry about. Let's just hope this volcano's lava moves as slowly as Whitehall bureaucracy.

The word that a 'new' volcano had started letting off steam spread like wildfire among the volcanology community. To be honest, faces lit up. New eruptions to these experts are like plane crashes to journalists. No one wants them to happen, but if they do, everyone wants to be first on the scene.

It was the Cameroonian William Ambeh and Jamaican Lloyd Lynch from the Seismic Research Unit in Trinidad who were first to arrive on 19 July, the morning after the venting. Lynch had visited Montserrat a year earlier, putting up posters explaining the dangers of a volcanic eruption. 'What Is A Volcano?' the posters were headed, above a list of explanations. The islanders had pretty much ignored them. They assumed the posters were about volcanoes in far-off places. On 19 July 1995, Lynch hiked up The Mountain for a closer look.

'The first thing was to rearrange the seismic network,' he said. 'The seismic stations we had put up there were not recording all the events. You need at least four stations recording to locate the earthquakes. There had been no big bang, no explosion, just two vents opening up. I put up new drum recorders to give us a real-time display of seismic activity. It was hard to see up there, there was a lot of cloud, but I saw enough to convince me it was the early stages of a phreatic eruption.' That could mean little. Or it could pose a mortal threat to everything below the volcano – the capital, Plymouth, the village of St Patrick's, in fact the entire south and most of the 11,000 population. When Lynch passed that on to the authorities, evacuation became the keyword. Was an eruption likely? Should some people be evacuated? How many? Maybe even the whole island?

After getting two of HMS *Southampton's* four Rolls Royce turbines replaced in Puerto Rico and urgent repairs carried out to its vital Lynx helicopter, Commander Keith Winstanley sailed into the little harbour at Plymouth, Montserrat, British West Indies in early August. It wasn't easy. The warship barely fitted alongside the jetty. (Not long afterwards, another British warship clobbered the pier and knocked its tourist telephone cabins into the ocean.) Winstanley and many of his crew had had to cancel shore leave in Florida, sending their disappointed loved ones back home to Britain without seeing them.

The Lynx helicopter pilots, Rick Anderson and 'Swampy' Marsh, had been reading up on volcanoes. As it happened, they'd already seen this one a couple of months earlier, in June. Before Keith Winstanley took over the warship, they'd been called to take part in the Queen's official birthday celebrations on Montserrat. They couldn't resist a peek at The Mountain, and when they realised it had an ancient crater they decided to 'pop inside' for a look. The big bowl was lush and green. Anderson took the Lynx inside and hovered for a while, admiring the view. They had no idea at that time that this old volcano was far from extinct.

Montserrat was a British colony. But it was far closer, geographically, to the United States and, in the era of modern communications, had become increasingly Americanised. Its currency, the East Caribbean dollar, colloquially the EC, was pegged to the US greenback. 'EC come, EC go,' the locals liked to say. Most of the tourists came from the US or Canada, as did the 'snowbirds' who bought villas and came down to flee the harsh northern

winters. American TV programmes were the most popular and island youths were increasingly turning from the
traditional cricket to basketball, from the old calypso and
reggae to the hip-hop and rap of black youth up north.

So it was no surprise that American volcanologists,
rather than Brits, were the first to arrive in numbers and
with up-to-date equipment to back up Lloyd Lynch and the
SRU, whose resources and equipment were strictly limited.
Peter Burton's ODA Disaster Unit in Victoria Street came
up with some emergency funds, and the United States
Geological Survey (USGS), the biggest and best-equipped
geological team on the planet, sent down a five-man
SWAT-style team of troubleshooters – the men who have
been dubbed 'volcano cowboys'. In some professions, you
might call them 'firemen', but you can't put out a volcano.
At least, no human being has so far. The American team's
official title was the VCAT, the Volcano Crisis Assistance
Team. It was headed by a legend in the field, Dan Miller.

As it did for most of his generation of volcanologists,
the 1980 eruption of Mount St Helens had changed
Miller's life. He was one of the first people to see an early
phreatic eruption from that volcano. Later, on 18 May that
year, when the big mountain blew its top and one of its
flanks, he lost friends and colleagues including fellow
volcanologist Dave Johnston. Before that day, Miller had
respected volcanoes as much as anyone. Afterwards,
respect was not a big enough word.

Some of the VCAT team in Montserrat had been
involved in the world's last big eruption, at Mount
Pinatubo in the Philippines in 1991. Lessons learnt from
Mount St Helens had been heeded at Pinatubo and the
American volcanologists' judgement calls saved probably

tens of thousands of lives. The biggest American military installation outside the United States, Clark Air Base, 15 miles from the summit of the volcano, was evacuated just in time, but hundreds of Filipinos died from resulting mudslides. Miller's respect for these fiery mountains grew even more. And so did his caution.

He and his men, along with their Caribbean colleagues from the SRU in Trinidad, began operating in Plymouth in a row of green Nissen huts that had once been used as a school. Formally, they became the Montserrat Volcano Observatory, or MVO, but everyone just called them the Green Huts. They were only yards from Frank Hooper's police station and the little EOC, the Emergency Operations Centre, set up by the governor in the police station's grounds. The fact that the Green Huts looked directly up to The Mountain's peaks had initially been seen as an advantage. Initially. 'Line of sight' works both ways. It didn't take long for the Americans to realise that the Green Huts would be in the direct path of anything that came down from the western peaks of the volcano. Staying there could become seriously hazardous to their health.

Police Commissioner Frank Hooper, trying to come to terms with something he'd never envisaged, asked one of the Americans exactly what this phreatic venting signified, and what was likely to happen next. 'I think we ought to evacuate this observatory, Frank. I think we ought to get the hell away from this mountain,' the American said. Plymouth and the Green Huts were only two and a half miles from Chance's Peak as the oriole flies, and not much more, following gravity and the contours of the land, as the lava flows. Clark Air Base in the Philippines had been

15 miles from Mount Pinatubo but still got hit. 'They started telling me about Pinatubo,' said Hooper. 'I looked up at The Mountain. It suddenly looked a hell of a lot less friendly than before. Its veil of clouds seemed to get darker. I remember thinking the Americans were all a bit shell-shocked from Pinatubo. But that was the first time I realised we were all in some danger.'

The scientists from the SRU in Trinidad, used to living on Caribbean time, took almost the opposite approach. One of them drove the Americans crazy by strolling around the Green Huts whistling and singing 'Don't worry, be happy.' The SRU men felt there was no need to press the panic button. There had been earth tremors and The Mountain had let off steam. That was all. It did not necessarily augur an eruption. Chief Minister Reuben Meade and his local government agreed. Thinking of vital tourism, they were happy to play the whole thing down. And if the American experts pulled back from Plymouth, what kind of signal would that send to tourists and the capital's residents alike?

Governor Frank Savage had been toying with evacuation plans since day one, including the idea of total evacuation to Antigua, but had tried to keep them close to his chest to avoid panic. Anti-colonial feeling was oddly polite on this island, but it was very much there. Decisions taken in London fell under immediate suspicion, particularly among black nationalists who emphasised their African roots. Rumours quickly spread that Britain might declare direct rule, a return to full-scale colonialism, or 'pull a Diego Garcia'. That was a reference to Britain's forced removal of islanders from the British Chagos islands, including Diego Garcia, in the early 1970s to allow the

United States to set up a military base in the Indian Ocean. In the secret deal, the US reportedly paid Britain to 'sanitise' the islands of their residents. Like Montserratians, these were mostly descendants of African slaves. The Americans had decided against another island, Aldabra, fearing a backlash from ecologists because it was a breeding ground for rare turtles. 'We were less important than turtles,' Diego Garcia islanders later complained. But by then it was too late. The turtles got to stay, and the Chagos islanders had to leave. Montserratians began to fear a similar fate.

But Frank Savage felt it would be 'grossly irresponsible not to have a contingency plan'. He drew up a strategy for a retreat to the north of the island, putting the 2,000-foot Centre Hills between evacuees and the volcano, as well as a contingency plan to ship everyone to Antigua. Owners of all types of craft, from ferries and fishing boats to private yachts, had already begun volunteering for a Dunkirk-style evacuation if necessary. 'I've got responsibility for eleven thousand people. What happens if they're in mortal danger? It would be irresponsible not to have an off-island evacuation plan in place, simply as a contingency,' Savage told a meeting of the EOC, 'but obviously, I don't think we're going to need it.' He hoped to God he was right.

To help with the contingency planning, Savage asked London for a military advisor. He didn't have to wait long. The ideal candidate was already in the Caribbean. On 25 July, only ten days after arriving in Barbados to train local security forces, Major Steven Bruce of 45 Commando the Royal Marines flew into Montserrat. He had to cancel his thirty-sixth birthday party for the following day, but the Caribbean would make a pleasant change from Northern

Ireland and Kurdistan, he thought. Less than two weeks earlier, he had been in his hometown of Poole in Dorset, training Royal Marines to storm ashore on landing craft. Now he was to plan the opposite: getting people off an island if a volcano were to blow. He grinned when told of his grand new title: Commander, Land Forces, Montserrat, British West Indies. In command of all land forces, and not yet 36 years old. Mind you, there *were* no land forces, at least not yet. So far, he was it.

The American scientists remained uneasy. Their Caribbean colleagues were still taking the chill-out approach. The pragmatic Frank Savage, as well as police chief Hooper, felt the need for further guidance, preferably from back home. 'We had blind faith in the scientists. But we were getting mixed signals,' the governor said.

So a few days later, English seismic hazards expert Dr William P. Aspinall, known to friends and colleagues as Willy, kissed his Trinidadian wife goodbye at their home in Beaconsfield, just off the M40 between London and Oxford. His title would be Scientific Advisor to the Governor and Her Majesty's Government. Aspinall was the obvious choice. He knew The Mountain intimately. He had worked in the Seventies for the SRU in Trinidad, where he met his wife, Felice. His two daughters were born in Trinidad and, although he himself was white, he considered himself 'as much West Indian as British'. That was bound to give him a bit more street cred with the islanders. He himself had placed some of the existing monitoring devices on the Soufrière Hills, way back in the Seventies. They were still working.

Aspinall, an expert in earthquake hazards, had been working in England on a 'calldown' assignment for the

British Geological Survey, looking into the safety of proposals for an underground nuclear waste storage tank at the controversial Sellafield nuclear power plant in Cumbria. He had put a micro-earthquake monitoring network around the Sellafield site, not unlike the devices he had planted on the Soufrière Hills many years earlier. The aim was to study whether earth tremors, even those imperceptible to humans, could endanger any underground nuclear waste disposal 'cavern'. In the end, the proposals were scrapped and the plant continued to pump radioactive waste water into the Irish Sea.

'My first thought was, hmm, this could be interesting,' Aspinall said of the Montserrat venting. Like most of his colleagues, he talked of volcanoes with passion, the way other men talk about football. 'I find them compellingly interesting,' he said. 'The heat energy in the Montserrat volcano's dome is the equivalent of a million nuclear power stations. It's a force of Nature that is magnificent, more than anything man can build.'

Aspinall was delighted to get back to the Caribbean. His PhD at Durham University had been in atmospheric electricity, or thunderstorms, but he was not averse to a spot of sunshine. 'We were always well aware this was a "young" volcano,' he said. 'It was active in what we consider recent times, a few hundred years ago, and perhaps thousands of years before that. In geological terms, that's but a micro-second.'

At the first meeting with his American and Caribbean volcanologist colleagues in the Green Huts, Aspinall quickly realised, as he put it with typical understatement, that 'there was a slight difference of emphasis'. Another participant was more blunt. 'It was like the Tower of

Babel in there.' The usually sedate Frank Savage became increasingly frustrated. 'Look, we've got to get some kind of consensus here,' he told them. 'I can't have all of you telling me something different, gentlemen. Where's that going to get us? Thousands of lives are at stake here.'

Aspinall took on the role of what he called 'synthesiser', eliciting the opinions and predictions of each scientist, interpreting them for the governor and trying to agree a course of action. But after almost a month, it was all beginning to look academic. The Mountain began behaving itself again. The beach bars were full; the Guinness was flowing: it was business as usual in paradise. Until 21 August 1995.

5

Ash Monday

Under the volcano, all appeared quiet on the evening of Sunday 20 August 1995. Except at Government House, where a good old-fashioned colonial-style party was in full swing. Winston, His Excellency's dog, slept through the clink of glasses, the rising chatter and the laughter. Given that creature's strange preoccupation with The Mountain, the fact that he was having a snooze was a good sign, the governor thought. Desmond the butler was scuttling around between salon, balconies and lawn, offering chunky glasses of golden Appleton rum, downed swiftly but appreciatively, as in centuries gone by, by thirsty English sailors.

The governor was throwing a farewell party for HMS *Southampton*, due to pull out at nine the following morning. The volcano had gone quiet during August and the WIGS, the West Indian Guardship, was no longer needed. There were other islands to watch, shore leave to catch up on. The ship's Lynx pilots had taken the scientists on to The Mountain several times a day, dodging clouds of steam and ash. But lately The Mountain seemed to have gone back to sleep.

'Give us a toot on your horn as you pull out in the morning,' Police Chief Frank Hooper said to HMS *Southampton*'s commander, Keith Winstanley, 'and I'll give you a wave from the police station.' The two men, both from

England's south coast, had become friends and planned to get together, along with their wives, back home.

By 8 a.m. the following day, Monday 21 August, Government House was quiet, the debris of the party long cleared away. It was a typical Caribbean August morning, already as warm as a fine English summer afternoon. Governor Savage noted that the palm fronds and leaves throughout his gardens were unusually still. There was not a breath of wind, rare so close to the ocean. He saw PC Kelvin White pull up at the end of the driveway in a white jeep and drop off a fellow officer, the Government House sentry for the day. Security was hardly an issue here. The sentry would spend most of the day guiding tourists into the house's gardens and posing for their photographs. Sentry? More like a guide at Kew Gardens, the governor thought.

On the terrace of the Vue Pointe hotel, north of Plymouth on a seafront slope facing Chance's Peak, Dr Willy Aspinall was having breakfast, his camcorder on the table. He planned to shoot some footage from the crater rim during a hike later in the morning. A fuzzy clump of white cloud lay motionless below Chance's Peak, giving the summit the look of a green-clad Santa Claus. In the background, via ZJB Radio, Bob Marley was singing 'Don't worry 'bout a t'ing, cos every little t'ing gonna be all right.' George, the pearly-eyed thrasher bird who lived in the Vue Pointe's rafters, was singing along in agreement. It was a perfect morning, but Aspinall's glance kept returning to The Mountain. He was trying to read its mind.

At the ZJB Radio studios on Lovers' Lane, on the northern outskirts of Plymouth, Rose Willock was presenting the 'Good Morning, Montserrat' show. The studio cleaning lady was getting ready to go home. The fears of the last few weeks had eased and Rose was back to her normal fare, interspersing reggae with calypso, Bob Marley with the soca of local boy Arrow. All over the island, feet were tapping.

Among these were the dancing toes of fisherman Danny Sweeney. He was down in Kinsale, just south of Plymouth and Government House, where the first ash had fallen on 18 July. Danny was selling fresh wahoo fish to his friend Moose Meade, owner of the Seaquarium seafood restaurant and bar which jutted out into the ocean on a wooden jetty and was renowned for Moose's disinterest in taking your money. Moose's wife Idabelle – Ida to most – was a politician and sometime cabinet minister, and the daughter of one of the island's most famous activists, union leader Bob Griffith. But when she got home from her day job, she changed her clothes and cooked fish in the restaurant's little kitchen.

Danny had often danced the night away at Moose's to the sounds of Mick Moloney, the Irish folk singer and banjo player who was a regular visitor and who would rattle the pier boards and make the tropical fish dance when he jammed with the local string band musicians into the wee hours. Driving back through Plymouth, Danny passed the seafront Yacht Club. He smiled when he thought of the time he and his partner Margaret were 'puttin' down a storm' (dancing all night) at the club when Mick Jagger's wife Jerry Hall tried to cut in. 'No way! He's my man,' said Margaret. Passing Plymouth jetty, the windsurfing fisherman saw HMS *Southampton*, already getting up steam, ready to pull out within the hour.

Governor Savage was on his rear balcony, ready to go to work in his outhouse office, when he noticed that Winston was acting up. The dog was on his haunches, nose in the air, staring up at The Mountain. But this time he was not whimpering. He was deathly silent. Everything was.

That's when the governor heard the blood-curdling scream.

It came from the garden and he thought it must be Catherine, the maid and cook. He'd never even heard a real scream on this island before. Agatha Christie novels flashed through his mind. 'Who Killed the Colonial Governor's Maid? Was it the butler?' When he got down to the garden, Catherine stood transfixed. Her mouth was agape, her jaws cupped in her hands. It was as if she had just seen Jesus. She was staring up at The Mountain. Frank Savage looked up too.

An enormous, thick, black cloud, as though from an oil-well fire, was shrouding Chance's Peak. But it was not rising, not even hovering. It was rolling and churning down the mountainside, hugging the slopes, headed straight towards Government House and Plymouth. It looked like some kind of living, breathing monster, black as night, relentless and angry. What kind of cloud could run downhill? Frank Savage thought. But by then it was almost upon them.

'Everybody inside the house!' the governor shouted. Even Winston seemed to understand. Savage and his staff did not have time to close the shutters. The black cloud enveloped Government House no more than 60 seconds after the maid had screamed. The air turned pitch black. The governor stumbled and fumbled for a light switch and flicked it on but nothing changed. He held up his hand and realised he couldn't even see that. Savage had been reading up on volcanoes. He knew that flows of deadly red-hot rock, gas and ash can ride the coat-tails of such black clouds. If that were the case, he, his wife Veronica, Winston, the little town of Plymouth and maybe 8,000 of the islanders would be incinerated within seconds. In his mind's eye, he saw visions of Pompeii and its inhabitants, killed by the AD 79 eruption of Mount Vesuvius before they knew what hit them. Savage said a swift, silent prayer.

At the time the governor's maid let out her scream, Frank Hooper had just arrived at police headquarters, in Plymouth's Dagenham district, in a particularly good mood. His personal Suzuki Vitara jeep, complete with wide wheels, cowcatcher, and what he called 'all the boy-racer go-faster bits', had just been shipped in from Sussex. He was in his office facing the seafront, watching the *Southampton* build up steam and wondering whether Commander Winstanley would remember his promise to toot the ship's horn.

Hooper heard 'a bit of a babble' in the corridor and went out of his office. His entire clerical staff, his secretary, the superintendent, the deputy commissioner, all the CID people, were out there, pointing up towards The Mountain. He looked up and saw an enormous black cloud, dense, dark, rolling down the mountainside. 'Close all the shutters,' he yelled. It wasn't long before he realised that would hardly help.

'Just as I said that, I heard a ship's hooter blast and ran back to the front window. The *Southampton*, which had been berthed bow inwards, was going backwards at about twenty knots,' said Hooper, himself a keen and experienced yachtsman. 'I don't know whether you've ever seen a destroyer going backwards but they can go as fast backwards as they can forwards. She was powering astern out to sea as if she were trying to avoid a torpedo. She was throwing up this enormous bow wave, except in this case it was a stern wave. Keith was blasting his horn as they went. I ran back to the back window. The cloud hit us like some kind of black hurricane. It carried its own wind with it. Then everything went black. You had a feeling of total helplessness.'

Seconds earlier, Constable Kelvin White had arrived back at the station after dropping off the Government House sentry. He had seen the cloud come down The Mountain and screeched into the police station car park just before it hit him. He noted that the street lights had come on automatically. 'I ran into the radio room,' White said. 'There was this policewoman just screaming. I had to tell her to shut up. She was hysterical. Then the place went pitch black and I couldn't see her. That's when I started to feel a bit scared. I'd read *National Geographic* and heard about Pompeii. But I'd never heard or seen anything like this before.'

At the ZJB studios, Rose Willock was waiting for a music track to finish when her technician burst in. 'Rose, Rose, de volcano blow this time.' Rose laughed and told him it was too early in the morning for jokes. 'Yeah, yeah, yeah, this time it blow, Rose,' he insisted. 'It blow, it blow.' Still sceptical but knowing the technician must have seen something, the announcer put on a soothing Lou Rawls track, 'Time will take care of everything, there's no need to rush . . .', walked to a rear window and looked up. Sure enough, there it was, a huge black cloud, tumbling over itself, down towards the studios. As day began to turn to night, she saw pinpoints of light on Lovers' Lane, the headlights of cars fleeing Town, headed north. The panic was tangible.

When she ran back to the live studio, the phone was ringing off the hook. Rose told the cleaner and her technician to try to get home. Then she called the scientists. It was, they said, a phreatic eruption, more worrying than the first venting of 18 July, but not necessarily a threat to lives. 'Not necessarily' was for the radio audience's consumption. But, they said, a real eruption was possible later. Alone in the studio, gathering a bunch of easy-listening discs around her, Rose clamped on her big headphones and went on the air. Virtually everyone on the island – at home, in businesses, in schools where children had just arrived, many panicking – was tuned in. The Voice of Montserrat cleared her throat, prepared her most soothing Caribbean lilt and went on the air.

'Okay everybody, listen up. I know you're scared. That's understandable and that's okay. But I've just spoken to the scientists and they say this is a phreatic eruption, a combination of ash and steam.' She lowered her voice another notch and tried to sound even more reassuring. 'Don't be afraid. I know you can't help being afraid because we've never seen anything like this before. I know it's very intense where you are. I know you can't see anybody. Some of you might be at home alone. I know you're scared stiff but please don't leave your homes. If there's somebody there with you, you may want to hold their hand and just stay together, talk to each other, reassure each other. Just stay where you are. It's going to clear. I don't know how soon but no one's going to get hurt.'

Throughout the island, people listened. Many could not even see their radio sets. A few feared Rose was bluffing and that they were going to die. But hearing her calm voice made them feel better. Many held hands.

In Government House, Frank Savage and his staff were huddled round a radio and heard Rose Willock continue. 'It's all right to be frightened,' she said. 'If you're crying, it's okay to cry. If you're praying, it's all right to pray. Any of those things. But it will get better. I promise you.'

Fifteen minutes after the cloud came down, the governor's phone rang. It was still as dark as night but no longer a total blackout. The house lamps now gave off enough light for him to find the phone. It was Commander Keith Winstanley, calling from HMS *Southampton*. 'We got out of the harbour just in time, Governor,' he said. 'We're looking at the cloud now. It's black, hanging over Plymouth, but we can see the mountain and I can tell you there's nothing more dangerous behind the cloud.' Frank Savage breathed a sigh of relief and told his staff. They were safe. For now.

Finishing breakfast at the Vue Pointe hotel, English volcanologist Willy Aspinall had captured the cloud on video. 'It was hugging the ground,' he said. 'That told me it was a cold ash surge cloud. It stuck to the ground because it didn't have any heat. That was good news. But it still put the wind up the American scientists. In the Green Huts, they were looking up the gun barrel. They were thinking of Pinatubo and seeing the analogy. It raised the interest level, I can tell you that.'

The solid blackness eased. Some light came through. But Plymouth and the rest of southern Montserrat were still dark and it was not yet 9 a.m. Ash was falling like black snow, like Christmas in hell, and there was chaos in the streets. From the police station, Frank Hooper could see an endless line of cars headed north up Church Street and Lovers' Lane. Despite the gravity of the situation, he noticed, they were staying in single file, anxious but patient, nobody trying to overtake. These people just won't break the law, he thought. Even running away from a bloody volcano.

David Lea, the American missionary, had been up The Mountain when it started to shake and spew ash. He had got himself a nice video camera and hoped to put together a historic record of The Mountain's moods for future generations. What the heck am I doing up here now, he thought as he stood on Chance's Peak. The once lush foliage was now uniformly grey from ash falls. The normally bright green elephant ear plants now looked exactly like that, like elephant's ears. They were a dull grey, covered in a thick film of ash. You couldn't tell from down below but this mountain has been spewing a lot of ash, Lea said to himself. It was then that The Mountain started shaking.

'It's right up here you start to hear it,' he said to the camera. 'And it makes your heart beat fast. Don't do this at home, folks. Anybody watching this, don't be stupid enough to come up here. This is my last trip and it's hot already and it's spewing right now.' He was breathing heavily and you could hear pebbles, then stones, then rocks hitting him and the camera. 'Oh, my, that's hot stuff. It's falling down. I'm not going to stay long. What you hear there is rocks coming up and I'm gettin' outta here. The whole mountain's shakin'. I'm outta here.'

Lea kept the camera on but all you could see were his boots. The light grey, ash-veiled foliage whipped by faster and faster as he raced downhill. 'The mountain's quiverin'. It's shakin' harder and harder,' he said. 'She's blowin' hard and heavy behind me. She just let loose.' He turned the camera on to his face, red and sweating and bouncing up and down and in and out of the frame. 'Do I look scared? I think that's the closest I ever thought about . . .' There was a brief gap as he sought the words. '. . . being dead. The whole top of the mountain is just shiverin', shiverin', shiverin'. Up and down under your feet. You can feel this positive power underneath, vibratin', wantin' to come out.' Lea made it downhill safely.

Throughout the south of the island, the blackout caused panic. 'I was getting calls from all over the world,' Rose Willock said afterwards. 'Some people grabbed a suitcase and headed for the airport, and Antigua. Some headed for the banks, which were open and got swamped when the ash cleared. By the afternoon, one thousand people had flown out by small plane to Antigua. Many were scared, they were completely out of it. There were reports from Antigua of Montserratians roaming around the airport in a daze, with no place to go.'

Ash Monday, as it became known, plunged Governor Frank Savage into a dilemma. To evacuate or not? The whole island, or just the south? The American geologists had been pushing from the start to evacuate Plymouth and the south. The local government and the Caribbean scientists, who recalled the evacuation of the French island of Guadeloupe in 1976, had been reluctant to pull out of Plymouth – the capital, the only port, hub of the economy and tourism. Guadeloupe suffered major tourism and other economic losses after the evacuation but the volcano never blew. It was a false alarm that cost several hundred million dollars. An off-island evacuation would set Montserrat back years, if not decades. That could prove more damaging than Hurricane Hugo.

Dan Miller, of the American volcanology team, recalled his experiences in the years after Mount St Helens. When he and his colleagues warned of the dangers of an eruption of the Mammoth Lakes volcano in the Sierra Nevada in 1982, they were abused by locals because of the fall-off in business. The geologists were told to get out of town. Miller even received a death threat. But threats had not made Miller pull his punches. On an observation flight in Montserrat in the Royal Navy Lynx, he told Swampy Marsh, 'This mountain's like a shaken champagne bottle with the wire removed.'

Willy Aspinall recalled a report by leading American volcanologist Barry Voight on the 1985 eruption of the Nevado del Ruiz volcano in the Colombian town of Armero. There, the authorities had not heeded the warnings. When the snow-capped volcano blew in November 1985, melting snow turned into a massive mudslide which swept away everything in its path. That included Armero and almost all its inhabitants – 23,000 of them.

'It's a tough call,' Aspinall told Savage and his colleagues. 'If you make the call too early, people will eventually go back. If you're too late, you take casualties. It's far too facile to talk of getting it right or wrong. There's no right or wrong. You evaluate, and you make a decision. If you evacuate and nothing happens, it's not a mistake. The threat is still there.'

It was a tough decision for Savage. But he was helped by the belated emergence of a volcanology report on Montserrat written in 1987 by a pair of young scientists, Geoff Wadge of the University of Reading and Michael Isaacs of the SRU. No one on the island had previously heard of it, but it surfaced after the July venting as volcanologists dusted off their files and searched the internet. Frank Savage later speculated that the original report might have been blown from Government House with other papers during Hurricane Hugo in 1989.

The Wadge Report, as it became known, had used computer image processing and now looked uncannily accurate in its predictions. 'The Soufrière Hills volcano is active and will erupt again,' it started. 'Although only moderately active in the geological past, [it] poses a considerable potential threat to the inhabitants of southern Montserrat.' The governor read on, and became increasingly concerned. The report spoke of the possibility of a 'pyroclastic flow' – an avalanche of red-hot ash, gas and rock first described by French volcanologists as *nuées ardentes*, or scorching clouds – and even the kind of 'lateral blast' that had blown out one side of Mount St Helens in 1980. For the first time, it dawned on Frank Savage that this volcano might emit something other than just slow-oozing lava like the famous Mount Etna. And it might not give much warning.

That left Savage in no doubt. He would have to evacuate Plymouth and the south. The Wadge Report suggested that the intervening Centre Hills would be likely to stop volcanic material reaching the sparsely-populated north of the island, beyond the Belham River valley. So Savage and the scientists chose the Belham valley as the safety line. It would be wagons ho towards the north. 'Like moving all Londoners to the Scottish highlands,' as one local put it.

The governor went on ZJB Radio to announce a 'limited state of emergency', including a two-day phased evacuation from Plymouth and southern villages such as St Patrick's. 'The scientists have told us they can no longer guarantee six hours' notice of an eruption,' he said in the best grave-but-calm voice he could summon. Up to 8,000 people, more than two thirds of the island's population, would have to move. Schools, churches and community centres north of the Belham River were being opened as shelters. Evacuees should be sure to pack their passports, birth and marriage certificates, house deeds or land certificates and enough food and clothes for three days. 'I ask you to leave calmly, in an orderly fashion, and within the deadline,' Savage told the southern islanders. 'I shall be evacuating Government House.'

He promised them he would be the last one to leave. He was to keep his word.

6

'Indiana Jones and the Volcano of Doom'

The residents of Plymouth, St Patrick's and all points south packed what they could into their cars and headed north. Those who could afford it flew to Antigua. No one carried much. They hoped to go home soon and anyway there was nowhere to put their stuff. Those who had relatives in the north squeezed into their homes. Rose Willock, who had to abandon her new villa below Chance's Peak, also had to help move the ZJB studios. In the coming days, the station's disc jockeys wore out Jamaican reggae singer Jimmy Cliff's song 'Many Rivers to Cross (but I can't seem to find my way over . . . And it's only my will that keeps me alive)'. It became something of an unofficial island anthem.

Irish priest Larry Finnegan put preaching into practice and slept on the floor of the St Martin de Porres Catholic Church in Salem along with a hundred evacuees. Constable Kelvin White was among many who slept in their cars. Chief Minister Reuben Meade allowed 20 people to share his Salem home.

To the relief of the American scientists, the Green Huts – the Montserrat Volcano Observatory, close to the police station – were abandoned. The volcanologists moved into the Vue Pointe hotel in Old Towne, on the northern edge of the island's one little golf course and the Belham River valley. Some of the scientists slept on the floor of the makeshift observatory in the hotel's conference room. The Vue Pointe, whose rooms were individual hillside cabins, had a direct view of Chance's Peak, but with the deep Belham River valley in between. It was to become the hub of island activity, its ballroom and conference room serving alternately as volcano observatory, government offices, parliament, courthouse, church, concert hall and community centre.

The American scientists, never really taken to heart by the islanders because of what was perceived as their 'doom and gloom-mongering', pulled out, but they left behind their badly-needed equipment for the Englishman Aspinall and his Caribbean colleagues from the SRU. In theory, the American troubleshooters' tour of duty, financed by Lynda Chalker's ODA, had been due to end anyway, but according to police chief Frank Hooper, 'the Yanks were all a bit shell-shocked. So they got disinvited.'

Before they left, the Americans expressed another concern. The island was on a major route for commercial airliners travelling between US airports and South America. Ash clouds from the volcano could easily clog up and stall planes' engines. It had happened before in other volcanic areas, though the aircraft had managed to restart their engines after falling thousands of feet. After an eruption in Alaska in 1989, a Boeing 747 with more than 230 people on board lost power in all four engines while coming in to land. Volcanic ash had coated the turbines. After the longest eight minutes of their lives, the pilots got the engines restarted only a few thousand feet above the ground. The plane landed safely, though the engines were written off, and the passengers had no idea how close they had come to disaster.

In the Caribbean, where there is more ocean than land and where few runways can take the big international jets, the effects of volcanic ash could be even more catastrophic. So Willy Aspinall and his colleagues issued advisories to regional air traffic controllers to follow their volcanic reports. Pilots on Caribbean routes heard the reports and were on alert, but passengers crossing the Caribbean were blissfully unaware of the potential danger.

Just before midnight on the third day of the evacuation, 23 August, Frank and Veronica Savage locked up the front door of Government House, stuffed a few bags into the governor's white Land Rover Discovery, registration M1, along with Winston and eased out of the tree-lined driveway. They were headed for Olveston House, the colonial mansion offered to them by its absent owner, George Martin. Living up to his promise to be the last one to leave, Savage had sent the sentry and his staff home earlier.

The Savages drove through Plymouth slowly, looking around as they went. Not a soul. The little capital was a ghost town, lit only by a clouded moon. They drove past the tall white War Memorial clockstand and the old red phone booth on the seafront. For the governor, that sturdy phone box somehow symbolised the stubborness of the island's continuing Britishness in the face of the American cultural onslaught.

Winston began to bark. He had spotted the group of skinny brown mongrels that considered the area around the phone booth their turf. Now they had it all to themselves. The humans had gone. No taxi drivers to toss them scraps. It occurred to the governor that these dogs must already be getting hungry, with the humans gone and everything locked up. And they would soon get hungrier. He knew there must be hundreds, perhaps thousands such strays in the south. Many residents would have left their domestic pets behind, too, and some had probably left dogs behind specifically to guard their homes or farms. He also knew that hungry animals would eventually become wild animals.

The governor noticed that many residents had not even bothered to put up shutters on their houses or businesses. They were expecting to be back soon. The word 'looting' did not seem to be in their vocabulary. The other English Frank, Police Commissioner Hooper, was not so sure. He was still pretty new to the island – six weeks now – and preventing crime, not to mention the possibility of civil unrest, was what he was paid for. He and the governor's military advisor, the Royal Marines' Major Steven Bruce, the Land Forces Commander who was still commanding only himself, decided to call in a detachment of Marines from England 'just in case the locals get restless'. Apart from the 95-man police force, the island had only a part-time civil defence outfit, the Montserrat Defence Force (MDF).

Hooper and Bruce later admitted with hindsight that their fear of looting or unrest had been unwarranted. It wasn't something Montserratians would do. But the Marines did prove useful, even vital in the early days of the crisis. They were welcomed warmly by the locals. The Marines would help put up big military tents in the north to shelter refugees. Someone was also going to have to keep the power station running on the edge of Plymouth, inside the evacuated zone.

Some 100 Marines, most of them, appropriately enough, based in the original Plymouth with 42 Commando, arrived within days under the command of Falklands veteran Captain Paul Mansell. If they thought they were in for just sun, sea and sand, they got an early surprise. One group, on board an RAF Hercules transport plane, ran smack into the high winds of Tropical Storm Iris and had to turn back to Antigua. HMS *Southampton*, by now staying clear of the ash-covered Plymouth harbour and steaming in what the Navy calls a 'patrol box' off Old Road Bay, eventually shipped the Marines across.

Using the back of his Suzuki as a desk, Frank Hooper swore the Marines in as temporary police officers, allowing them to man roadblocks and discourage looting. Sheila Hooper wrote in her diary: 'Francis has increased his police force by 100 per cent with the arrival of the Marines. He has a portable police officers' swearing-in kit in his briefcase, with a pocket bible, which was difficult to find here, and a card with the words of the swearing-in ceremony written on it. The Marines all get sworn in by the roadside. It's good to have them here. I defy anyone to break through a Marines' roadblock.'

The evening his fellow Marines arrived, Major Bruce briefed Captain Mansell and his men in their billet, a disused villa, nicknamed the Taj Mahal because of its white dome, above the Vue Pointe hotel. 'Look, lads. I know you're thinking scorching sunshine, beautiful beaches, great surf and scuba diving,' he told them. 'But keep your eye on the ball here. That's a real volcano up there. It could go at any time. So don't get cocky, yeah?' In case they didn't believe him, the volcano backed him up right on cue. One of the strongest earth tremors to date rattled their cots and toppled their backpacks. There was a split second of wondering whether they should hit the deck, then a burst of laughter and a cheer. 'How did you do that, sir?' said Mansell. 'Friends in high places,' replied the major.

The next day, Steven Bruce decided to 'wander up the mountain' for a first-hand recce of Chance's Peak, looking for potential sites for a real-time video camera that could send back images to the MVO. He found some, marked them and sent two of his men up with a camera. Just as they reached the top, the volcano vented dramatically and rained ash and boulders. At first the Marines, from the Fleet Stand-by Rifle Company, lay on their backs to keep filming, rolling from side to side to avoid the falling rocks. Then they ran down the jungled mountainside at record speed. Their video showed running boots, a lot of fast-moving grass and fern and a sound-track that seemed to consist entirely of 'Oh, fuck, oh, fuck.' But their eye-witness account confirmed the threat. And despite their 'retreat' – a dirty word to Royal Marines – the two men later received bravery awards for going up there in the first place.

Chief Minister Reuben Meade told an influx of foreign reporters there was 'a relatively high probability that the volcano will erupt any day now'. The figure going the rounds was a 70–80 per cent probability of 'a big eruption'. A visiting British reporter, referring back to past hurricanes and earthquakes, put it to Meade at a press conference that his island might be 'cursed'. The young, lightly-bearded government leader was unfazed. 'We were born to disaster,' he said. 'Our ancestors came across from Africa chock-a-block, like sardines in a can. That has created a certain resilience, my friend.' The reporter asked no further questions.

Resilience was certainly required by the evacuees in the north of the island. Tropical Storm Iris's 50-mph winds battered the big olive military tents housing refugees by the cricket pitch at Gerald's Bottom. The plateau seemed safe from the volcano, but it was exposed to the windward side of the island and took the full brunt of the winds. The big tents filled with air and all but took off like hot-air balloons. Hundreds of refugees, including children, struggled to get free from the heavy-duty military canvas and wandered around in torrential rain. 'We are in considerable disarray,' said Governor Savage in a message asking the Royal Marines to help. The people forced out of the tents had to squeeze into already packed private homes, business premises, schools and churches. Frank Savage feared there might be worse to come. They were, after all, in the heart of the Atlantic hurricane season.

The rain-soaked trail up The Mountain did not make life any easier for the scientists attempting to monitor the volcano's moods. At the end of August, in what they called Operation Harlech, a group of Royal Marines hiked up to Chance's Peak along with two scientists. One was Jamaican Lloyd Lynch of the SRU, the other an Englishman, John Shepherd of Lancaster University. A bespectacled 56-year-old physicist from Warrington, he was an unlikely choice for the title but was inevitably dubbed 'Indiana Jones' by the British press. 'Indiana Jones and the Volcano of Doom', read a headline in the *Independent* of London above a story relating his exploits on the island. On their way up the lower slopes, past deserted homes, the group passed the bodies of dead dogs lying on street corners. They had apparently starved in the absence of the human hand that feeds. There were the remains of dead cows, too, ravaged by animals unknown.

Hiking up a rumbling volcano may at first have seemed routine enough for the commander of the Marines, Captain Paul Mansell. He had taken part in the famous 'Great Yomp' from San Carlos Water to Mount Kent in the Falklands War of 1982 and led a rifle troop up Two Sisters Hill in the battle for Port Stanley. But as he felt The Mountain tremble beneath his feet, it occurred to him he might have more chance facing heavy gunfire from Argentinian soldiers than he would up here if this volcano blew. 'If she blows, we're dead meat. Archaeologists will probably discover our bootprints a couple of thousand years from now and wonder what kind of species we were.'

Dr 'Indiana Jones' Shepherd, wearing a bright yellow hard hat, stopped at a rocky outcrop beside an ash-shrouded mango tree to set up some equipment. Captain Mansell and Sergeant Kevin Foster, of the Marines' elite Mountain and Arctic Warfare Cadre, kept walking. Without the middle-aged scientist in tow, they doubled their pace to a jog. The plan was for the Marines to place reflectors, each the size of a baked-beans can, and mark them with large white crosses as targets on the crater's rim. Shepherd set up a tripod to fire laser beams at the crosses. 'That will tell me, by distance and angle, whether or not the crater is bulging,' he explained to two visiting reporters from *The Times* and the *Telegraph*. A bulge would be the precursor of an eruption. 'There's a one-in-three chance of a little rumble while we're up here. You're standing looking up the gun barrel. But if I thought it were about to happen, I wouldn't be standing here smoking a cigarette.

'If this one blows, it would be what we call a pyroclastic

eruption,' Shepherd went on. 'As any of your readers will know, having studied Greek, that means "broken by fire". It wouldn't be molten lava, like Etna. Volcanic rock, anything from ash to boulders with a temperature of around 800 centigrade, would explode upwards, while gas would engulf the island.' The reporters abruptly stopped taking notes and looked at each other. 'We really should be getting back, Dr Shepherd. Early deadlines, you know.'

Lynch climbed farther up the slope and listened through headphones to a solar-powered seismograph he had placed there on a previous trip. It was emitting an uneven drone. 'If it starts going weee-oooo, weee-oooo,' he said, sounding like a police car siren, 'that's when we're out of here.' Lynch was a serious volcanologist, but, like many of them, he liked a bit of fun. He began dancing a kind of Irish jig on the dried grey mud around the ultra-sensitive seismograph. 'That'll put the fear of God into them down at the observatory in the Vue Pointe. The needles will be going haywire.' It was a prank he would not dream of playing a few months later.

At that moment, directly below the volcano on Lovers' Lane outside Plymouth, facing Rose Willock's now aban-doned ZJB Radio studios, two cars were parked on the downhill slope between the open gates of the island's power station. Both drivers' doors were open and both had keys in the ignition. There was, after all, no one around to steal them. The place was a ghost town, except for the two men who had parked the cars: two British servicemen, assigned to keep the power station running in a zone considered unsafe. Two men under the volcano, playing cards. They did not realise it then, but they were also playing Russian roulette.

Royal Marines' Lance-Corporal Chris Taylor and Royal Navy Petty Officer Rob Smith from HMS *Southampton* were looking after the power plant's two diesel engines which provided electricity, phones and water to the islanders now packed into the north, and, no less importantly, to the vital instruments of the MVO. The keys were in the ignition in case they needed to make a rapid getaway. Neither of the British servicemen glanced up at The Mountain, although they could have seen it clearly from the window behind them. They were relying on radio contact with the scientists and their own officers.

They'd already had two false alarms earlier in the day. 'The scientists detected two tremors and we were ready to rock 'n' roll,' Taylor said. 'But they called us off within thirty seconds. If a tremor lasts two minutes, we're out of here. That's our orders. Anything that hurtles down that mountain, we'd obviously be the first to see it. We'd crank up the siren,' he said, pointing to a grey-painted Second World War antique from England, 'in case there's any idiot wandering around the danger zone. Then we'd get the hell out of Dodge. We've been practising Le Mans starts, but let's face it, if it comes down, it'll come down like a red-hot express train. And we're driving Hondas.' They did not yet realise that they could be facing not oozing lava but what Dr Shepherd had explained earlier to reporters – a pyroclastic flow, an avalanche of red-hot gases, ash and rock that could exceed 100 mph. It could reach the power plant and Plymouth within a couple of minutes of leaving the top of The Mountain. If she blew, Taylor and Smith could be incinerated between turning on the siren and running for their cars.

Having abandoned her villa below Chance's Peak, Rose

Willock was living in the 'safe zone'. She had been watching the news and was about to switch off. Then she saw the familiar profile of the weatherman pointing to a giant screen linked to the National Hurricane Center in Miami. She turned up the volume. The weatherman was pointing to two swirling cartwheels, real-time satellite images, in the western Atlantic ocean. They were churning westwards, one right behind the other, their centres crimson with yellow rims and white edges foaming like waves. They looked like images out of a cartoon, but they represented deadly weather systems. Above the cartwheels were two names, Luis and Marilyn. 'The Leeward Islands are facing a double whammy from Hurricanes Luis and Marilyn,' the weatherman said. 'And they look mean. Luis is packing winds of up to 140 miles an hour. Its forward movement is slower than usual, so its effects will last longer when it hits. It's a textbook hurricane, with a well-defined eye and tight circulation, and it could score a direct hit on Antigua, Barbuda or Montserrat.'

Oh, Lord, Rose Willock thought. She remembered the 1989 Hurricane Hugo as though it were yesterday. To face a deadly hurricane like that was bad enough. Now, she thought, we've got a simmering volcano on one side and two hurricanes on the other. Talk about Scylla and Charybdis. She packed her kit, including her sleeping bag, and set off for ZJB's makeshift studio. This was going to be a long shift.

The day Hurricane Hugo had hit Montserrat, 17 September 1989, became known as Black Sunday. The storm, one of the biggest of the twentieth century, hurtled in from the Atlantic and hit the Caribbean's Emerald Isle head on.

Although its spinning winds were lethally rapid, gusting up to 165 mph, its body mass moved west excruciatingly slowly, like a crawling but unstoppable train. It took 12 hours to cross the little island, 12 hours of hell for those who lived through it, huddled in basements, sometimes simply under their beds. In the end, 11 people died, hundreds were injured and barely a home was left unscathed. Although the island's houses were relatively well-built and upmarket, only two per cent were left undamaged. Roofs vibrated and rang out like steel drums, then flew through the air like paper aeroplanes. By the end of the day, 3,000 people – almost a quarter of the population – were homeless.

Hugo whipped round The Mountain from the east, funneled itself through the peaks and valleys and down the ghauts, and slammed into Plymouth harbour. The pier was washed away, castrating the vital tourist industry. Phones and power lines were down for weeks. Sailors from the West Indies Guardship of the time, the frigate *Alacrity* normally based in the original Plymouth, stayed in the region for most of the rest of the year, helping get things back up and running. 'It was as if someone had put grenades in every house, then exploded them all at once,' said the *Alacrity*'s commander, Colin Ferbrache. 'The whole place looked like a giant field of stubble. There was not a leaf on a tree, no foliage left on bushes.'

Islanders emerged to discover that a favourite landmark, the old tamarind tree outside St Anthony's Church on the edge of Plymouth, had been toppled. The tree had meant a lot to the locals. Under its branches slaves used to listen to hymns and pray silently while their masters worshipped inside the church. A sign by the door read, 'No dogs, no slaves.'

The ancient ficus tree known simply as the Evergreen, the symbolic centre of Plymouth where locals gathered to lime, or gossip, had been broken from its roots, too, and lay horizontal and twisted. But, with care from the locals, it would later sprout new branches and defiantly grow again.

As phones and other communications went down, the Caribbean and the world heard the ongoing news of Hurricane Hugo from Rose Willock, at that time broadcasting for the Montserrat-based regional station, Radio Antilles. The station beamed its programmes in several languages throughout the Caribbean from one of the world's biggest AM transmitters – nicknamed Big Bertha – at O'Garra's, beyond St Patrick's on the exposed southern tip of the island. Rose and the station staff had evacuated to Plymouth when the hurricane hit and continued their broadcasts from there. That was when she became known as The Voice of Montserrat.

So now, six years later, Rose and her 11,000 compatriots had good reason to respect and fear a major hurricane, never mind two coming at them in tandem. Six years after Hugo, Rose was in front of the microphone again, wearing her big, ear-warming headphones, this time at the makeshift studios of Radio Montserrat ZJB. She had been forced to evacuate the Plymouth studios as well as her own villa above the town, a few hundred yards below the crater of a bubbling volcano. So far, her house and others had been affected only by volcanic ash, 'black snow'. But now, in September 1995, here she was watching TV satellite images of a pair of mean, relentless storms barrelling in from the Atlantic. Hurricanes Luis and Marilyn, deceptively attractive and mesmerising as brightly-coloured, cartwheeling images on the TV screen, were edging closer to Montserrat's shores.

Fuelled by weather and sea conditions off West Africa, the two storms had built up steam across the Atlantic in what the weathermen call 'hurricane alley'. Ominously, both were so far following the same path followed by Hugo six years earlier. 'Luis is a stunning 350 miles wide from tip to tip,' the TV weatherman said. 'It's packing 140-mile-an-hour winds but is moving forward at only eight miles an hour. That means it will last longer and could cause more damage over a longer period of time. This could be the most destructive hurricane to hit the Caribbean since Hugo.'

Rose Willock dug out some soothing music, took a slow, deep breath and prepared to do what she did best. Normally, she thought, she'd tell folks to stay home and batten down the hatches. But most of the islanders were no longer *at* home. They were refugees. They'd be tuned in to her from tents, churches and schools. What to tell them? Not a lot more to do now, she thought, but pray.

She did, and then she went on the air. It was the evening of 4 September 1995.

7

Between volcano and hurricane

As Hurricane Luis's cartwheeling 140-mph winds bore down on Montserrat, Royal Navy Commander Keith Winstanley did what all ship's captains do when faced with a mighty Atlantic storm, if they get enough warning, that is. He steamed south-west, keeping the storm off his port quarter. His plan was to hook round south below the island of Martinique and end up behind the hurricane. In the Caribbean, you can't sail west for ever. You'd hit the mainland of the Americas, where you would be a sitting duck in port or at anchor. And you don't want to go north to get round a hurricane. They generally veer north-westwards and their winds spin anti-clockwise. That means you don't have to be in the hurricane's direct forward track to get hit head-on from its circling winds. You can get caught off guard by a right hook.

Sea captains divide hurricanes into four quarters. If you're caught in the storm, the south-west quarter is the least dangerous place to be. But wherever you're caught, your best bet is to turn directly into the hurricane's path, steam at your slowest speed, hold tight and pray. You don't want to be caught in port. A sturdy Type 42 destroyer like HMS *Southampton* could handle it, but lighter vessels can end up as matchsticks. (The MV *Fantôme*, which, like its sister ship the *Mandalay*, used to visit Montserrat, disappeared in the Caribbean during Hurricane Mitch in 1998 with 31 crewmen including its English captain on board. He had offloaded the schooner's passengers in Belize but decided the vessel itself would be safer at sea than in port.)

The Lynx helicopter crew from the *Southampton*, Rick Anderson and Swampy Marsh, had initially based the big grey-painted chopper mostly on land, at Sturge Park cricket ground on the northern edge of Plymouth. That made it easier for them to fly the volcanologists over The Mountain several times a day to analyse the air for sulphur dioxide content. The Sturge Park ground was where the whole island used to turn up to watch big cricket matches. The government would give everybody the day off. No one present could forget the day Richie Richardson hit a six far over the surf and into the ocean for the Leeward Islands against Guyana.

After Plymouth was evacuated, the crew moved the Lynx to a helipad at the Vue Pointe hotel, just inside the safe zone. They called it NAS (Naval Air Station) Vue Pointe. But the hillside, above Old Road Bay jetty and Danny Sweeney's watersports business, was vulnerable to storm winds, so Rick and Swampy finally flew the chopper back on to the *Southampton* and battened it down tight.

It didn't stay battened down for long. The two fliers had barely secured their craft and were headed for their cabins when the ship's tannoy told them to scramble for take-off. The *Southampton* had picked up a distress signal from a tiny island, Isla Aves, the 'Isle of Birds', south-west of Montserrat. It was barely an island at all, just ten acres of rock, under water for much of the year and inhabited only by sea birds and turtles for the rest – as well as a unit of Venezuelan troops. Although the little island lay 350 miles north of Venezuela, the mainland South American nation laid claim to the Isle of Birds. No one was quite sure why until a passing yachtsman spotted the troops scooping up bird droppings. The Venezuelan government, it transpired, considered the island an important source of guano, a fertiliser made from bird excrement.

The 13 men had been dropped on the island by a Venezeluan coastguard vessel, but it had been unable to come back for them because of the rough pre-hurricane seas. They'd tried to contact the US coastguard cutters that ply the area looking for drug smugglers or illegal immi-grants. But it was HMS *Southampton*, and Royal Navy Lynx number 334, that happened by. 'The American vessels don't have helicopters on board,' said Commander Keith Winstanley. 'And frankly their coastguard pilots just don't fly in the same conditions as ours do.' In any case, the American Navy and coastguard had sent all their regional vessels, based in Puerto Rico, hundreds of miles south, to be clear of the approaching hurricanes. They didn't want to be broadsided by those kinds of winds in port.

Hurricane Luis was already putting out feelers. The Isle of Birds was being buffetted by a tropical storm and the Atlantic waves were threatening to wash over the entire little land mass. It occurred to Rick Anderson that the helicopter's callsign, Castaway, had never seemed more appropriate. Judging by their radio calls, the trapped Venezuelans were extremely nervous. They were in pitch darkness, and their little atoll was about to be submerged. But winching them up to the Lynx was out of the question in this wind, and time was limited.

On a Royal Navy Lynx, the flight pilot flies. But his partner, the flight observer, is also the flight commander. He does everything bar the flying, from navigating to firing the Sea-Skua missiles, the Stingray anti-submarine torpedoes or the big machine-gun. Anderson had to take the big grey aircraft down on a sandy patch between the rocks. The sand was liquefying fast. It would be below the ocean soon. So he stayed 'wheels light', touching down but without resting the helicopter's weight, while Marsh, the flight observer and commander, hustled the Venezuelans into the Lynx from the windswept rocks. They were visibly scared as they were flown back to the warship four at a time by the two Royal Navy pilots, but they all wanted to take their bags and their rifles. 'No way, José,' Marsh told them through a Navy interpreter from HMS *Southampton*. 'You're going to have to leave your kit behind. Not compatible with a Royal Navy helo, I'm afraid. And if we don't get you out of here right now, you won't be needing any kit. You're going to get more than your feet wet.'

There was still the small matter of landing the big grey Lynx on a deck smaller than half a tennis court on the stern of a warship sailing full steam ahead into tropical storm winds. Commander Winstanley, on previous assignments, had seen two Lynx helicopters lost. One missed the flight deck completely, the other hit it smack on but too hard. The first sank as its occupants jumped free. The second was a write-off, but again the crew survived.

It may seem odd, but landing on a ship at full steam is easier than trying it when the vessel is stationary. Helicopter and ship can better coordinate their speeds and can use the head-on wind as a kind of stabiliser. Coming in from the usual 15 degrees off the starboard side of the stern, to avoid turbulence from the ship and remain visible to radar, Rick Anderson had to pull the stunt off three times to get all the Venezuelans on to the ship. 'Landing on a Type 42 is easy,' he liked to say. 'That's because you can't see the deck just before you land. If you could see the size of that deck as you came down, you'd never dare try it.'

All 13 Venezuelans were safe and well and were handed over later, beyond the reach of the hurricane, to a Venezuelan vessel bound for Caracas. Their clothes, supplies and rifles were under water by the time the last four men jumped from the Lynx on to HMS *Southampton*'s deck. Back on the ship, Anderson and Marsh had a strong cup of tea and put their feet up. But they wouldn't be able to rest for long.

Back on Montserrat, as Hurricane Luis bore down, Frank Hooper drove around deserted, evacuated Plymouth to check that no residents had slipped back into their homes in the volcano's danger zone to weather the storm. He saw no one, but, like the old western cowboys in Indian territory, he felt as though he was being watched. He was sure some folks would have slipped through the checkpoints to ride out the hurricane in their own homes, volcano danger or no. They were probably peeking from behind their curtains as he drove by, he thought. Probably listening to Rose Willock, as was he on his car radio, telling the islanders: 'Stay indoors, folks, stay away from the windows, and keep some candles and batteries close at hand so you can stay tuned to ZJB. We'll keep you up to date on Hurricane Luis's movements.'

Down by the War Memorial and the old red phone booth, the police chief came across dozens of stray dogs. Most were lying down and gazed at him lazily. He reckoned they must be hungry, too hungry to bark. And he would have betted there were many more tethered in or outside houses because evacuees were not permitted to bring their pets to shelters. There were goats, donkeys and cows all over the road, too, forcing him to swerve and weave. With farmers relocated to the northern safe zone, the animals in the south were running free. It was only a matter of time, Hooper thought, before the dogs were hungry enough, and wild enough, to attack the farm animals.

He drove north, across the Belham River valley, and into the safe zone. Driving alongside the lush fairways of the Royal Montserrat Golf Course, he saw Danny Sweeney hauling his surfboards and two fishing boats, the little *Jumping Jack* and his twin-engined 26-foot pride *Jumping Jack Flash*, out of Old Road Bay and securing them close to the golf clubhouse. Danny had learnt his lesson during Hugo in 1989. His fishing boat at that time, a 13-foot Boston whaler, had been wrecked. That ruined much of his livelihood on the fishing side. And Hugo also trashed the beach and jetty at Old Road Bay, setting back his watersports business. It was also Hugo that put paid to George Martin's Air Studios, on the ridge above Old Road Bay.

Danny and his partner Margaret, close friends of the Beatles' former producer, had sheltered from Hugo inside Air Studios along with friends who worked for Martin. When the hurricane blew in the windows of the living area, they scrambled downstairs to the studios themselves and huddled beneath the recording panel that had mixed so many famous sounds. No one was hurt, but Danny had to chainsaw and move aside dozens of fallen trees to get out of the isolated estate.

Now, six years later, with Hurricane Luis approaching, Danny finished securing his boats and equipment and drove up the hill to his home in the village of Salem. There were already nine people there, mostly family, wanting to weather the storm together. Among them was a neighbour and the oldest man on the island, Mr Isley Bobb. He had reached 102 years despite his fondness for a tot or two of rum. 'Me mout' cold, Danny,' he said as the fisherman walked in. His mouth was cold. Danny smiled. He knew what that meant. He produced a bottle of Mount Gay rum and poured the old man a Caribbean measure.

Just along the road from the Sweeneys in Salem, Chief Minister Reuben Meade was giving shelter to 20 refugees in his own home. Anyone who had any space was helping out in the face of these twin threats. But Meade was worried about the hundreds of refugees huddled in the big olive military tents set up by the British servicemen on the northern plateau known as Gerald's Bottom. He had protested strongly to Governor Savage over the stinking latrines the evacuees were forced to use, a 50-yard walk from the tents. Now he wondered whether the tents themselves could withstand 140-mph winds.

Father Larry Finnegan was helping out his congregation as always, but suffering alongside them at the same time. As the hurricane approached, the Dublin-born priest had received permission to return to the village of St Patrick's to remove the Blessed Sacrament from the church for safekeeping, as well as the baptism and marriage records. Now he was sleeping on a military cot alongside 100 refugees from St Patrick's in the Catholic church in Salem. Well, most of him was. Since he was six foot two, he had to add a plastic chair for his feet. He cooked donated food with the refugees in a vestibule that had been turned into a kitchen, washed his clothes with them in the churchyard, used the same toilet and makeshift showers and felt their discomfort every time he tried to sleep. There were no partitions. The pews had been pushed aside, along the walls. The popular priest and his parishioners, some of them fairly well-off business people or farmers, slept with nothing between them but suitcases, in some cases only plastic bags, containing the possessions they had fled with.

Completing his pre-hurricane rounds, Frank Hooper felt lucky to be on his way home to weather the storm. Since their arrival on the island two months earlier, he and 'Mistress Police' had lived in a villa near the Vue Pointe, just inside the safe zone. He had had to evacuate the island's police HQ in Plymouth but not his new home, which had the added advantage of an underground bed-room now stocked up as a hurricane shelter.

Alone in the villa, Sheila Hooper was getting edgy. First a volcano threat, now a hurricane. It was a far cry from Sussex, where lowland floods had been the worst scenario. She scribbled a few lines in her diary. 'Managed to put clean sheets on the bed.' And she stayed tuned to Rose Willock on ZJB Radio, following the experienced broadcaster's advice on how to batten down the hatches. 'Spent an anx-ious morning,' her diary continued. 'Removed our personal belongings to the basement. Covered all the electrical appliances with bin liners to keep out water. All ornaments safely stored. Put all the poolside furniture into the pool, said to be the safest place for it. Nothing left outside that could blow away and injure people. It's very still outside, very eerie, very tense. Not a single bird singing. Just the hammering and banging of plywood as people protect their windows.'

Frank Hooper was making a final check on his men at

Salem police station, next to the church taken over by Father Larry and the refugees. The station had been built to withstand hurricanes and was listed as an official storm shelter. It was already crammed with people who felt safer there than in their homes. Most of the Royal Marines had remained in their billet, the big white villa known as the Taj Mahal, but those on stand-by duty were laid out on cots or on the police station floor alongside local police officers. Among the latter was Constable Kelvin White.

Kelvin's father John, who ran a cattle, sheep and goat farm in the village of Trant's as well as working for the island's communications network, Cable and Wireless, had stayed on in Trant's to tend his livestock despite the evacuation order. The policeman's mother, special-needs teacher Linda White, had rented a bungalow in the safe zone with other family members, but it was jam-packed. So, since the evacuation of the south nearly two weeks earlier, Kelvin had opted to sleep in his mum's Mazda saloon outside the little Church of God of Prophecy in the northern village of St John's. He preferred the privacy to a crowded shelter, found the reclining passenger seat more comfortable than a military cot and was able to wash and change in a nearby relative's house. But as Hurricane Luis approached, he had decided to join the British lads in the police station. He had to smile when he saw a young Royal Marine sound asleep and snoring on the cot next to his. On the Marine's stomach, cosy and comfortable, was Bébé, the stray brown terrier puppy that hung out in the police station yard.

Frank Hooper drove home via the hillside Vue Pointe hotel. Its owners, Cedric and Carol Osborne, were boarding up windows and their open-air bar, the one they never used to bother locking up at night after closing time. In 1989, Hurricane Hugo had blown off the roofs of the hotel's 30 hexagonal luxury cottages as if they were parasols on a windy beach.

The British and Caribbean volcanologists from the Montserrat Volcano Observatory, who had abandoned their green Nissen huts in evacuated Plymouth, had taken over one of the Vue Pointe's conference rooms and set up their seismographs and gear there. Along with a few of the hotel's guests, they planned to sit out the hurricane in the hotel's underground kitchen. Surviving the storm was not the scientists' only concern. At an emergency meeting earlier in the day, someone had raised a disturbing question. Couldn't the low pressure in the eye of the hurricane trigger a volcanic eruption? At least they knew pretty much when and where the hurricane would hit. They could batten down the hatches and lie low. But no one had a clue what a hurricane could do when its forces of suction and its low-pressure core passed over the crater of a venting volcano. Only time would tell.

Just before HMS *Southampton* steamed to safety in advance of the hurricane, some of the island's emergency officials had come up with an idea, seen as rather off-the-wall by many of the volcanologists but discussed with some seriousness. Why wait in uncertainty for an uncontrolled eruption of unpredictable magnitude? Could we not take control and trigger an eruption ourselves after getting everyone well out of the way or even off island? Someone pointed out that the island had all the weaponry of the British Royal Navy at its disposal. If HMS *Southampton* could sink submarines, maybe it could blow up a volcano. A few weeks earlier, in a joint exercise with the US Navy codenamed Burmese Chase, the *Southampton* had fired a couple of hundred rounds from its four-and-a-half-inch Bofors gun at another Caribbean island, Vieques, and scored 'magnificently'. Part of Vieques is used, controversially, by the US Navy as a bombing and firing range, even though the island has a civilian population of Puerto Ricans.

Commander Keith Winstanley was called in. The Lynx helicopter crew, Rick Anderson and Swampy Marsh, based at the Vue Pointe along with the volcanologists, came too. 'There was incredible frustration,' said Marsh. 'There was a tremendous sense of wanting to bring this thing to an end.' Winstanley at first thought the idea was a joke. Then he realised it was under serious discussion. 'Well, I'd have to get permission from the Navy and the MOD [Ministry of Defence],' he told the meeting. 'Our biggest weapon is our four-and-a-half-inch gun. Can we hit a volcano? Well, if we can't, we might as well go home. We might not hit her dead centre, bull's-eye, with the first round. But with Rick and Swampy in the air, acting as spotters and correcting our fire, we'd hit her all right.'

Swampy Marsh mused briefly to himself on what would happen if he fired a Sea-Skua, an anti-ship missile, at The Mountain, or dropped a depth charge into the crater, or riddled it with hundreds of .762 calibre rounds from the Lynx's mounted machine gun. What a nutty idea. Who comes up with this stuff? He was relieved when the whole thing got dropped. A gunfight at the okay corral between a destroyer and a volcano was not his idea of a good time.

Frank Hooper arrived home just as the electricity and water were cut off throughout the island, a precaution against electrocution from severed cables or loss of water supplies through burst pipes. Still listening to ZJB Radio on a transistor set, he and Sheila were heading downstairs to the basement bedroom-cum-shelter by torchlight when there was a knock at the door. It was Governor Savage's staff officer. Veronica Savage had cooked a large end of ham, and the governor had just been given two bottles of Glenfiddich malt whisky. Would Frank and Sheila like to join 'H.E.' to see the storm through? Hooper was never one to let a hurricane come between himself and a fine malt. He and Sheila drove the few hundred yards to the governor's temporary residence at Olveston House. Somehow the thought of a steaming ham, and more especially the Glenfiddich, put Hurricane Luis into perspective. The Blitz spirit would prevail.

After dinner, in the lull before the storm, the governor, his wife and the Hoopers sat on the steps of the mansion, sipping their Scotch. Inside, the governor's staff, with Hurricane Hugo still fresh in their minds, chatted in whispers. Frank Savage had told them they could go home if they wished, but they felt safer in this sturdy mansion. They also felt a duty towards this amiable governor.

The atmosphere outside turned suddenly sultry. The leaves on the trees were as motionless as if they were part of a still-life painting. And it was eerily quiet. Birdsong had ceased. Not a single dog was barking. Even the millions-strong choir of tree frogs seemed to have lost their beeping voices. The only sound was that of Rose Willock on ZJB Radio, thanks to the governor's generator. Broadcasting from a kitchen not far away, Rose was telling the islanders that the outer rim of Hurricane Luis was almost upon them. In between hurricane updates, she played upbeat music – local boy Arrow, some calypso, a bit of gospel, a touch of reggae, all aimed at keeping spirits high.

Hooper sipped his malt appreciatively. He noticed that Winston, the governor's green-eyed terrier, was ignoring a huge ham bone that would normally have been a canine dream. He was sitting up stiffly, sniffing occasionally, as though checking on the quality of the malt. The police chief thought of the hundreds of less fortunate dogs in abandoned Plymouth, as well as the cats, parrots, other pets and farmyard animals out in the open and about to be hit by 140-mph winds.

'Notice he's facing the ocean,' Governor Savage told his police chief. 'He senses that something big's coming in. He always senses a storm when it's about fifty miles off.'

'Let's just hope he doesn't turn to The Mountain and start running around in circles,' said Hooper.

It was then that the big wind came. And it sounded like a non-stop express train hurtling through a rural station. Winston whined, did a few circles at the governor's feet, then scampered away to the master bedroom to bury himself among the gubernatorial pillows. Within minutes, phone lines went down. The closed louvres of Olveston House chattered like castanets, the wind hissing between them. The vanguard winds, coming from the direction of Antigua, first battered the windward east coast, but they picked up speed as they found the cracks in the island's contours – the valleys between the three mountain ranges – turning them into high-speed air tunnels and barrelling across to the more inhabited west.

In Salem, Danny Sweeney huddled with his family, listened to the winds try to tear off his roof and prayed that his boats would be safe. Down the road in the police station, Constable Kelvin White saw that the little brown puppy, Bébé, was trembling. The young Royal Marine was awake and cuddling her. Almost next door, in the Catholic church, Father Larry Finnegan asked his fellow refugees to join him in prayer that they and their abandoned homes, in the village of St Patrick's on an exposed slope in the south-west, would survive the storm. In her makeshift studio, Rose Willock massaged the groove her large-rimmed spectacles had imprinted on the bridge of her nose and kept on broadcasting. Hurricane updates, soothing music. Hurricane updates, soothing music. She prayed the roof of her own villa, below Chance's Peak and not far from St Patrick's, would hold fast.

Almost a day later, after a brief lull as the hurricane's eye passed over, the anti-clockwise motion of the storm's tailwinds hit the west coast like an uppercut to a punch-drunk boxer. The scientists, however, were relieved to see that neither the winds nor the storm's low-pressure eye appeared to have affected the volcano's activity. Travelling forward at a painfully slow eight mph, and 350 miles long from its vanguard to its tail winds, Hurricane Luis pounded the little island for almost two days. But the islanders were lucky. Keeping their transistor radios tuned to Rose – now the only link between Montserrat and the rest of the world – they heard that the storm had veered slightly northwards just before it hit the Lesser Antilles. Little Montserrat was certainly being battered, but it would not be the bull's-eye. That would be further north.

As the winds began subsiding, Governor Savage was among the first to emerge. He wanted to be able to go to the radio station and give the islanders an overview of the damage. The first person he saw was David Lea, the

American missionary who had dedicated himself to chronicling the volcano's activity on video. Lea had packed his wife Clover off to the island of St Maarten with their three young boys for safety, but he had ventured out three times during the hurricane to get video footage. Savage met him on the seafront in deserted Plymouth, where waves were still breaking over the road past the War Memorial, the Customs shed and the red phone box. There was no sign of the usual crowd of dogs.

'Looks like it could have been worse, Governor,' said Lea, removing a huge sheet of galvanised roofing from the road. The missionary did not yet know that the island of St Maarten, where his wife and sons had fled, had been worse hit.

Frank Savage drove on to check out his official residence, the historic Government House, which he'd been forced to evacuate two weeks earlier. Waves still crashed over the seafront and torrential rain pounded his windscreen. On the car radio Rose Willock's voice faded and a familiar guitar riff took its place: 'Dum, duh-dee duh-dee-dum . . . dum, duh-dee duh-dee-dum . . . I got sunshine on a cloudy day . . .' Savage smiled. Rose certainly hasn't lost her sense of humour, he thought.

He found his recently evacuated residence looking forlorn but intact. The gardens, the pride and joy he and Veronica – with a bit of help from Her Majesty's prisoners – had recultivated after Hurricane Hugo and which had become a tourist attraction, were another matter. His rose garden was trashed, his mango trees blown bare of not just fruit but leaves and even branches. He and Veronica would have to start over from scratch.

On his own tour, Frank Hooper ascertained that no one

appeared to have been killed or seriously injured. But he found his own villa flooded with 15 inches of rainwater. A number of homes around the island had lost their roofs but the fact that they were so few was almost a miracle, especially to those who'd lived through Hugo. Worst hit was the coastline. Hooper saw that Old Road Bay, the silky black sand beach where Danny Sweeney ran his water-sports centre, had been trashed. Danny was going to be out of business for a while, but at least he had got his boats out of the water in time. The Nest, the light blue wooden beach bar below the Vue Pointe, was wrecked. The line of trees that separated the beach from the little Montserrat Golf Course had been flattened. A little to the south, the mangrove swamp and forest that formed a bird sanctuary at Fox's Bay had been devastated. Hooper wondered how many of the area's egrets, pelicans, frigate birds or the oddly-named brown boobies had managed to flee or shelter, and how many had perished.

A little further south, the ocean had come close to claiming the Las' Call beach bar, where tourists from the tall-masted sailing ships MV *Fantôme* and MV *Mandalay* used to sip Mount Gay rum between dips in the famous Hot Water Pond. Windswept waves had also taken what looked like a large bite out of the Sturge Park cricket ground. There was now a 15-foot cliff where the western boundary used to be. On the road south to St Patrick's, the rickety pier that housed Moose's Seaquarium restaurant had survived, but only just. An ocean-going fishing boat, the *Montserrat*, had run aground only yards from the pier. St Patrick's village itself was battered but standing.

At the other end of the island, at Little Bay in the extreme north, a makeshift jetty of giant boulders built by Major

Steven Bruce and his Royal Marines to replace the evacuated port of Plymouth had been demolished, the boulders blown away and scattered as though made of papier-mâché. It was a major setback. The island relied heavily on tourism and rice exports and could not survive without seaborne fuel imports. You can't bring in many tourists, export much rice or import any fuel on the kind of light aircraft that landed at the tiny airstrip. A jetty was vital.

But not everyone was sorry to see the new jetty disappear. Germans Wolf and Inge Krebs, who for years had been running a popular scuba-diving business on the island, had condemned the building of the jetty at Little Bay, site of one of the Caribbean's finest shallow reefs. They said the construction and the subsequent shipping could destroy the reef. After Hurricane Luis, Inge Krebs went diving in the area and wrote in the local weekly paper, the *Montserrat Reporter*: 'The beach was terrible, all the sand was gone. Big boulders were scattered around. The underwater world in Little Bay had changed dramatically. We used to know every sponge, every coral. Now it took us a while to recognise familiar structures. The bottom was two to five feet deeper. Old coral rock was washed free. Black corals, barrel sponges and tube sponges were severely damaged. Nature took its revenge. Luis destroyed the jetty in Little Bay and I am glad.'

In the northern village of St Peter's, David Lea's hillside house survived. But he had heard nothing of his wife Clover and three sons on the island of St Maarten. From listening to Rose Willock, he knew Luis had veered north and hammered St Maarten head on. Its international airport was closed and likely to be so for weeks. Its tourism was virtually ruined for the upcoming winter season.

With phone lines still down, Rose Willock remained Montserrat's only link with the rest of the world. She spent most of her airtime now exchanging messages between concerned relatives on her own and other islands. But Lea still heard nothing of his family. After a couple of days, he managed to get on a small private charter plane and found Clover and his boys, Sunny, Jesse and Noah, unscathed. The house in which they weathered the storm was badly flooded but intact.

Well south of the hurricane, HMS *Southampton* was curving back northwards to come in behind it. Commander Keith Winstanley wanted to be ready to return to Montserrat to lend assistance in the hurricane's wake. But then he received an emergency call from 'down the hole'. That was what they called the Navy's Ship Movements Controller, so named because it is a shelter three storeys underground at the FOO, the Fleet Operations Office at Northwood, north of London. '*Southampton*, proceed with all dispatch to the island of Anguilla,' said the controller. 'There are reports that a hurricane shelter collapsed.' An initial report said up to 150 people might have been been killed. Like Montserrat, Anguilla was a British 'dependent territory'. Now, it was depending on the WIGS, the West Indies Guardship, currently HMS *Southampton*.

The destroyer anchored off Anguilla before dawn on 6 September, 1995. Anchoring was not easy. The offshore sandbanks that served as navigational landmarks around the island had been swept away by the storm. And with power down, the island had been pitched into blackness. Rick Anderson and Swampy Marsh flew ashore in advance to locate British Governor Alan Shave and his police commissioner. The reports of 150 dead proved unfounded, but the two Navy fliers, the *Southampton*'s sailors and its Royal Marines contingent remained on Anguilla for ten days. They repaired the airport, rebuilt the control tower and restored communications. That allowed the airport to re-open, initially only for aid flights, a few days later. It would be almost two months before it re-opened to tourists. In the end, Luis turned out to be the eastern Caribbean's most destructive hurricane since Hugo six years earlier, causing $2.5 billion of damage. Remarkably, only 16 people were killed in the entire Caribbean.

Caribbean islanders had little time to regroup. Ten days after Luis passed, Hurricane Marilyn churned in, its centre targeting the US Virgin Islands of St Thomas and St Croix to Montserrat's north. President Clinton declared the islands a disaster zone and sent in US troops to rebuild. Marilyn's winds were less powerful, hitting 115 mph compared to the 140 mph of Luis's, but they carried more rain. The storm killed eight people, mostly in the US Virgin Islands. Montserrat was badly flooded but no one was killed and few homes were damaged.

One casualty was Iggy, a friendly iguana that had moved in to the home of Frank Hooper and his wife. To shelter from the hurricane, Iggy took refuge up the vent of Sheila Hooper's tumble dryer. Unfortunately, Sheila liked to do a wash before a hurricane, just to be prepared. She had no idea the iguana was hiding in there. Iggy would have had more chance in the hurricane.

By the time the 1995 Atlantic hurricane season was over, the weathermen said it had been the 'busiest' in 60 years, with more than 120 people killed. 'This year, the Atlantic definitely won,' said one US hurricane forecaster.

On Montserrat, the islanders were at least able to weather Hurricane Marilyn at home, rather than in refugee shelters as during Luis. Governor Frank Savage had consulted the volcanologists and they predicted no imminent danger from The Mountain, so he had lifted the ban and allowed the islanders to reoccupy the south, including Plymouth and St Patrick's. There was an overwhelming sense of relief. Islanders began to look forward to their colourful month-long Christmas festivities.

Local soca singer Arrow had become a symbol of the defiant islanders who refused to flee Montserrat despite the dangers and continued to rebuild their businesses despite constant relocations. Just before Christmas, he released a new song, which could be heard constantly on ZJB Radio.

On the map you can hardly find it but it's always my
    paradise
And everyone who have seen it has always been
    hypnotised
But between the green and the mountain a volcano
    has been sleeping
And now he is awakening, I don't know what to do
    (what can I do?)
Ah just can't run away,
Ah just can't run away,
As long as there's breadfruit and mango down there
I'll be holdin' on . . .

Like Hugo, Hurricanes Luis and Marilyn were now history. And this time Montserrat had survived pretty much intact. All was well on the island.

Except for the small matter of a bubbling volcano.

8

'Mountains don't grow'

Before they were distracted by the hurricanes, Montserratians had been complaining of a lack of information from the British and Caribbean scientists as to the state of the volcano. The scientists were brave men. They went up there every day, after all. But they were not the best of communicators, and when they *did* issue statements, their specialist jargon meant little to the layman. The island's young chief minister, Reuben Meade, decided he had to check out The Mountain for himself so that he could tell his fellow islanders first-hand what was going on. Soon after Hurricane Marilyn had passed, Meade hiked up The Mountain to see what he called 'the front line' for himself. He saw steam, he saw ash-covered foliage, but what struck him most was a magnificent yellow butterfly.

That night, he went on ZJB Radio and assured Rose Willock and his compatriots that all must be well. Such a butterfly would not be up on the rim of the crater if the volcano were about to blow. Meade was a popular leader, a man of the people, seen as having struck just the right balance between defending the island's own identity and maintaining good relations with the mother country as represented by the governor and the Foreign Office. But his butterfly broadcast was to haunt him. Within days t-shirts, perhaps sponsored by opposition politicians, appeared bearing his image and the logo 'Butterfly scientist'. Teasing calypsos on the same theme inevitably followed.

Local photographer Kevin West, who had built up his little photo shop in Plymouth partly through his moody postcard pictures of The Mountain in the days before any-one thought of it as an active volcano, was more realistic. He sensed that The Mountain had moods he had yet to encounter. He took to tramping up there with the volca-nologists, sometimes with American missionary David Lea and his video camera, or often alone. In late September 1995, two weeks after Hurricane Marilyn had passed, West and Lea looked over the back of Chance's Peak and saw a 20-foot-high spine of pointed rock they could swear they hadn't seen before. Its rusty reddish colour stood out against the once lush and green but now ashy grey land-scape. West went home, printed the film and, as always, hung the pictures up outside his photo shop in Plymouth, a town fully populated again since the passing of Hurricane Luis and the quietening of The Mountain. He also hoped to sell some to the Montserrat Volcano Observatory – they paid rather well with British taxpayers' money.

Police Commissioner Frank Hooper's wife Sheila spotted the photos, bought one and gave it to her husband. In the hope of showing it to one of the scientists, he took it to a party thrown by Frank Savage at Government House. He was in luck. Fellow Englishman Dr Geoff Robson, a geologist from the University of Lancaster currently work-ing with the MVO and advising Savage, had gate-crashed the party to express his own concerns to the governor.

Hooper pointed to the pinkish chunk of rock in the photo. 'What do you make of that, Geoff?'

Robson looked at the photo, glanced at Hooper, then back at the rock in the photo. 'That, Frank, is a dome.'

Had he said that to Hooper before the volcano first announced itself in July, a week after he arrived on the island, the retired copper from Sussex wouldn't have known what he was talking about. Domes were what architects put on cathedrals. But, like everyone else on the island who had lived through regular earth tremors, venting and ash falls, Hooper had become familiar with the terminology. He knew that discovery of a lava dome would mean a whole new ball game. In volcano terminology, a dome is a growth of new volcanic rock, magma that has been pushed through the old surface. In effect it is a new, growing section of mountain. And it could eventually collapse.

Since the first venting caught the islanders by surprise on 18 July, the volcano's steaming and ash clouds could have been put down simply to ground water activity. The Mountain's plumbing was playing up, but there had been no sign that anything was growing. If the protrusion in the photograph was a lava dome, it meant The Mountain could explode. It depended on the nature of the rockpile: whether it was old rock, or the new, molten rock which the scientists call magma before it bursts through the surface and is then termed lava. Depending on the type of volcano, lava is not always the liquid red variety seen oozing slowly from Mount Etna. It can be more solid, a viscous rock, growing and growing like a whole new mountain until often it collapses to form the high-speed avalanche of rock, ash and gases scientists call a pyroclastic flow.

Again, the Caribbean scientists, and most of all the Cameroonian Dr William Ambeh from the Trinidad-based

SRU, took a laid-back approach. But Geoff Robson was wary. Dr Willy Aspinall, English seismologist and long-time observer of this mountain from his younger days at the SRU, had gone back to England when the venting and ashing eased, but Robson now called him back to the island to get the benefit of his experience and expertise.

After a late-night meeting at the MVO, studying further photographs of the rockpile inside the old crater rim, Robson and Aspinall decided it was worth waking Governor Frank Savage despite the ungodly hour. Aspinall called him at 1.15 a.m. 'Frank, this rock could be old material, like the old toothpaste at the top of a tube you haven't used for a while. But even if it *is* old material from a previously blocked conduit, something has pushed it out. It might have been plugging a rising slug of magma. This photograph is consistent with magma having risen, possibly from six miles or so underground. We don't know how volatile it might be. But if this *is* magmatic, our volcano's almost certainly going to blow sooner or later, and maybe with little warning.'

The governor had trouble getting back to sleep. He went to his desk, pulled out his work diary and wrote some notes on what Aspinall had told him: 'I believe this is dome-forming activity. It could be benign. There are three potential scenarios: 1. non-explosive dome growth, 2. the dome could collapse, causing pyroclastic flows to the east, or 3. if the dome grows larger, it could collapse to the west.' To the west was Plymouth. That's where Frank Savage was now, in Government House. There were perhaps 8,000 people in Plymouth, St Patrick's and other southern villages and he had ultimate responsibility for their safety. The governor went back to bed with much on his mind.

The big grey Royal Navy Lynx helicopter had become a familiar sight to the islanders. Rick Anderson and Swampy Marsh took MVO scientists up over the volcano, and sometimes into the caldera, the bowl inside the outer rim of the old crater, several times a day. Anderson became expert at edging through thick cloud until he could see The Mountain. 'We were pretty much in a cul de sac, playing the game of trying to clear the cloud with our blades,' said Marsh. 'You got to the base of the cloud and you couldn't go any closer. But if you went in slowly, you could do it. The energy of the blades would clear some vision for about fifty feet. Sometimes Rick couldn't see The Mountain at all. One minute we were looking out the window, next minute we couldn't tell east from west, or up from down. We ended up in total whiteout, like being in a blizzard on a ski slope when you can't tell the ground from the sky.' Fortunately, Navy pilots are trained to go quickly from visual to instruments.

'When that happened, we'd have to just hover,' said Marsh. 'I always ensured we had a safe heading, an escape heading for when you can't see jack shit and you know there's mountain all around you. It was compass heading 065, east north-east. Rick would pedal the aircaft until we were on heading 065, then he'd fly and climb like the clappers, as fast as he possibly could.'

It was late November 1995 before the governor, the scientists and the islanders knew exactly what they were up against. Another photograph showed that the new protrusion of rock in the area known as English Crater appeared to have grown. But that was not all. The light in the photo was poor, but the rock appeared to have a slightly pinkish tint, almost a glow. 'It's incandescent lava,

Frank. It looks a bit like an old coal fire that's going out,'
Willy Aspinall told the governor. 'This is proof beyond
doubt that we have fresh magma rising. The Mountain is
erupting, and magma means it is likely to explode, sooner
or later. The only real question now is whether it will be
gentle, or violent.'

Before 18 July, The Mountain had been a favourite place
to hike, to watch the little fumaroles, to sit on the warm
rocks, to explore the Bamboo Forest, to hunt mountain
chicken, to spot the national bird, the oriole, or to romp
beneath the invigorating Great Alps Falls. Now, knowing
it was an active volcano, the islanders had taken to
observing its moods, its steam and its ash from a safe
distance below. The Vue Pointe hotel, with its direct line
of sight, became just that: a favourite viewing point.
Carol and Cedric Osborne would sit on the wicker bar
stools with their guests, sip cocktails and watch the
volcano at the same time. Carol nicknamed it 'Old
Smoky'. Pointing to the new spine of rock, virtually a new
mountain, she told visitors: 'The view never used to
include that piece of rock. You can see it grow almost
from day to day. It's hard to believe. Mountains don't grow.
Trees grow.'

At dusk one evening, Police Constable Kelvin White was
outside his parents' house in the east coast village of
Trant's, next to the little airport, gazing up over the two old
clamacherry trees in his garden towards The Mountain. As
a little boy, he had looked up there and been fascinated by
its greenery, its clouds, its changing moods. Now, like
everyone else, he was preoccupied by its threat. For a
moment, he thought he was seeing things. He screwed up
his eyes. Sure enough, the top of The Mountain, around

Castle Peak on the north-eastern side, seemed to be glowing like a Hallowe'en pumpkin lantern.

Sheila Hooper had seen it, too. In her diary, she described The Mountain as 'like a huge barbecue just at the right temperature for cooking. Absolutely awesome.'

As the Englishman Dr Willy Aspinall had pointed out, the glow meant the mountain would almost certainly blow sooner or later. No one knew when, no one knew how big. But it would blow. The previous steam explosions and ash clouds had been phreatic events or eruptions. Subterranean magma had heated the ground water, turning it to steam and making The Mountain a leaking pressure cooker. Now, it was clear the magma was pushing upwards and oozing above ground to form a new rock mass. It glowed because it emerged red-hot from underground. And domes that grow usually explode or collapse, sending lethal pyroclastic flows downhill at speeds of over 100 mph.

The MVO scientists knew a small eruption and pyroclastic flow could affect mountainside villages on the east coast such as Long Ground. A bigger eruption might threaten the airport and villages of Harris, Farm and Trant's. Bigger yet and Plymouth, St Patrick's and the entire south would be in danger. Frank Savage wrote in his diary on 30 November: 'Volcano at its most advanced stage. No advance warning might be given of a collapse of the dome.'

The British volcanologists, including Willy Aspinall and the newly-arrived Englishman, Dr Simon Young from the British Geological Survey, knew any collapse would be difficult to predict. The study of dome collapse was a science in itself. But there was one man who knew more about it than probably anyone on the planet. He had predicted the strong possibility of an eruption and collapse at Mount St Helens in 1980. There had been friction between the American and Caribbean scientists on Montserrat earlier in the year, with the Britons caught in between, and the Americans had left somewhat abruptly, virtually personae non gratae. But there was only one man for this job. And he happened to be an American.

Barry Voight wished he had a dollar for every time he had been described as the actor Jon Voight's brother. But to volcanologists around the world, the men who risk their lives to study these fiery mountains, it should have been Jon Voight's claim to fame that he was Barry's brother. Jon may have played a 'Midnight Cowboy' on the big screen, but Barry, his big brother by a year, was what some call a 'volcano cowboy'. He was one of that small group of men and women who like to visit an active volcano, climb it, photograph it, sketch it, even talk to it in an attempt to read its mind: was it harmless, or was it a potential 'Wild Thing'? That Sixties hit song just happened to have been written by a third, younger Voight brother, known by his showbiz name Chip Taylor, and became a big hit for the Troggs. And Jon Voight's daughter, Barry's niece, just happened to be the actress Angelina Jolie, later to star as Lara Croft, Tomb Raider.

The aim of volcanologists is first and foremost to save lives. But Voight and his colleagues were the first to admit they'd climb those bubbling mountains for the pleasure of it anyway. A man could develop a relationship with a mountain.

So the British and Caribbean volcanologists on Montserrat called in Barry Voight in March 1996. The 'differences of emphasis' with the US Geological Survey team the previous summer had been set aside, if not entirely forgotten. One of the top Americans, Rick Hoblitt, had already returned to help out. Besides, the original concerns of the Americans had turned out to be justified. This volcano was no longer just steaming. It was growing and could well explode. Voight, a landslide expert and a professor of geosciences at Penn State University, was known among his peers for his definitive report on the 1985 eruption of the Nevado del Ruiz volcano in Colombia which wiped the town of Armero from the map, burying 23,000 of its residents in an avalanche of mud. The report was a classic of its genre. Its sprinkling of quotations from Albert Camus's *The Plague* might normally have seemed incongruous in a highly technical scientific report, but in this case they seemed eerily relevant. 'People in town are getting nervous, that's a fact . . . and of course all sorts of wild rumours are going around. The Prefect said to me, "Take prompt action if you like, but don't attract attention." He personally is convinced that it's a false alarm.' If you wanted to save lives, you wanted Barry Voight on your team.

Voight, a gravel-voiced, silver-bearded 57-year-old from Yonkers, New York, who had the same soft blue eyes as his brother, left his beloved two labradors and a beagle with his daughter and son-in-law in Pennsylvania and packed his bags for Montserrat on 17 March 1996 – St Patrick's Day. At the little airport, he was welcomed by green bunting, cardboard leprechauns and posters carrying this year's slogan in the local patois: '100,000 welcomes, cause all ah we ah one' (because we're all one). He knew he wouldn't have time to join the week-long celebrations. This growing dome worried him. He didn't yet know much about the lush mountain on this paradise Caribbean island. No one really did. It had burst into life too suddenly. It reminded

Voight uncannily of the Merapi volcano on the Indonesian island of Java where, a year earlier, he had seen the aftermath of a tragic eruption which left an indelible impression on him.

Voight had climbed the 9,500-foot Merapi (meaning 'Mountain of Fire') volcano many times in earlier years, often donning a gas mask against sulphur dioxide, even though it was considered one of the world's most active volcanoes. It had erupted 70 times in the last 1,000 years. Voight considered these decent enough odds to go up, along with Indonesian colleagues and students, and place the kind of devices that would take the volcano's pulse in the hope of saving lives. But the devices proved virtually useless when the mountain actually blew. So did the offerings of the local priests and medicine men who considered the mountain sacred and used to climb to the crater to leave handcrafted works of wood or silver.

On 22 November 1994, Merapi's dome collapsed without warning in a series of massive pyroclastic flows and surges. When he interviewed survivors, studied ash deposits and analysed data recorded on seismic equipment, Voight realised that the 66 people who died never had a chance. Like ground-hugging hurricanes, the red-hot surges of ash and gas had careened down the mountain, overflowing canyons and instantly incinerating everything and everyone in their path. They either burnt or choked to death, or died of shock, or in lingering agony in hospital.

Although the number of victims was not overwhelming, what got to Voight was the unpredictable suddenness of the event. One pyroclastic surge had churned through a village wedding ceremony on the rim of a canyon. The bride, groom and most of the guests may not even have heard the grey monster approach until it was too late. It swept over the ridge at up to 100 miles an hour, almost silently, engulfing them before they knew what hit them.

On Montserrat, Voight gave a slide presentation to Governor Savage, local government officials, Police Commissioner Hooper and the rest of the scientists, showing what had happened at Merapi and stressing that a similar dome collapse and lethal pyroclastic flow could easily occur on the little Caribbean island. Then, on 27 March 1996, he joined his English colleague Simon Young on a helicopter overflight for an aerial look at the dome. HMS *Southampton* had gone and with it the Lynx helicopter and its crewmen, Anderson and Marsh. To replace them, Britain had hired a small chopper from a private company, St Lucia Helicopters, from the island of that name. The new pilot was Jim McMahon, a Canadian veteran of southeast Asia. He and his compact Bell 206 Jet Ranger, with its goldfish-bowl cabin, would become a local legend in little more than a year. Forgoing the traditional pilot's jumpsuit, he favoured a denim shirt, shorts and jungle boots. Like almost everyone else on the island, that quickly got him a nickname, at least behind his back – 'Knees'. 44-year-old McMahon, from Ontario, had recently been chasing polar bears across the high Arctic for a group of scientists trying to tag them. He had also joined a gold rush, and helped put out forest fires, but he'd never tried to outrun a pyroclastic flow.

The scientists knew that the most immediate threat came from Castle Peak, on the north-eastern flank of the volcano. That was where the last eruption had clearly occurred, centuries earlier, and where the new dome had emerged. The dome faced a glaring, horseshoe-shaped gap in the crater rim, like a chip on the side of a bowl, where the experts estimated a huge collapse had taken place before the island was colonised. The gap reminded Barry Voight of the one at Mount St Helens after it blew in 1980. If there was a big enough collapse now, any material was likely to spill through the gap.

On the slopes below the gap lay the village of Long Ground, site of a popular hillside restaurant renowned for owner James 'Mountain Man' Lee's home-grown fruit and vegetables. Lee had been advised to evacuate but refused to abandon his restaurant and farmland. Below and to the north of Long Ground lay the villages of Harris and Farm. In the seaside plain lay Trant's, Spanish Point and the little airport, now renamed W.H. Bramble airport after the island's first Chief Minister. More than a thousand people lived or farmed in the area.

Of most concern to Barry Voight was the western flank, in particular the part of the crater rim known as Gage's Wall, a rock face towering above Plymouth. The expanding dome was already pushing against the wall. If the dome grew enough to break through or overflow the wall, gravity itself would ensure Plymouth took a direct hit from a pyroclastic flow. Gage's Wall was some three miles from Plymouth harbour. A pyroclastic flow was liable to travel at 60 mph or more: a mile a minute, at least. So a flow could hit Plymouth harbour in under three minutes. People in Town, unless they saw the flow begin and were sitting in a fast boat in the harbour with the engine running, would be fried.

It was the clearest day in weeks as pilot Jim McMahon wheeled over St Patrick's, the lush Bamboo Forest and the Great Alps Falls. Looking down from the little Bell helicopter, Barry Voight thought of his childhood, fishing for trout or playing Tarzan with his brothers, swinging from trees in the woods around Yonkers. Although areas around the crater were ashy grey, most of The Mountain had the green-black sheen of a duck's neck. It looked so peaceful, Voight thought.

McMahon eased the little chopper over the village of Long Ground and towards the Tar River Valley, inching towards the steaming lava dome for an 'up close and personal' look. Simon Young, a native of Cirencester who had studied at both Liverpool and Lancaster universities, was taking pictures, as always, through the open front left side. When they passed over 'Mountain Man' Lee's restaurant on the edge of Long Ground, Voight had an uneasy feeling. He had awoken at 6 a.m. with what he later descibed as 'much discomfort' over the fact that people were still living in Long Ground. He felt an explosive 'event' in that direction was a distinct possibility. He had not been able to get it out of his mind all day.

The scientists had strongly advised the villagers to move out because of the threat of a pyroclastic flow. But Mountain Man had only recently returned from London and put his life savings into his restaurant and farm. The fruit and vegetables were not doing well. The soil seemed to be drying up, as if something was draining it. But he wasn't inclined to give up now.

Although they were wearing headphones with microphones, those on board the helicopter were silent. This was not a good moment to distract a pilot who had your life in his hands. In any case, McMahon knew what the scientists needed. He made a series of 'aerial switchbacks' to gain altitude and get the Jet Ranger close to the dome. When he was less than 100 yards from the monster, he held the chopper motionless in the air and swivelled to the right to allow Young to film from the left front seat. That's when somebody broke the silence: 'Holy sh . . . , look at nine o'clock low . . . I think she's blowing . . .' McMahon looked over his left shoulder. He knew every split second would count if the volcano erupted. But he had to know what was happening. He had to know which way to run.

A large chunk of the lava dome, equivalent to a fair-sized hill, was collapsing and plummeting down the flank of the dome, throwing up an expanding, turbulent, pale tan cloud. McMahon had to make an immediate decision. If the cloud turned into a fast rising plume from a large pyroclastic flow, he had to work out which direction it would move. He'd want to go the opposite way, fast. Even if they were far above the ground-hugging pyroclastic debris, the hot ash in a rising plume could choke the engine and down the little chopper. If the collapse turned into an explosion and a full-fledged eruption column, it could engulf and incinerate them before they had a chance to flee.

McMahon had done his homework. He'd never seen a fast-moving cloud like this before, but he was an experienced military pilot who had flown some of the Cold War missions you don't get to read about, and he'd prepared himself for various hazard scenarios around this angry mountain. He knew the winds on this clear day were easterly as usual, the trade winds, so any rising ash plume would move west. He had also listened closely to the scientists, who believed that the island's first pyroclastic flows would be down the Tar River Valley, just south of Long Ground. They were right.

The scientists saw the hot flowing debris rush down and

swill around inside the ancient crater. It banged against the crater rim, climbed it, then thundered down the Tar River Valley towards the ocean. They could feel the heat through the chopper's open doors. Just to the north, in Long Ground, the villagers saw a plume of fine ash rise from the valley like a rapidly-growing cauliflower. They'd never seen anything like it. Some gazed in awe. Some jumped in their cars and raced north.

To the scientists, this 'event' was what they had long feared and more recently predicted. It was a searing avalanche of ash, gas, and red-hot giant blocks broken from the dome. The rolling avalanche followed the twisting path of the Tar River, descending by precisely the route that Jim McMahon had earlier flown up. Had the chopper been low in the valley now, and McMahon and his passengers not fixing their eyes on the dome, they might well have been engulfed by the rising plume. But the Canadian had wheeled to the south and then eastward over the sea. Voight and Young were able to watch and photograph the scorching debris roll down the valley like a bubbling tan streamer.

As the dust and debris settled, McMahon took the little chopper back in close. On the banks of the Tar River bed, the searing current had left trees and brush burning in its wake. The people down in Long Ground were lucky. Had the flow been larger, enough to come over the top of the Tar River's northern banks, they could have been hit by the red-hot ash hurricane. Death would have been almost instant.

So this was the island's first pyroclastic flow. It could have been a lot worse. If a larger portion of the dome had collapsed, the flow would have been bigger and faster. The scientists in the chopper knew that if the dome kept on growing, the pyroclastic flows would increase in size and power. If it collapsed in the other direction, to the west, it could bury or roast large parts of Plymouth in a matter of minutes at most. Of the island's 11,000 population, some 8,000 lived in Plymouth, St Patrick's and villages nearby. The first pyroclastic flow had shown what The Mountain could do. The lives of these 8000 people, and their homes, businesses and farms, were now under serious threat.

On 30 March, 1996, Frank and Veronica Savage flew to England for some long-awaited leave and Foreign Office debriefings. As always, the head of the island's legislature, native Montserratian Professor Howard Fergus, took over as acting governor. The Savages felt Winston, the green-eyed terrier with a nose for storms and earth tremors, would be lonely and maybe nervous in the big Government House, despite having the staff to look after him, so they left him with a dog-sitting friend in the village of Salem. The 'First Dog' was never to see his first real home again.

Not all the scientists believed Long Ground was seriously threatened. But Voight did, and he explained the threat to the acting governor. Fergus needed little convincing. He was a native of Long Ground and had been well briefed on the potential effects of pyroclastic flows. The scientists also called Rose Willock to enable her to explain to her listeners what had happened and urge them, in her inimitable way, not to panic. The sky in the south had been darkened by the flow's accompanying ash cloud and, as it blew west, was seen by those in the safe zone. On the advice of the scientists, the acting governor had to make what would turn out to be a momentous decision. But first he had to make a phone call.

9

The leaving of Plymouth

His Excellency the Governor of the British Dependent Territory of Montserrat, British West Indies – Frank Savage from Preston – had just attended a debriefing at the Foreign and Commonwealth Office in Whitehall. He was on the train to his home in north Kent when his mobile phone rang. Savage hated that sound, especially in crowded carriages. It was usually somebody's wife calling to ask hubby if he'd be home in time for dinner. Even worse were the loud-voiced husbands on the train who phoned to say they'd be home early. Late, he could understand. But early?

This was a call from Montserrat, and he could just make out the quiet-spoken voice of acting governor Howard Fergus, breaking up as the train thundered into tunnels. Savage had to repeat Fergus's words out loud to make sure he was getting it right. As he did so, dozens of pairs of eyes were raised discreetly from books and *Evening Standard* crosswords.

'Serious threat? Okay, Howard,' said Savage. 'Evacuate Plymouth? Yes, of course. Evacuate the entire south? Okay, Howard. Today? Fine. I'll return as soon as possible.'

He could not help but wonder what his fellow passengers made of *that* conversation.

★

In her radio studio at 2 p.m. on 3 April 1996, Rose Willock introduced acting governor Fergus, best known as the island's leading academic, poet and historian but also something of a black nationalist and anti-colonialist despite his constitutional role. To Professor Fergus, the annual St Patrick's Day celebrations on Montserrat were most definitely to commemorate the slave revolt, not Ireland's patron saint.

As always after a major event, virtually the entire island was tuned in to ZJB. 'The scientists at the MVO have advised the government that the Soufrière Hills volcano has undergone significant changes since 6.52 a.m.,' Fergus said softly. 'Ash emission has been continuous and, in addition, there's an opening in the eastern flank of the lava dome which may suggest eruptive activity. The scientists have advised that it would be prudent to immediately evacuate people living in the danger zone, as to do otherwise would be to act irresponsibly. The chief minister, his government and myself have agreed on such an evacuation, to take place today.' The previous shelters – schools, churches and community centres – would be open again. He asked southerners, the vast majority of the population, to lock up their property and be out by 6 p.m. That gave them four hours.

As a historian, Professor Fergus was well aware of the import of his statement and its impact on his fellow islanders. They were being asked to abandon their homes, farms and businesses again. This time the volcano threat was very real. Fergus knew they would comply, and they did.

Rose Willock had to repeat the evacuation order throughout the day. 'You are asked to take your passport, your birth certificate, savings account book, all those important documents,' she told the islanders. 'Bring your marriage certificate, your land certificate if you own land, and an overnight bag, with enough food to last three days.' She was not only broadcasting. She was living the news. In between broadcasts, she rushed home to her own villa at Upper Amersham to pack those items herself. Then she helped ZJB staff move vital broadcasting equipment out of the state-of-the-art studios on Lovers' Lane.

Three days' provisions. The residents of Plymouth, St Patrick's and the rest of the south, around 8,000 people, assumed they'd be home within days. They had no idea what lay ahead.

While Governor Frank Savage prepared to fly back from England, his staff packed some of his and his wife's clothes from Government House, the most important documents from his outhouse office and the terrier Winston's bed. They shut the wooden louvres tight, in the hope of keeping out volcanic ash, and locked up.

One of Frank Hooper's men, Constable Kelvin White, started his shift at 4 p.m., helping move equipment from the Plymouth HQ to Salem police station. But he had his own family on his mind. His father John and mother Linda were at their home and farm in Trant's village, next to the airport, below Long Ground and directly below The Mountain's north-eastern flank. With permission from his superior officer, he sped home to try to help his family. Sped is the word. He was stopped by a fellow cop on the Cork Hill road for doing 65 mph in a 40-mph zone. There may have been a volcano erupting, and almost the entire island may have been relocating, but this cop was not to be distracted. He had a new toy, a speed gun, the first ever on the island. 'What can I do, Kelvin?' White's fellow officer asked. 'It's switched on. Your speed's recorded. I've got to book you.' He did.

Across the road from the Plymouth police station, Mark and Tricia Bridge, expats from Surrey, ushered their lunch guests out of their restaurant, Moles, as soon as they heard the evacuation order on the radio. They scooped up the day's takings, grabbed the inflatable pink 'flying pig' from above the bar and headed south to their home outside St Patrick's to pack a suitcase. They left behind the island's only traffic light, an old English one that decorated the bar, and headed north to seek accommodation with friends.

On the road to St Patrick's they passed Father Larry Finnegan. He'd thrown some clothes into a suitcase before locking up the presbytery in Plymouth's George Street, as well as the Catholic church next door. Now, he was headed for St Patrick's village to pick up the Blessed Sacrament once more and return to the St Martin de Porres Church in Salem. Tonight he'd be sleeping there, on his hard military cot by the door, alongside as many refugees from St Patrick's as would fit into the church. Mass would be said in the conference room at the multi-purpose Vue Pointe hotel down the road.

Danny Sweeney and his partner Margaret, the lass from Sunderland, already lived in the safe zone, in Salem, but Danny went into Town to help friends pack and evacuate. He'd never seen anything like it on the island. A line of vehicles headed north. It was like a gold rush. Everybody gave him the usual toot of their horn as they passed. 'Ahl-right, Danny?'

On the corner of Strand Street and Houston Street, a block from the War Memorial and the red public phone booth, Danny saw his friend John Watts loading essentials on to a pick-up truck from his Harbour Court restaurant, bar and renowned 16-flavour ice-cream parlour. Danny had danced the night away often in that place. He'd seen Elton John in there after recording sessions. He'd seen Stevie Wonder, Paul McCartney, Eric Clapton. He'd taken the members of Dire Straits there to taste Watts' superb soursop fruit-flavoured ice-cream. And he'd seen 53-year-old Watts, from Kinsale near St Patrick's, give Boy George the cold shoulder on account of what he termed the singer's 'peculiar proclivities'. John Watts was famed for not closing until his last customer left. Rare was the Saturday that Rose Willock didn't enjoy her goatwater, the island's national dish and Irish stew lookalike, in the Harbour Court.

Watts was removing his precious ice-cream machines to a relative's flat in Olveston, in the safe zone close to the Vue Pointe hotel. He was leaving his crushed-ice equipment and his expensive walk-in freezer behind, but he hoped to sell ice-cream from the garage of his relative's apartment. He had also thrown up a tiny wooden hut, little bigger than a phone booth, in Salem, where he hoped to sell his mango, guava, coconut, soursop and other flavours until everyone returned to Plymouth and to normal.

James and Mildred Farrell were neighbours of Watts in Plymouth with their tailor's shop and Bird's Nest bar on the seafront. James was a black Montserratian, a retired soldier in the British army, a master tailor and formerly the world's only black kiltmaker. Among his clients were Prince Charles and several Scottish regiments. His wife Mildred was German and spoke a unique mix of English and local patois, sprinkled with lots of German *mits*, *vons* and *unds*. They packed as much Heineken and Guinness as they could carry, and they, too, built a temporary replacement for the Bird's Nest bar, a wooden shack in Salem close to Watts' ice-cream booth.

Between these two shacks, on the same former brushland, another, larger wooden structure had been built. It was Arrow's Man Shop, the new temporary clothing and music store of Alphonsus Cassell, part-time shopkeeper, part-time world-touring soca singer. Among the CDs on sale was his own latest. It captured the mood of the island and encouraged the islanders to persevere.

The island's in despair, destruction everywhere,
People living out in the air, in the aftermath of
    Nature's wrath.
Oh, oh, oh, oh, oh, have a little faith.
I say to the survivors, in time we will work wonders,
Mourn not your loss, forget the cost, it could have
    been worse.
In time our wounds shall mend, let us rebuild again,
Have a little faith.

When Danny Sweeney finally drove out of Plymouth at the tail of the evacuation convoy, it was all but deserted of humans. But there were dogs all over the place, barking or whining, confused by the exodus, aware something was wrong. Dozens of stray brown island terriers were roaming George Street. A few remained in their usual spot around the red phone booth. Others were around the seafront Public Market, sniffing out scraps of fruit and vegetables. In gardens and front yards there were many more, house pets or guard dogs these, but left behind, many of them chained, by owners who planned to be back soon. There would be no pets allowed in shelters, the radio said.

Danny drove round the Evergreen roundabout and thought he saw a white-haired figure disappear behind the famous Evergreen Tree. Looked like it might be Never Me, the friendly oldtimer whose home was a plastic bag on the seafront. Danny looked again, but the figure had gone. The tree, though a tangled mass of branches since Hurricane Hugo, looked rather eerie in the early evening light. He had rarely seen it without people sitting around it, limin' or playing dominoes.

The whole place was spooky. Danny thought of the old stories of jumbies, or ghosts, passed down through generations. Some older folks used to walk into their homes backwards at night, to make sure jumbies didn't follow them. If you saw one, you had to light a match, but make sure not to drop it. If you did, the jumbie would follow you home and beat you to death. But they only come out at night. Danny laughed to himself at the thought and drove on. As soon as the evacuation order was lifted, he thought, he, Margaret and their little daughter Sarah would come back for a seat, for a ginger beer and to lime with friends in the cool shade of the Evergeen Tree's umbrella branches.

10

Furnaces of the gods

Montserrat was now an island threatened by a volcano. The irony was that, like most of the other islands in the Lesser Antilles, it owed its very existence to one.

The word 'volcano' conjures up images of exotic snow-capped conical mountains, of the agonisingly-twisted victims at Pompeii, of glowing orange lava oozing down Mount Etna. But volcanoes are a geological foundation of our world. The landscape of the planet Earth, its mountains, valleys and lakes, is largely the result of volcanic eruptions over hundreds of millions of years, of molten rock bursting through the Earth's crust, hardening and then being gradually sculpted by natural erosion. Even the two thirds of the Earth's landscape we cannot see, the ocean floor, is made up of volcanic lava in the form of rock known as basalt.

Some palaeontologists believe massive volcanic eruptions may have played a role in the worldwide extinction of sea and land species, including the dinosaurs, 65 million years ago. In recent years, space travel and images suggest there are active volcanoes elsewhere in the Solar System, including on Mars and Venus and possibly even the Moon, though the required source of heat remains unidentified.

Most of us have read of Vesuvius and its victims at Pompeii, or have followed the regular eruptions of Etna on television. But there are many volcanic sites in more familiar places. The famous Giants' Causeway tourist attraction of polygonal columns in Northern Ireland is made of volcanic basalt lava, sculpted over 50 million years of erosion after the eruption of a volcano, long since extinct and deflated. So is its Scottish cousin, Fingal's Cave on the isle of Staffa, which resembles a church organ and inspired Mendelssohn to write one of his greatest works. Arthur's Seat, the landmark crag looming over Edinburgh, is the site of an extinct volcano. In France's Massif Central, the Chaine des Puys or Chain of Peaks in the Auvergne region is, in fact, a chain of 90 volcanoes. Some were formed only a few thousand years ago, babies by geological standards. The fertile soil around the Volvic volcano is credited with the quality of the area's mineral water.

Tenerife and Lanzarote, the most popular tourist resorts in Spain's Canary Islands, are sitting on active volcanoes that could erupt again out of the blue. The El Teide volcano on Tenerife was erupting on the very day Christopher Columbus sailed past in 1492 at the start of his first attempt to reach Asia by a westward route.

Volcanoes, like all contours of the Earth's surface, are caused by 'plate tectonics', the constant shifting of the slabs that form the jigsaw of the Earth's crust. The plates covered by ocean are termed 'oceanic', the others 'continental'. The seven main plates and a similar number of smaller ones shift only a few centimetres a year but grind into, over or under each other, changing the shape of the Earth's surface.

If two continental plates collide, the Earth's surface gradually compresses and folds to create mountains. The mighty Himalayas are the result of the collision of the

Eurasian and Indian plates. If two oceanic plates bump together, one is forced down below the Earth's crust, into the hot viscous rock of the 'mantle', the largest area of the globe's internal structure. This process, known as subduction, causes the mantle to melt and the molten rock – magma – to rise through the overlying crust and burst out on the Earth's surface as lava. Thus a volcano is born.

This is how many islands were created, including Montserrat and the rest of the Caribbean string known as the Lesser Antilles. These islands were the result of the Caribbean oceanic plate being squeezed by the North and South American continental plates. Montserrat, like its neighbours Guadeloupe, Martinique, St Vincent and St Lucia, emerged millions of years ago, first breaking through the sea bed and eventually surfacing above the ocean. Most of the eastern Caribbean islands do not just house volcanoes. They *are* volcanoes.

To the ancient Greeks and Romans, volcanoes were the legendary furnaces of the gods, subterranean forges for the crafting of weapons of war. To the Greeks, the God of Fire was Hephaistos, his forge the bowels of the fiery mountain they called Hiera. The Romans believed their God of Fire, blacksmith to the other gods, toiled in the same mountain with his helpers, the one-eyed Cyclops, hammering out a shield for Achilles, invisible armour for Hercules and bronze arrows for Apollo. Their name for him was Vulcan and they later named the mountain near Sicily after him, Vulcano. It gradually became eponymous for all such fiery mountains, the 'u' becoming 'o' in some languages.

While some volcanoes deflate and sink after erupting, new ones continue to emerge. On 13 July 1831, a diplomatic incident broke out after a new island miraculously appeared in the Mediterranean between Sicily and Tunisia. It was the result of a submarine volcanic eruption. Sicily claimed it, but the British Navy and French scientists showed up and both planted their national flags. A war was averted when the island diplomatically sank just after Christmas the same year, just as swiftly as it had risen.

In the 1940s, a native Indian peasant in Mexico, Dionisio Pulido, used to throw his rubbish into a five-foot-deep hole in one of his cornfields near the village of Parícutin. He wondered why it never got filled up but put it down to the Lord of the Miracles, a crucifix figure revered by the local Tarascan Indians. In February 1943, Pulido heard rumblings around the hole and saw that a cone of ash and cinders had filled it in, rising above the height of his head. Spitting sparks, it grew and grew for a year until it reached over 1,000 feet and spread out across the peasant's farmland. Then it spewed lava, destroying Parícutin and other villages within several miles. It erupted for almost a decade before it went back to sleep.

By many peoples worldwide, volcanoes are worshipped as sacred. To others, they house evil spirits which must be appeased. Around Mount Fuji, the Japanese have temples where pilgrims can make offerings to the Sun God. In Nicaragua and El Salvador, native Indians used to throw young virgin girls into the lava lakes beneath their volcanoes to appease the gods after an eruption. The Nahuatl Indians who live on the foothills of Mexico's mighty Popocatepetl volcano, backdrop to Malcolm Lowry's novel *Under the Volcano*, worship it as a provider of rain and fertile soil. Around the Bay of Naples in Italy, below Mount Vesuvius, residents invoke St Januarius as their protector

Rose Willock, 'The Voice of Montserrat', on the air.

Leprechauns, including Sarah Sweeney (centre), on St Patrick's Day 1995.

Police Commissioner Frank Hooper and Governor Frank Savage.

The mountain explodes.

'The Mighty Arrow'.

Danny Sweeney chasing wahoo.

Cricketers ignore a pyroclastic flow.

Rick Anderson and 'Swampy' Marsh fly their Royal Navy
Lynx over Old Road Bay and the Vue Pointe Hotel.

Two-pronged pyroclastic flow,
25 June 1997.

Barry Voight …   … amid devastation after Boxing Day 1997.

Father Larry Finnegan with his flock, including Sarah Sweeney (right).

George Street, Plymouth, including Father Larry's church, almost buried by pyroclastic flows.

Postcard of Montserrat seafront, including War Memorial, pre-1995.

Partly-buried War Memorial and phone booth, 1998.

The War Memorial and seafront in 2002.
The old phone booth is long buried.

from eruptions. Below Etna, they pray to St Agatha, believing a miracle occurred in the third century AD when inhabitants of the town of Catania saw a lava flow threaten their city. They laid the veil of the martyred Agatha in front of the flow and the lava, believers say even now, miraculously stopped.

Despite the prayers, gifts and sacrifices, volcanoes have killed around a quarter of a million people in the last 300 years. In the Caribbean alone there have been 20 eruptions since the time of Columbus, killing 50,000. Around the world, many millions are still at direct risk from volcanic eruptions. Some two million people live within sight of Vesuvius which, scientists say, could erupt again at any time. One million live on the slopes of Indonesia's highly active Mount Merapi.

Although the study of volcanoes as a science lay many centuries ahead, the title of the world's first volcanologist might fairly have gone to the Roman naval officer, scribe and intellectual Gaius Plinius, known nowadays in English as Pliny the Elder, from the Bay of Naples. But his nephew, also named Gaius Plinius and so known as Pliny the Younger, who recorded the eruption of Vesuvius as a teenage scribe, tends to get the credit as the first true volcanologist. When Vesuvius blew on 24 August AD 79, Pliny the Elder, who was 56, tried to get closer, using a pillow to protect himself from falling pumice stone. He eventually succumbed either to volcanic ash and gases or heart failure. After speaking to eyewitnesses, his nephew provided the first written account of a volcanic eruption, accurately previewing what others would later record on film. There was a cloud 'like a pine tree, which rose to a great height like a tree trunk, spreading at the top into numerous branches. We saw the sea sucked back, as though repulsed by the convulsions of the Earth and many sea animals now lay captive on the sea shore,' Pliny the Younger wrote. It was the first description of the suction that precedes a volcano-induced tidal wave, or tsunami.

The eruption of Vesuvius, which buried the towns of Pompeii, Herculaneum and Stabiae and killed several thousand people, remains probably the world's best-known volcanic event, even though the same volcano has erupted 200 times since and other volcanoes have caused many more deaths. The three towns lay buried under solidified volcanic ash for hundreds of years, ensuring their perfect archaeological preservation as examples of the Imperial Roman world. And when proper excavation got under way in the mid-nineteenth century (it is still going on – part of Pompeii is yet to be uncovered), Italian archaeologist Giuseppe Fiorelli had the simple brainwave that was to turn Vesuvius into a legend and Pompeii into a world-renowned tourist attraction. Discovering that the dried, clay-like volcanic ash had encased the victims and pre-served their shapes like moulds even though their bodies had decayed, Fiorelli pumped plaster of Paris into the hollows. Then the ash encasement was carefully dug away. He was left with the now famous life-like forms of human and animal victims contorted in agony in the positions in which they died.

Vesuvius will almost certainly erupt again, and volca-nologists fear the next explosion will be far worse than that of AD 79. The difference now is that perhaps two million people live within the radius that the volcano's deadly pyroclastic flows could reach. Prediction and timely evacuation will be vital.

Vesuvius's destruction of Pompeii may be the best-known volcanic event, but Sicily's Mount Etna may still lay claim to being the world's best-known volcano. It is far bigger than Vesuvius and is almost continuously erupting, yet it has been much less deadly over recorded history. That's largely because it emits not the fast-moving pyroclastic flows of Vesuvius, but the slow-moving, glowing, molten red lava most associated with volcanoes until pyroclastic flows became noticed and analysed by volcanologists in the early twentieth century. Etna's worst eruption was in 1669, when lava oozed out for four months, destroying a dozen villages, damaging part of the busy town of Catania and leaving tens of thousands of people homeless. But no one was killed; people were able to flee in time. Once again, timely evacuation was the key, saving thousands of lives. No doubt it will be the key again if the mountain blows, but next time, as around Vesuvius, the stakes will be far higher. Hundreds of thousands of lives, in the area around Catania, will be at risk. Still, in the case of Etna, things are simpler. You can see Etna's lava coming. And you can outrun it unless you're caught unawares. But you can't outrun a pyroclastic flow.

The fact that the big Vesuvius eruption of AD 79 involved a pyroclastic flow did not become clear until after the excavation of Pompeii. The term itself did not become widely used until the turn of the twentieth century. Until 8 May 1902, to be precise.

Until that date, the picturesque town of St Pierre on the French West Indian island of Martinique, south down the Lesser Antilles chain from Montserrat, was known as the Paris of the Caribbean, a favourite retreat for wealthy white French who hired local blacks as servants and often took them back home. With a lush green mountain, La Montagne Pelée (Peeled Mountain), directly behind it, St Pierre bore a striking resemblance to the Montserratian harbour town of Plymouth, though several times bigger and more populated. Like Montserrat almost a century later, the town and island had just returned to normal after a devastating hurricane a few years earlier which killed 700 people. In St Pierre, horse-drawn trams carried the wealthy to and fro among the bright yellow-painted houses while sailing ships, steamers and rum and sugar boats sat at anchor offshore. Unlike Plymouth, there was no harbour. The summit of Montagne Pelée was five miles north of the town, twice the distance between Plymouth and its own green mountain.

At 8.02 a.m. on 8 May 1902, the Peeled Mountain erupted. There was a flash from its summit and a roar like Alpine thunder. The mountain burst open, sending a grey mushroom cloud billowing into the sky and a *nuée ardente*, a scorching cloud of gas-propelled ash and rock of at least 400 degrees centigrade, hurtling southward straight at St Pierre. Witnesses on boats estimated the churning grey ribbon came down at up to 300 mph. From the moment of the explosion, it took little over a minute to hit St Pierre. Almost all 27,000 inhabitants were cremated where they stood, sat, walked or lay.

In the town proper, only two people survived. One was a cobbler who was badly burnt. The other was destined for some renown. He was Louis-Auguste Sylbaris, a huge, muscular, 25-year-old, heavy-drinking black labourer known to everyone as 'Samson'. When the mountain blew, he was in solitary confinement in a bare stone cell outside the town prison after a brawl. Somehow the cell saved his life, although he too was badly burnt by the hot ash and gases. Rescuers found him three days later and he was eventually paraded as something of a freak in the big Barnum and Bailey circus in the United States – 'the only living object that survived the silent city of death'.

The Montagne Pelée eruption was the worst volcanic disaster, in terms of victims, of the twentieth century. It motivated a new generation of scientists devoted solely to volcanoes and brought the term 'pyroclastic flow' into their language. But it was a mountain in the United States, in the area known as the Pacific North-West near the Canadian border, that brought the term, and the phenomenon, to the attention of the modern world.

In early 1980, Mount St Helens, in Washington State, was a picture-postcard cone-shaped, snow-capped mountain, a tourist attraction towering above an area of forests and lakes. Geologists knew it was volcanic; it had erupted in the mid-nineteenth century. But, as in Montserrat, the locals and even the scientists had paid it little attention. As it turned out, it was to change the face of volcanology. What had been something of a nerds' pastime became a precise, fascinating and dangerous science and vocation. The modern 'volcano cowboys' were born. At Mount St Helens, one of them died.

Earth tremors under the mountain began in March 1980. Then, as its smaller cousin in Montserrat would do later, it began to spout steaming ash and rock. Scientists and journalists flocked to the area. The geologists warned it might explode and suggested evacuating tourists and residents. That did not go down well. As in Montserrat, tourism and property sales were the backbone of the local economy. Visiting scientists from the United States Geological Survey were heckled and barred from local bars and restaurants for 'scaremongering'.

Concerned by a growing bulge on the volcano's northern flank, the USGS called in a landslide and rock fall expert, a certain Barry Voight from Pennsylvania State University. After studying the volcano and the data, Voight warned that this mountain might not erupt in the usual fashion. He feared a lateral blast, a sideways explosion rather than one that would erupt vertically from the crater. His full report was circulated among scientists on 16 May 1980. He was proved right even sooner than he had expected.

On the morning of 18 May 1980, 30-year-old volcanologist Dave Johnston was at his observation post, a mobile home six miles north of Mount St Helens. It seemed a perfect spot from which to monitor the volcano. It was within the 'red' danger zone, and Johnston knew the risks better than most, but he was high above the valley floor. If she blew, he knew he might get valuable data and great pictures. After dawn, he radioed HQ to say all was normal. Then, at 8.32 a.m., he radioed again, this time with an excited, though professional voice. 'Vancouver, Vancouver, this is it!'

That was all he had time to say. He knew he was witnessing The Big One, every volcanologist's dream, until it becomes their nightmare. Johnston probably had a few seconds to realise that this collapse and pyroclastic explosion was so big and fast – more than 200 mph – that it would engulf his position almost immediately. He was dead within seconds of his radio transmission. The 'volcano cowboys' insist they have no death wish, but they know only too well what their mountains can do and they know the risks. Dave Johnston accepted the risk and paid the price. The explosion killed 57 people in all.

Five years later, the inexactitude of the science, the unpredictability of these fiery mountains, and the vital importance of timely evacuation was brought home to the world. In 1985, the South American nation of Colombia was not flavour of the year. It was best known as the cocaine-processing and exporting capital of the planet, its 'King' a drug baron called Pablo Escobar, and Marxist guerrillas ruled the roost in much of the country.

On 13 November 1985, while the nation was still in mourning over a shoot-out in the heart of Bogota which had left 100 hostages dead, Colombia's Nevado del Ruiz volcano blew its top. It wasn't the biggest eruption of the twentieth century, not by any means, but it would prove to be close to the deadliest.

'Nevado' in Spanish means 'snow-capped'. The volcano stood almost 18,000 feet high, three times as high as the average Alpine ski resort, and was capped year-round by snow and ice. In a river valley on its foothills, fully 35 miles from its peak, lay the picturesque town of Armero, population 25,000, not unlike a small Swiss or French town on the lower slopes of the Alps. Although the mountain had been rumbling and spouting ash, the mayor of Armero and local priests had been on the radio throughout the day telling townsfolk not to panic, that there was no need to evacuate.

They might have been right. The eruption was not a major one. The pyroclastic flows were minor. But they were enough to melt the snow and ice glacier around the mountaintop, millions of tons of it, effectively a giant reservoir whose dam had broken. The meltwater, like a fast-moving flooded river, followed the contours of the mountain down the course of the Lagunillas River, heeding gravity and sticking to the path of least resistance. As it descended in a raging torrent, it picked up mud, then rocks, and then, as its force grew, trees, boulders and anything else in its wake. By the time it turned a river bend above Armero it had travelled 35 miles, growing as it came. By then, it was a towering wall of thick mud, like a tidal wave inside the riverbed, no less than 120 feet high and hundreds of yards wide. Most people were at home, many in bed, but those in the streets must have looked up in terror as an inescapable wall of mud and boulders surged beyond the riverbed to engulf them.

Only 2,000 people survived by running to higher ground early enough. Some 23,000 perished, many slowly. Around the world, the human face of the tragedy became that of a single victim. Omaira Sanchez, a 13-year-old girl, was found alive and in good spirits but her body, though upright, was trapped between blocks of concrete and covered by muddy water up to her neck. Only her face and short, curly black hair were visible for three days as rescuers tried in vain to free her. The little face appeared on every TV station and every major magazine cover in the world, first smiling but later despairing and, as the cameras continued to flash and film, fading into a very public death.

Armero was the second most deadly volcanic eruption of the twentieth century, after the Montagne Pelée disaster on Martinique. The town was never rebuilt and Pope John Paul II later visited to consecrate it as a holy site.

Six years after Armero, the world's volcanologists were put to another life-or-death test, another to-evacuate-or-not-to-evacuate dilemma, and the Nevado del Ruiz disaster remained very much on their minds. Mount Pinatubo in the Philippines awoke in 1991 for the first time in at least half a millennium, threatening half a million people within striking distance of its crater. Like Montserrat, Pinatubo hadn't even been included in lists of the world's active volcanoes, and the developed world might have taken little notice had it not been for the fact that 16,000 American servicemen and women lived and worked at Clark Air Base, the biggest American military base outside the US. It was just 15 miles east of the crater. After Armero, lessons had been learnt. The United States Geological Survey sent in its equivalent of a police SWAT team, the Volcano Crisis Assistance Team (VCAT).

(Two of the top volcanologists, who would not have missed this one for the world, were tragically absent from Pinatubo. The French couple Maurice and Katia Krafft, legends in their lifetime for their daring escapades filming eruptions around the world, had fallen victim to their lifelong passion on 3 June 1991. They were filming the eruption of Mount Unzen in Japan, up close and personal as always. Like Dave Johnston at St Helens, they thought they were far enough away to be relatively safe. They were on a hill across a valley from the volcano, a valley that had previously diverted pyroclastic flows. Not this time. As they filmed, a pyroclastic surge just kept on coming. The Kraffts, along with American volcanologist Harry Glicken, a former student of Barry Voight, and 40 Japanese journalists, were incinerated.)

At Pinatubo, the American VCAT team together with Filipino scientists advised that a wide area around the volcano be evacuated. The American forces pulled out of Clark Air Base gradually, some of them in the nick of time.

When the biggest eruption came, on 15 June 1991, it buried areas where tens of thousands of people, many of them native Indian farmers, previously lived. The abandoned US base was covered in a thick layer of ash. Pyroclastic flows followed the lie of the land, hurtling helter-skelter down ravines, similar to the ghauts of Montserrat, that had themselves been carved out by volcanic flows in ancient times.

Because of a passing typhoon, the Pacific equivalent of a hurricane, rain compounded the problem and several hundred people were killed by lahars – the Indonesian word used by volcanologists worldwide to describe mudflows – or by collapsing roofs. Several hundred more, mostly native Indians, died within months from various diseases in refugee camps. In all, more than 1,000 people probably died, directly or indirectly, as a result of the eruption. Even that was relatively few in the circumstances. This had been one of the most powerful and violent eruptions in history. The volcanologists felt they had got it right. Evacuation had saved tens of thousands of lives and averted potentially the most lethal volcanic disaster in history.

Pinatubo also drew attention to another volcano-related problem. Its blast sent a column of ash no less than 25 miles high, well over 100,000 feet, spreading laterally in a mushroom cloud resembling a nuclear explosion. Commercial airline pilots had been warned for weeks about possible ash clouds in the area but some took them less than seriously. Few had ever seen an ash cloud climb higher than a high-flying airliner. Some pilots even flew closer to volcanoes, pointing them out to passengers like tourist guides. On 15 June 1991 at least a dozen commercial aircraft, carrying several thousand passengers between them, were caught up in Pinatubo's ash cloud as it rose and drifted with the westerly wind, even though they were several hundred miles from the volcano. None crashed but several lost altitude as ash clogged up engines. It was a danger that put further pressure on and caused further concern to the volcanologists. It meant that their judgement calls could affect not only lives on the ground, but thousands more in the skies.

The eruption also dramatically highlighted the threat of a worldwide 'volcanic winter'. Pinatubo's ash particles went on spreading for two years, covering the entire planet and countering the contemporary effects of 'global warming'. Despite the warming trend, average temperatures around the world fell between 1991 and 1993 as a result of Pinatubo's volcanic ash in the stratosphere. It brought early snow to Scotland in the winter of 1992/93, and some scientists believe the sulphuric acid from the eruption significantly increased the hole in the already dwindling ozone layer.

It was a reminder that volcanoes, wherever they may be, can and do affect us all.

II

'Now she puffs, but will she blow?'

In the spring of 1996, few Montserratians were concerned with the hole in the ozone layer. They were concerned with the holes in the roofs of their refugee tents and with the stinking holes in the ground many were forced to use as toilets. And they were concerned with the lava-plugged hole in the top of The Mountain, which was still showering them with heavy black ash, even in the so-called safe zone.

For the whole of the following year, from April 1996 to April 1997, they would live in hardship, in fear, often in the pitch blackness of ash clouds, and, most of all, in suspense. 'Now she puffs, but will she blow?' read the front of a new t-shirt with a picture of the volcano. And on the back: 'Trust the Lord and pray it's no.'

When Governor Frank Savage returned post-haste from his trip to London, the historic Government House in Plymouth was out of bounds and abandoned, its once magnificent gardens already coated in ash. In the village of Salem, across the Belham River valley from Plymouth and just inside the safe zone, residents walked around with construction-style hard hats or cardboard Carib beer cartons on their heads to protect them from falling ash and small stones. Drinkers in the rum shops wore surgical nose masks to keep out the ash, pushing the masks up whenever they needed a sip.

The Savages picked up Winston from their dog-sitter and moved back into the rented villa they nicknamed 'Camelot', in the centre of the island. Winston was glad to see them but Frank Savage noticed he was trembling more than usual. This was not the storm season, and the little terrier could not see The Mountain from here. The governor guessed he was feeling tremors beneath the volcano that only animals and the seismographs could detect. Sometimes he would just run to the governor's bedroom and hide among the pillows.

The governor quickly ran into a lot of flak. On 3 April 1996, during his absence, people had been told to pack provisions for three days. Weeks later, they were still crammed into schools, churches or stifling, tent-like huts, relying on government food handouts. They wanted to go home. But the volcano's dome, the new mountain that had burst through from beneath the earth as molten rock, was growing visibly by the day. The scientists knew it would almost certainly collapse sooner or later and that could mean a massive pyroclastic flow. 'The Big One Coming?' read a banner headline in the *Montserrat Reporter*, announcing that all events scheduled for Easter had been cancelled. '12,000 Body Bags?' asked another front-page headline a month later. It referred to rumours that the British government had flown in that number to be used in the event of a catastrophe. With typical humour, the newspaper cited jokes going the rounds about ordering your own colour of body bag in advance, or reserving two 'in case you're blown into two pieces'. The little black island was in crisis. But black humour was helping people cope.

For the first time, the world's media took notice of the little island in the Caribbean. Maps in newsrooms were hastily dusted off and the big names flew in. 'Will it? Won't it? When?' asked ITN's Michael Nicholson in an evening news report, shot with The Mountain behind him. 'Only one thing is certain. If it does finally open itself, much of this island will be destroyed. This mountain is holding people hostage.'

With the south evacuated, the islanders were now living in the west-central strip of the island or, mostly, in the rugged north. All except four. Two stubborn American couples, who had upped roots in the US and moved to the island to start a new life at the start of 1996, refused to budge. The couples did not know each other. The Kleebs lived on the island's west coast, with a couple of hillocks between themselves and The Mountain. The Chloupeks were on the east, directly below it.

Bob and Beverley Kleeb were newly-retired white Americans who had found the Michigan winters harsh on their ageing bones. Bev, a medical doctor and psychoanalyst, had also been diagnosed with cancer, so the couple decided to seek out a place in the sun to pass the rest of their days. They had first tried the Cayman Islands but were won over by the friendly reception they got from Montserrat islanders, these black folks with a hint of Irish brogue in their patois.

They bought a plot of land next to a steep cliff on Garibaldi Hill, north of Plymouth but still south of the Belham River valley that marked the border between the safe and evacuated zones. Then they built a villa with a pool and a magnificent view over the little golf course, down to the Vue Pointe hotel and across the sparkling ocean. The plan was to sip rum on their terrace and watch the sun go down until it no longer did. They had spent their life savings on this home. Evacuation order or no, the Kleebs weren't going anywhere. These scientists and this limey governor had their knickers in a twist over nothing, Bob Kleeb insisted. At night, after the evacuation of April 1996, anyone looking south from the Vue Pointe or the village of Salem towards the evacuated zone would see a pitch-black void, except for one cluster of lights on Garibaldi Hill, where Bob Kleeb was puffing on his pipe and having a rum on the rocks. The Kleebs could not know it then but their name was to become part of the language on the island. 'To kleeb it' would come to mean 'to tough it out'. It's still in use.

On the other side of The Mountain, on the island's windward east coast, Lewis Chloupek, a 50-year-old pig farmer from Nebraska with a handsaw mid-western drawl, had only just begun renovating a badly-damaged property that had been abandoned since Hurricane Hugo. His life savings of US$ 60,000 had bought him what used to be a large house, a restaurant, a small supermarket, a bar and a warehouse. His plan was to convert the whole thing into a series of apartments he could rent out to American and Canadian winter tourists, the so-called 'snowbirds'. In the mean time, he thought he saw a gap in the island's fruit market and planned to grow and sell pineapples. Chloupek's surname originated in Bohemia, but you could hardly imagine anyone less bohemian than this slight but wiry country boy from a village that apparently didn't get or expect many visitors. It was called Surprise, Nebraska, population 35. Lewis Chloupek, an old-fashioned God-fearing Baptist, had begun suffering from arthritis and decided to start a new life in the sun with his wife Sandra and three-year-old daughter Mary.

The property was at Spanish Point, facing Antigua, just

south of the little W.H. Bramble airport and the Trant's village farm and home of police constable Kelvin White and his family. From the back of the Chloupeks' new home, except for the historic Bethel Methodist church, there was nothing blocking their view up the slopes of The Mountain, past Long Ground, to the north-eastern rim. That, of course, meant there was nothing to block anything that came down in the other direction. Except perhaps the old stone church.

By early May, a month after the evacuation, pressure was building on Governor Savage and the local government of Chief Minister Reuben Meade to let islanders return to the south. People had fled with almost nothing. The Royal Marines had now departed and Police Commissioner Frank Hooper's police were hard pressed to keep people out of the exclusion zone. There had been several cases of looting, though most appeared to have been carried out by 'pirates' coming in by boat from other islands. Hooper had only one small patrol boat, the MV *Shamrock*, to watch the island's shores. The scientist currently in charge of the Montserrat Volcano Observatory, Dr William Ambeh from the SRU, felt the volcano was quiet enough to justify a return to the south. Like most of the islanders themselves, he was black and that won him particular respect among them. Rumours of racist differences had swept the island after reports of shouting matches at meetings involving white Governor Savage, black Chief Minister Meade, white Police Commissioner Hooper and an MVO currently including the Cameroonian Ambeh, several black scientists from the Caribbean, Willy Aspinall and other white British scientists, and white American landslide specialist Barry Voight.

The black men had stayed in cheap accommodation, constrained by the low budget of the Seismic Research Unit, whereas the Britons and Americans were put up in the plush hillside cottages of the Vue Pointe hotel or in rented luxury villas with pools. From the start of the crisis in July 1995, Ambeh and the Caribbean scientists consistently took the 'chill-out' approach which sat naturally with most of the islanders, strongly religious people who believed God would provide. The Brits and Americans had more experience of what volcanoes could do and tended to stress the dangers and err on the safe side. 'It was rather like seeing the glass as half empty or half full,' said Voight.

In the end, The Mountain made the decision for them. On Mother's Day, 12 May 1996 (the Montserratians celebrated the American date), the islanders were making the best of a fine, warm Sunday. The black sand beach at Old Road Bay, where Danny Sweeney ran his watersports business beneath the Vue Pointe hotel, had always been the favourite family spot for a Sunday outing. It was still in the safe zone, though only just. It had been cleaned up after the previous year's hurricanes and on this Mother's Day it was packed. Danny's partner Margaret was building sandcastles with their five-year-old daughter Sarah, whose brown hair was bleached almost as blonde as her mum's from spending most of her young life on the beach. Looking down from their clifftop villa inside the evacuated zone were the stubborn Kleebs. On the opposite hill, in the Vue Pointe hotel and in the safe zone, guests were enjoying the hotel's Mother's Day barbecue brunch. From the poolside tables, they had the perfect view of Chance's Peak, Gage's Mountain and the entire northern sweep of the Soufrière Hills.

Danny helped little Sarah clamber on to her favourite surfboard, a full-sized one he'd used to teach Sting and other stars to surf. Sarah was only five but Danny had fitted her a tiny sail the size of a headscarf. She was a natural but he stayed alongside her and made sure she stayed in the shallow waters beside the jetty.

It was then that he heard what he thought was a clap of thunder, subdued at first but rumbling louder. 'Daddy, daddy, look, look at The Mountain!' Sarah shouted. There was a thick column of bubbling grey ash directly above The Mountain, rising fast and expanding sideways. The cloud seemed to be plunging downwards to the windward eastern shore and the ocean, somewhere around Spanish Point, Trant's or the airport. Almost on the edge of the cloud, Danny could see the silhouette of Jim McMahon's little helicopter, probably carrying the scientists and getting some film footage.

On this, the western side, a separate cloud of black ash began drifting with the wind towards Old Road Bay, the Vue Pointe and the safe zone. As the cloud closed in, starting to block out the sun, people left the hotel's barbecue brunch, jumped into their cars and headed north.

Jim McMahon had been looking forward to his Mother's Day barbecue at the Vue Pointe, and to calling his own mum in Canada, but he had taken the Bell helicopter into the air at the first sign of a volcanic 'event'. With him went a couple of scientists, as well as Dave Williams, a young local cable TV technician who had joined the MVO team. Harnessed but balanced precariously with one leg on a skid of the doorless chopper, Williams caught some of the most dramatic volcano footage ever seen, the pyroclastic flow thundering down the Tar River valley, a swirling avalanche of grey, all the way to the eastern shoreline. Williams kept on filming and the volcanic flow kept on going. It surged on into the ocean, rolling out over the surface, sending up further clouds of steam and creating a liquid grey delta that would later consolidate and become a new land mass.

McMahon spotted a lone figure on the ground, a man trying to attract their attention. He was close to the shore, just south of the now-settled but still red-hot flow debris. Despite the heat, the Canadian eased the little chopper down on the only piece of land he could see that had not been covered by the ash and rock fall. It was rocky, and McMahon had to sit the aircraft down at an uncomfortably steep angle. One of the scientists leapt from the helicopter and physically bundled the man, still in shock from his close call, through its open door. He had wanted to get photographs of The Mountain from inside the abandoned zone. As it turned out, the pyroclastic flow came so swiftly, so quietly and so close that he forgot to press the shutter.

Up in New York City, Alphonsus Cassell, better known as Arrow, was about to go on stage at Madison Square Garden in the annual Mother's Day Caribbean All-Star Festival. The place was packed with the city's Caribbean population, swaying and jumping to calypso, reggae and soca, when Montserrat's most famous singer got a phone call from his sister Veronica in Arrow's Man Shop in Salem. A pyroclastic flow into the sea. Ash everywhere. Arrow's villa on Fox's Bay, the one with the arrow-shaped swimming pool, had been covered in ash. More and more people were leaving the island and there were fears of a total evacuation, she said. Arrow said he'd fly back right after the show. He went on stage and put his heart into his popular volcano song, 'Ah Just Can't Run Away', as Montserratians in the audience sang along:

> I know people are uneasy, some are depressed,
>   some frustrated
> But only the Lord Almighty controls our destiny.
> What is to be will be,
> I'll never forsake my country.
> You might run away from volcano, end up in
>   hurricane and tornado.
> Ah just can't run away, Ah just can't run away,
> As long as I can leave me door wide open
> I'll be holding on.
> Hold on, Montserrat, hold on to what you got.
> Oh, what a lovely country, I'll be holding on . . .

Back on the island, people were holding on as best they could. But many were packing to leave. John Major's government announced a voluntary evacuation scheme under which islanders who moved to Britain at their own expense would get state benefits for two years. As the summer of 1996 approached and temperatures rose, life in the shelters got steadily worse. Constable Kelvin White was once again sleeping in his car in the northern village of St John's. George Howe and his wife Annie, a local politician, who had had to abandon their Town and Country restaurant and store in Plymouth, had people sleeping in their other bar in the north, including on the billiard table.

Despite their cramped conditions in the St Martin de Porres Catholic church in Salem, Father Larry Finnegan considered that his former congregation from St Patrick's were living in relatively good conditions. Relatively. They did have a bathroom, showers and a kitchen, but they slept side by side in the church itself, with the pews removed, on rows of hard military cots and even on the altar. To avoid disrupting their 'home', the popular priest from Dublin held his Masses in the Pelican conference room at the Vue Pointe hotel. There, worshippers in the front left pews had a perfect view of the volcano. Hotel owner Carol Osborne and Governor Frank Savage used to vie to get a seat there so they could keep one eye on The Mountain. Once, Savage saw a black ash cloud rise and slipped out of the room, without disturbing Mass, to check with the scientists how serious it was. It wasn't, and he went back in.

In the summer, Carol Osborne, a practising Catholic who liked to remind visitors she was 'seven eighths Irish', persuaded an exhausted Father Larry to use a bed at the hotel, but he insisted on going back to the church to cook and eat with the refugees during the day. In the afternoons, he would take their children down to the beach at Old Road Bay to keep them clean and out of their parents' hair for a while. Some nights, Carol saw him slump, exhausted, in front of the TV in the hotel lounge, watching one of his beloved John Wayne or Clint Eastwood movies. She couldn't but smile as this peace-loving man spoke the actors' lines and urged them out loud to go get the bad guys.

It wasn't only the lack of tourists that made these tough times for Carol, originally from Boston but now Montserratian like her husband Cedric. With the capital, and all therein, abandoned, the Vue Pointe became the island's hub. After laying the hotel's Pelican Room out for Mass, then attending it, she had to remove the crucifix and other religious accoutrements and replace them with a makeshift dock and witness stand for the island's High Court sessions. After that she'd have to reshuffle again for meetings of the island's parliament before kitting it out again for whatever conference, cocktail party or big dinner came up. By Sunday, it would be back to square one and Mass.

Farther north, the 100-odd refugees in the old Anglican church in the village of St Peter's were not as well off as Father Larry's flock. They were crammed even closer together, though some of the evacuees draped sheets between poles for a degree of privacy. Entire families shared a few square yards of floor space. Wet underwear was hung on the altar to dry. A shack outside in the grave-yard served as the kitchen, with a burner using bottled gas. Two other shacks served as pit toilets. The old, faded gravestones became multi-purpose. Tall ones gave privacy for those who could not endure the queue for the toilet. (Many of the refugees were old and incontinent, an embarrassment to themselves and a problem for all in the cramped conditions.) Flat gravestones became beds, not always for married couples. Refugees expressed concern that young homeless men had begun hanging out near the church because of the number of young refugee girls. Several teenage pregnancies were reported. As always, somebody wrote a calypso – 'Volcano Baby'.

The refugees had to get by on basic government food handouts and vouchers for other essentials. Local opposi-tion politician David Brandt, 'The Heavy Roller', laid into the British governor, Whitehall and Chief Minister Reuben Meade. Refugees were still paying not only their mortgages but telephone, water, electricity and cable TV bills for their homes or businesses in the ash-covered evacuated zone, Brandt protested. He also noted that refugees had been given tins of food that not only carried expired, five-year-old sell-by dates but also German-language instructions they could not understand. Where had Britain come up with this stuff? he asked. Children were getting sick; some of their tongues were turning green; others found worms or fungus among chocolates in handout packages. Diarrhoea was prevalent.

Brandt went so far as to compare the refugees' conditions with those of their slave forefathers while being shipped out from Africa. That was somewhat over the top, but his words began striking a chord and Meade's popularity slipped. In the meantime, the refugees often kept up morale by singing hymns. They were homeless. They were still under threat from a volcano. But you could hardly walk past St Peter's church without hearing refugees launch into a verse of 'How Great Thou Art'.

Bob and Beverley Kleeb, the retired couple from Michigan, continued to defy the evacuation order. In August 1996, they were still living in their villa on Garibaldi Hill, in the designated danger zone, with their dogs and parrots. But that month, the authorities cut gas, electricity, water and phone lines to the area. 'What are we gonna do now, kid?' Bev Kleeb asked her husband.

Bob took a deep puff on his pipe and looked out over the ocean. 'What the hell, I came to this house to die and I guess I'm gonna die right here.' He meant from old age. Bob Kleeb was convinced no pyroclastic flow could reach his home.

'Yeah, I guess if we're gonna be french-fried, may as well have it happen here,' said Bev. They would stay on. Now they really would have to 'kleeb it'.

The governor's bottom line was trying to keep people alive, trying to keep them out of the danger zone, but the retired couple from Michigan never forgave the Englishman for cutting them off. Now they were refugees in their dream home. No more swimming in their pool, the one that pelicans used to dive into, thinking the blue-tiled dolphin on its floor was real. The pool became their water supply, for washing themselves and their dishes and for flushing the toilet. They kept it well fluoridated and prayed for rain. And they still had their mobile phone. With a little help from their friends, they got themselves a petrol-run generator. If they needed petrol, they'd bring empty canisters to the barrier of the safe zone and Danny Sweeney would pick them up and bring the cans back full. The Kleebs still had their villa and plenty of space. The Montserratian refugees were not so lucky.

As for Frank Savage, he could have taken the easy way out. His assignment was due to end in September 1996, but in June he announced that he would stay on an extra year, out of solidarity with the islanders and to maintain continuity of crisis management.

Throughout the summer of 1996, the volcano belched ash clouds several thousand feet into the air. There were regular, but smaller, pyroclastic flows down the Tar River valley, still not breaching its sidewalls but getting perilously close to villages such as Long Ground. These had been officially evacuated but people were known to be slipping around police checkpoints to tend their animals or crops or to check their homes and businesses.

On 11 August 1996, Frank Hooper and his wife Sheila joined a group of the volcanologists on a fact-finding boat trip off the Tar River estuary, off the new land mass created by hardened ash and cooled volcanic rock earlier in the year. The idea was to measure the depth of the new pyroclastic material. The retired Sussex policeman was driving his force's new toy, a speedy commando-type RIB, or rigid inflatable boat, of the type used by Britain's Special Boat Squadron. In requesting it, he had cited the need to chase drug runners, smugglers or looters, but to a sailor like himself it also happened to be a hell of a lot of fun. It had awesome acceleration, but Hooper knew it would take more than this little beauty to outrun a pyroclastic flow. So he'd brought along the police force's only other vessel, the patrol boat MV *Shamrock*, as a communications back-up.

Sheila Hooper stayed on the *Shamrock* along with a group of MVO scientists, their walkie-talkies tuned into the observatory, their binoculars trained on the top of The Mountain. Hooper and one scientist moved in close to the new land mass on the RIB to make depth checks. The ocean was still warm, almost hot, from the pyroclastic material of previous days as the scientist took depth readings using old-fashioned technology – a piece of lead on the end of a string.

Hooper trusted the scientists' expertise, but not their eyesight. As he eased the dinghy in backwards towards the hot grey delta, keeping the bow pointed out to sea ready for the quickest of getaways, he kept his own walkie-talkie next to his ear and his eyes fixed on The Mountain. Several pyroclastic flows tumbled down the upper reaches of the Tar River as he watched, but they all ran out of steam – except for one. 'Big PF [pyroclastic flow], Frank, let's get out of here,' came a voice on his radio from the *Shamrock*. He didn't need the warning. He had hit the throttle. The little RIB caught up with the *Shamrock* in a couple of seconds and they both got to a safe distance.

The last thing Hooper recalled seeing before the flow was Sheila on the *Shamrock*, waving her camera at him, upset because she had run out of film. As it turned out, that pyroclastic flow did not reach the ocean.

At a series of meetings involving Governor Frank Savage, Chief Minister Reuben Meade, the MVO scientists and other key figures in the late summer of 1996, it was decided to tighten the cordon on the evacuation zone. The police, the volcanologists and Savage himself toured the south to seek out violators and urge them to leave. When Frank Hooper went through his own police checkpoint and cruised through Plymouth, now grey from coatings of ash, it occurred to him that it looked like a scene from one of Father Larry Finnegan's favourite Sergio Leone spaghetti westerns. A southerly wind coming round The Mountain howled and blew ash along the streets.

Governor Savage, alone in his white Land Rover Discovery, also drove down into the no-go zone. He had checked with the scientists that the volcano was quiet and he was tuned in to the MVO's radio frequency. Plymouth appeared deserted but for the hundreds of dogs, donkeys, goats and cows wandering around among the ash. As always, there were stray island terriers lounging beside the old red telephone cabin by the seafront clockstand, some of them more grey than brown from lying in the ash. It struck him how many of them looked like his own Winston. Quite a few had the same green eyes. He got out, put several opened cans of dog food on the street and watched them be hastily devoured. The London-based World Society for the Protection of Animals (WSPA) had contacted the island via Whitehall after Savage and others had made the plight of such animals known. The governor hoped its animal relief experts would arrive soon.

He drove south through Plymouth past the locked-up Government House, his former home and office, where Winston had been tossed over the wall as a puppy. He passed Moose's now ash-covered Seaquarium seafood restaurant on the old pier in Kinsale and drove on up to St Patrick's. At first sight it looked deserted, but then he heard thumping reggae music through his open car window. He followed the sound uphill to the Spreadeagle bar, which used to be a focal point of St Patrick's Day celebrations. The governor could hardly believe his eyes. Outside the bar, under the volcano, in the evacuated danger zone, there was bar owner Peter Dyer, eating barbecued lobster and drinking blond Carib lager with three other men.

Frank Savage was nothing if not a diplomat. He offered up a round of Caribs and Dyer gave him a piece of lobster. The bar owner had lived much of his life in London, on Riversdale Road close to Highbury Stadium, working for the Post Office, but his last known address was a cot near Father Larry Finnegan's in the Catholic church in Salem. Dyer remained a staunch Arsenal supporter and now joked about it with the governor.

'You can talk about the Gunners all you like, but did you ever see the great Preston North End side with Tom Finney?' asked Savage.

Dyer laughed. He was well aware Savage had not come by to talk about football. 'We just came in for the day, Governor, to check our property,' he insisted.

The governor smiled. These perishers are crafty, he thought. He was sure they were living there despite the ban, despite the danger, lying low when the police came by, keeping their lights off at night.

'Let me come tell you now, Mr Governor,' the oldest drinker interrupted. 'A ya me barn, a ya me rear [I was born and raised here]. Me live here seventy years, me goin' die on this mountain fuh true.'

'The problem is, I have to commit the lives of young Montserratians, the security forces, to save you,' said Savage.

The men promised to leave but the governor took it with a pinch of salt.

A week later, Savage returned. The Spreadeagle bar was open again. This time there were even more men, a dozen of them, sitting around drinking. 'The word had obviously got around that the governor was buying drinks,' he told his wife later. He did buy a round but this time skipped the football small talk. He was about to get straight to the point when The Mountain did it for him.

There was a deafening rumble like overhead thunder. The little bar trembled, and Carib bottles and rum tot glasses toppled from tables and shelves. 'It was quite a volcanic event,' he said. 'And it was unnerving, to say the least. Semi-solidified mud and pumice hammered the corrugated iron roof. It sounded like somebody was riddling it with machine-gun bullets.'

The governor tried to reach the MVO by walkie-talkie but got no signal. 'We waited for a bit but if you stay and it escalates, you're dead meat,' he said afterwards. 'I left and headed north. The others said they would do the same.' By the time Savage got out of St Patrick's and was down on the coast by Moose's, the Land Rover's windscreen-washer liquid was used up. His windscreen was a sheet of mud.

For a while he drove on by leaning out of the driver's window but his glasses got muddied and he finally had to stop. 'It was unbelievable. And eerie. Suddenly this smiling black face appears at my window and this hand is washing my windscreen,' the Englishman said. 'I told him to come with me but he told me the same old story. He was an old man and he'd rather die at home beneath his mountain. He'd lived in shelters in the north for nine months but had a bowel problem and couldn't stand the indignity.'

The clean windscreen was enough to get the governor out of the worst mud and ash fall. He made it to the safe zone and home, rattled but unharmed.

12

Acid rain

The date 17 September had for years been seen as something akin to the Ides of March by Montserratians. Disasters had befallen the island on that date as far back as records had been kept, the most recent being Hurricane Hugo in 1989. So it was with some relief that the islanders went to bed on the night of 17 September 1996. Recently the volcano's dome had been growing faster than ever, at a stunning ten cubic metres per second. As one scientist liked to point out, that was like adding ten household washing machines to an existing pile every second. Superstitious islanders had feared this massive dome might collapse on 17 September.

As if to tease them until the last moment, The Mountain went particularly quiet that evening. The silence was broken only by the howling and barking of stray dogs. Governor Savage noticed that his tawny terrier Winston appeared to be shivering although it was a warm night.

With only eighteen minutes left of the dreaded 17th, at 11.42 p.m. the seismographs in the MVO went wild. The Mountain was blowing its top, quite literally. And it would be the worst volcanic 'event' so far.

Father Larry Finnegan was in the Vue Pointe, watching *A Fistful of Dollars*, saying Clint Eastwood's lines out loud, twisting his lips as if smoking an imaginary cheroot.

'Suddenly I heard this freight train,' he said. 'I first thought, "I don't remember a train coming through in this scene." Then I realised the train was not on the TV. And it dawned on me there were no trains on Montserrat, either.' It could only be The Mountain blowing.

The singer Arrow had been working late in the sound-proof pre-production recording studio he had built in the basement of his house. When he took off his headphones and walked upstairs, he thought his home was under attack. The roof was being hammered by pumice stones several times larger than hailstones, still extremely hot despite several miles' trajectory from the volcano through the cool midnight air. 'I feel as though there's a whole army shooting at the house,' he told friends on the phone. When he looked out on to the sun deck, his pool was sizzling. Then the whole place went black. He was in the midst of an ash cloud.

Within minutes, in areas around The Mountain, it was raining red-hot boulders. In scientific jargon, it was the first magmatic explosion, the first time molten rock had actually exploded from the crater, driven by massive underground gas power. Previously, the magma had seeped to the surface, cooled, formed a dome, then collapsed in the form of pyroclastic flows. This time, too, the event had begun with a collapse – almost one third of the growing dome – launching a major pyroclastic flow. The hole left by the collapse on this occasion was so great that compressed gas-filled magma deep within the volcano was able to explode through the feeder conduit's roof. It then burst upwards for miles into the tropical night air, the way champagne in a well-shaken bottle blows out a loosened cork. The atmospheric shock wave sent an eruption column of ash, gases and pumice shooting like a fountain to more than 40,000 feet in a matter of minutes.

James 'Mountain Man' Lee had been something of an unofficial village chief in Long Ground, on The Mountain's north-eastern slopes. It was he who had installed a siren to warn his fellow villagers of a volcanic eruption. He had always said he would be the last one to leave. He and his wife Annette had abandoned their home, their renowned fruit and vegetable gardens and their popular restaurant at Long Ground, the closest eatery and watering hole to the peaks of The Mountain, after the first pyroclastic flows in the spring. It was just as well. Within minutes of midnight on 17 September 1996 their entire property was burnt down. It took several direct hits from the red-hot boulders. Everything the boulders hit burst into flames.

Large areas of Long Ground, a tourist paradise in years gone by, the place you started out on hikes or bike tours up The Mountain's eastern side, had been incinerated. The volcano had caused its first serious damage to property and given warning that it was capable of much, much more.

Mountain Man may have been the last one seen leaving earlier in the year. But one man had slipped back secretly and was in his home in Long Ground on 17 September. He became a local legend. Nathan 'Rock' Duberry, a stocky, balding farmer, builder and jack-of-all-trades with a greying beard, lived through the equivalent of a meteorite shower, not from outer space but from a crater not much more than a mile above him. He told David Lea afterwards on camera: 'I'm in bed, sleepin', and while I'm sleepin', I hear a funny noise above the house, sound like suckin' the house . . . I feel this heavy suction, like somethin' grabbin' under the bottom of the house. It was hell inside the house, the lightnin' was tumblin', the lightnin' started flash so hard it started to cut the louvres out the house. All the time rock was peltin' down. I realise my house, out front, is on fire at the same time. I throw some water in it. A small stone drop right through the centre of my house, next to the dinin' room table and start burnin'. I say, "Lord, how this stone get inside my house?" I say, "This is the end of it, Lord, forgive me for my sins." I say, "Lord, if I survive in this house . . ." It's my prayer that make me survive, and I say, if anything happens to me in this house, it's my own fault.' The story goes that Rock – his nickname long before this incident – ran barefoot towards the safe zone with a mattress over his head. It was the same survival instinct that led Pliny the Elder to cover his head with a pillow when Vesuvius erupted almost two millennia earlier. Pliny didn't make it. Rock did.

The magmatic explosion itself, and the hot rock bombardment of the south of the island, lasted 48 minutes, ending at half past midnight, now 18 September. But the 40,000-foot ash plume spread sideways throughout that day, both east and west, surprising several aircraft pilots. At around 3 a.m., the pilot of a commercial airliner 80 miles south of Antigua (around one hundred miles from Montserrat), radioed a message: 'We have problems with engine compression and we have smoke in the cockpit. Request permission to land.' The aircraft landed safely but its windscreen was scratched by ash. It later emerged that the 'smoke' in the cockpit had in fact been fine volcanic ash.

The scientists at the MVO, who were all on duty within minutes despite the lateness of the explosion, recalled the aftermath of the Mount Pinatubo eruption and the serious threat it caused to commercial airliners. They contacted the National Oceanic and Atmospheric Administration in the US, which in turn issued a Volcanic Hazards Alert to all aircraft. Planes crossing the Caribbean diverted as American satellite images reported two separate ash plumes, one moving swiftly east at around 40 knots, the other drifting west more slowly, at 15 knots. At 2.07 p.m. on 18 September, a commercial aircraft reported an 'encounter' with an ash cloud at an altitude of around 10,000 feet about 80 miles west of Montserrat. After ash blacked out the runway markings, Guadeloupe's busy tourist airport, south of Montserrat, was closed to all traffic. The two ash plumes, each tens of miles wide, reached 160 miles west across the Caribbean from Montserrat, and no less than 320 miles east into the Atlantic before dispersing the same evening.

Throughout 1996 and early 1997, pyroclastic flows continued down the same path, the already burnt-out Tar River valley. There were no big explosions but ash falls became as routine as the seasonal tropical rains. Much of southern Montserrat, the evacuated zone, as well as areas of the 'safe zone' including Salem, Olde Towne and Olveston began to look as though someone in the heavens had emptied a giant ashtray on them. 'Ash' became the most common word in island usage, expanding to become a verb, adjective and adverb. 'I'm all ashed out, man,' became a popular expression. 'It's ashin'' meant it was raining ash. Bar owner and businessman George Howe took up calypso singing and called himself 'The Mighty Ash'. Montserratians were taking the volcano in their stride, so far, but the ash had become a tangible hazard. It was causing roofs to collapse. It was destroying the island's magnificent flora, and many feared it was a serious health hazard to humans and animals alike.

The volcanic ash was full of sulphur. When it mingled with rain clouds or ground moisture, it created sulphuric acid. Effectively, what Montserratians were living under was nothing other than acid rain. It had already turned the mountaintop into a wasteland, with grey tree stumps the only relief. Tropical plants were being destroyed daily. With them went the animal, bird and insect life that depended on them. On the slopes of The Mountain, the scientists came across more and more dead creatures, including rare bats, the long-legged frog known as the 'mountain chicken' and, increasingly, the gold-breasted oriole. There were fears that the mountain chicken and the oriole could become extinct. One expert described the deepening quilt of ash as a 'Wall of Death' that would creep down The Mountain and kill off all plant life for decades after the volcano stopped erupting.

While the majority of the islanders just kept on shovelling and sweeping it from their roofs and gardens, fears grew that the ash could cause silicosis, the respiratory disease suffered by miners who inhale coal dust. A scientist with expertise in volcano-linked health hazards, Dr Peter Baxter of Cambridge University, was sent in to make an assessment. His first report concluded that the volcanic ash contained significant amounts of the mineral cristobalite, a form of silica which can damage lung tissue and eventually cause silicosis. Somebody at the MVO immediately dubbed Baxter 'Doctor Doom', a name that was to stick during his long stay. Despite detecting cristobalite, he concluded that it was too early to tell whether breathing the volcano's ash at current levels could be dangerous to health.

Dangerous or no, the ash became simply a major nuisance. This was not like dust, which could be swept into the air and would disappear. It was thick and heavy, like cement powder, and it didn't go away, at least not quickly and not easily. Islanders found themselves with a foot or more of it on their roofs unless they shovelled it off regularly. After 17 September, Carol Osborne and her staff at the Vue Pointe had had to dig their guests out after ash piles blocked the hotel cottages' outward-opening doors. And although finer, it was a lot like sand. It got into everything, no matter how you tried to seal yourself off – your car, your computer, your hair. When the volcano was active, every day became a bad hair day. Worst of all was what the scientists called 're-suspension'. When the ash fell it simply settled on the ground, but when it was stirred up, by wind, by traffic or by children playing in it like snow, it was inhaled more deeply. All in all, the ash itself drove many more people, locals and expatriates alike, from the island.

In October 1996, in office V527 at the ODA in Victoria Street, Britain's chief aid troubleshooter Andy Bearpark was drawing up a report on Montserrat's latest needs for his boss, Baroness Chalker. With him was his assistant, the head of the ODA's Disaster Unit, Peter Burton. Bearpark had just come back from a trip to the island and had drawn up a list of requirements, but red tape and interdepartmental wrangling, the scourge of their vocation, was driving him and Burton up the wall. 'Bring back Maggie,' said Bearpark, who had been Thatcher's private secretary. 'She'd sort this lot out in one meeting. In fact, in no meetings.'

The main issue was simple: Who was responsible for dealing with the Montserrat crisis? Chalker, Bearpark and Burton felt it was them. It was an emergency. The island needed aid. They wanted to get it out there without fuss. Unfortunately, the old rivalry between the ODA and the Foreign Office had reared its head. Montserrat was a 'dependent territory', a Crown colony, with a governor appointed by us, the Foreign Office pointed out. Hence, the Foreign Office's regional office in the Caribbean, the Dependent Territories Regional Secretariat in Barbados, should be in charge. Because of the regular presence of Royal Navy warships, the Ministry of Defence was involved as well. A series of meetings was held to try to sort it out.

Bearpark had reported that the island badly needed a new jetty in the northern safe zone. Plymouth port was still being used by emergency workers to load and unload rice and fuel vessels, but only when the scientists gave the all-clear, since the capital lay directly below the volcano. A new jetty in the safe zone was vital, Bearpark said. In addition, the refugee shelters were dire and had to be upgraded. Emergency generators were also needed.

On 17 October 1996, Peter Burton was glancing through his morning papers. A picture in the *Independent* caught his eye, as well as the headline: 'Clare's baby, and her happy ending'. Burton read on with interest. Labour's Clare Short had been moved from shadow transport secretary to shadow minister for overseas development in the summer. It was billed as a demotion, but, as an aid man, Burton didn't see it that way. What bigger job could there be than getting aid to those in need?

It turned out, the newspaper article said, that Short had had a son when she was a 19-year-old student in Birmingham in the mid-Sixties, but she'd put the baby up for adoption and had not seen or heard of him since. The son, now 31, had sought her out and they'd just been reunited. Peter Burton looked at the picture of the grinning mother and son and smiled himself. He'd always thought that, under Clare Short's often gruff exterior, her heart was in the right place.

Burton had more than a passing interest. There was likely to be a general election in the coming year. If Labour won, his and Andy Bearpark's boss would be none other than Short, the feisty Birmingham MP of Irish extraction. (Her uncle Paddy ran Short's bar in Crossmaglen, Northern Ireland.) Burton had nothing but respect for his current boss, Lynda Chalker. Like himself and Bearpark, she cared passionately about overseas aid. But she was not a cabinet minister. She was often outgunned by the Foreign Office. Getting funds was a constant struggle.

If Labour won, Short was likely to be in the cabinet. That would mean more clout and more funds. Labour had pledged to meet UN-specified aid targets as a percentage of Gross National Product. The Conservatives had fallen far short of the figure. Burton could imagine far worse fates than having Clare Short in charge.

In the wake of the the big 17 September eruption, the first destruction of property, the continuing ash falls and the ongoing hardship in the shelters, Montserrat's general elections of November 1996 were of secondary importance to the islanders, to say the least. Chief Minister Reuben Meade had been critical of the British government's perceived lack of interest in Montserrat, but in the end the islanders decided he shared the blame. He was defeated, and the veteran Bertrand Osborne was elected chief minister. Party politics meant little. The only surprise was that elections had gone ahead at all. Many had called instead for a Government of National Unity. The Mountain remained the number one issue. The only issue.

Christmas 1996 approached. A new dome was already emerging, a new mini-mountain, in the gap left by the September explosion. Earthquakes continued daily, mostly imperceptible except to the MVO seismographs and the island's animals. The scientists flew over the crater daily to monitor the growing dome.

Barry Voight and Simon Young went on an overflight with pilot Jim McMahon. 'Jim, could you take her down a bit closer there, by Galways Wall,' said Young. The Canadian obliged, hovering 50 yards from the narrow rock face that formed the south-west rim of the old crater, above St Patrick's. The MVO's electronic distance measurement devices had suggested the bulging dome was now bending the old Galways Wall. Only fractionally, a couple of inches a day, but when an ancient mountain bends, you take notice. 'Look at that crack. That definitely wasn't there before,' said Young, peering down at Galways Wall through the open side of the Jet Ranger. That could mean only one thing. New volcanic material in the crater was growing not only upwards but outwards, putting pressure on Galways Wall.

Voight and Young had to get down there. The next day, McMahon dropped them off on Chance's Peak and the two scientists hiked over to the edge of Galways Wall. Now they could see the cracks in the wall up close. Modern technology was vital for their work, but this was a case requiring old-fashioned methods. They hammered nails into trees on either side of the crack and tape-measured the distance between them. On successive days, they returned and measured again. It didn't take them long to see the crack was widening by more than two inches a day. That may not sound like much, but it meant that The Mountain, towering over the south of the island, was splitting apart.

Daily helicopter observation, coupled with data from the MVO instruments, showed that another new dome had emerged in the crater, another mountain within a mountain. A new bulge was emerging in the south-west corner of the crater, behind Galways Wall. Previous domes had grown on the eastern side, releasing pyroclastic flows down the Tar River valley in an area where no one now lived or, since 17 September, dared visit. But this new growth was directly above St Patrick's and other southern villages, putting these and nearby Plymouth under threat. Although formally evacuated, hundreds of people were still venturing into the western part of the exclusion zone every day – essential port and rice-mill workers, businessmen influential enough to get police passes, farmers tending their crops or cattle, or simply islanders fed up with life in the northern shelters.

There were also still a couple of thousand people living just north of Plymouth, inside the safe zone, in Salem, Old Towne and Olveston. People were still playing golf on the little 'Royal' golf course straddling the river's banks. Danny Sweeney's Watersports at Old Road Bay was right on the Belham River estuary, where he and Margaret were now also managing the Nest beach bar for the Vue Pointe hotel on the hill.

This was where Barry Voight came in. A growing volcanic dome. A cracked crater wall. It was impossible to know exactly what would happen next. But if anyone could make an educated prediction, it would be the big man from Yonkers, New York. Voight and Simon Young went up with Jim McMahon for another look at Galways Wall. The dome behind it had grown visibly, and now there was more than one crack in the wall. What had happened on the east coast was definitely possible here. If Galways Wall were to collapse, the wall itself and any pressured volcanic material behind it would follow the law of gravity. It would take the path of the White River all the way to the ocean, close to the villages of St Patrick's, Morris's, Shooters Hill and O'Garra's.

Voight and Young had the same thought – Mount St Helens. Voight had been there, had made his name there by predicting a rare 'explosive edifice collapse' and horizontal explosion – blowing out the side of the mountain – rather than a vertical eruption. Young had been a teenager at the time but it was reading about Mount St Helens and men like Voight that had pushed him into volcanology. Now, here they were together, hovering over a volcano in the Caribbean that could blow at any moment. Young had already been amazed, earlier in the crisis, at how the old-timer Voight could scramble up and down The Mountain 'like a bloody mountain goat'.

(He could also do a mean backward flip. Young once invited Voight on a yacht trip during a day off but the American had been working and literally missed the boat, so Jim McMahon flew him in the helicopter until they found the yacht, then hovered about 15 feet over the ocean. From the yacht, Young was astonished to see the white-haired Voight climb on to the helicopter's skids, do a backward commando flip into the ocean and swim to the boat. 'I bet your brother would get a stunt man to do that,' said the Englishman.)

The new dome in the south-west of the crater was now higher than Chance's Peak, formerly the island's highest point. If Galways Wall collapsed and fresh magma emerged, it could burst out sideways to the south and south-west. St Patrick's would take a direct hit within seconds. The village now had to be considered as much of a high-risk zone as Long Ground on the other side. If there were still folks using the Spreadeagle bar, the one Governor Savage had visited earlier, they were dicing with death.

The governor, new Chief Minister Bertrand Osborne, Police Commissioner Hooper and the MVO scientists launched an urgent campaign to hammer home the new threat and get people out of the danger zone. Frank Savage's policy had always been to urge them to leave but not to force them. But now he had to be sure they were 100 per cent aware of the risks. Rose Willock explained the new dangers, the deformation and cracks in Galways Wall, the size of the new dome, to the islanders over and over again. She brought in the scientists to give twice-daily briefings on ZJB Radio. The Voice of Montserrat was not just being professional. Galways Soufrière below the Wall and the Great Alps waterfall were her favourite picnic spots and she had done much to promote them. Plymouth was her adopted home, a town she loved. She was not merely broadcasting to her fellow islanders. She was talking straight from the heart.

Via Rose on the radio, people still living in St Patrick's were asked to attend a briefing in the village's Anglican church the following day, to be given by British volcanologist Dr Angus Miller, an Edinburgh-based freelance consultant with the British Geological Survey. As always, American missionary David Lea showed up to chronicle the meeting on video. His tape showed a couple of dozen villagers, most of them elderly, the women dressed up in their Sunday finery. They listened attentively as the ginger-bearded Miller pointed through an open window to Galways Wall above and urged them to evacuate.

'What could happen?' he began. 'The worst case is that that wall will collapse, the dome behind it will be released, perhaps explosively, perhaps just as a collapsed landslide which will lead to pyroclastic flows with hot material from the dome, starting off about 900 degrees centigrade. Very hot rock. If that rock gets released and starts coming down in this direction, anyone that gets caught by a resulting pyroclastic flow will not live. There's no way you will survive a pyroclastic flow.'

The villagers listened, then shuffled out and walked slowly back to their homes. Some evacuated as a result, but most stayed. They needed a more direct prod to drive them from their homes. It was to come.

Despite the increasing threat from The Mountain, and the deepening hardship of the refugees, the islanders were determined to celebrate Christmas 1996 as best they could. The usual month-long festivities were slashed back. Plymouth was covered in ash and out of bounds and so the little village of Salem, basically two short streets, became the hub of activity for the annual parades, the jump-up street dances and the calypso contest. Occasionally, The Mountain would light up at night and a crowd would gather outside the Desert Storm rum shop to watch a glowing pyroclastic flow head down the evacuated eastern flank. Then everything would go dark and only one set of lights would remain visible across the pitch blackness of the Belham River valley. Bob and Beverly Kleeb, oldtimers but young at heart, stubborn as ever and still living without facilities in the exclusion zone, had cranked up their generator and strung up their multi-coloured Christmas lights. It was a cheering sight for the islanders, one that helped keep alive their hopes of returning to their own homes. It was good to know the retired couple were still 'kleebing it'.

With Christmas almost upon them, the islanders were confounded by yet another threat. As current chief scientist, the Englishman Simon Young had the job of explaining it and issuing a warning. Young had been nicknamed 'Doctor Sex' by his colleagues after looking 'particularly hunky' when he appeared on a local TV show wearing his orange 'hot suit', but explaining the new threat to the island was to win him another nickname from the islanders. With Galways Wall unstable, Young said, a large avalanche of pyroclastic debris could hit the ocean with such speed and force, and push it back so far and fast, that it could launch another potentially deadly phenomenon, a tsunami or giant tidal wave. The laid-back islanders quickly dubbed Young 'Tsunami Simon'.

French scientists on the island of Guadeloupe, the nearest neighbour south of Montserrat, had expressed concern that the volcano might initiate a tsunami – a Japanese word meaning 'harbour wave' – capable of wreaking havoc on their island. They cited the renowned eruption of the Krakatau volcano in Indonesia in 1883. Krakatau island itself was uninhabited except for passing fishermen and woodcutters when the eruption virtually obliterated it, but the 80-foot seismic sea wave generated by the explosion powered through the Soenda Straits, even then one of the busiest shipping channels in the world. In all, an estimated 36,000 people died, mostly on the islands of Java and Sumatra. So powerful was the eruption that it was heard more than 2,000 miles away and the shock waves were recorded by scientific instruments on the other side of the planet. Its 120,000-foot ash plume drifted all the way round the world, creating unprecedented fiery purple sunsets in London that inspired many artists, notably William Ascroft, three months later. The very thought of another disaster with such global implications has frightened scientists around the world ever since.

Even today, some scientists believe a new eruption of the active Cumbre Vieja volcano on Las Palmas, one of the Spanish-ruled Canary Islands off West Africa, could cause a landslide that would thrust a tidal wave 150 feet high across the Atlantic at speeds of several hundred miles per hour. Such a wave would flatten coastal areas in North, Central and South America, as well as the Caribbean islands, these scientists say. Others say the theory is nothing but exaggerated scaremongering.

At Christmas 1996, no one on Guadeloupe, or Montserrat for that matter, really believed a Krakatau-type disaster could be repeated on their patch, but everyone was well aware that volcanic landslides could cause tidal waves and the possibility had to be studied. It was unlikely to be on such a scale as Krakatau, but it could happen. Just another threat the Montserratians could have done without. Especially at Christmas.

Governor Frank Savage invited a French team to the island – or rather they invited themselves. They told Her Majesty's representative they feared Montserrat's angry mountain could launch a towering tsunami that would thunder south and engulf Guadeloupe. With data from the MVO, the French team put together a dynamic computer model simulating what might happen. The results brought relief all round. This mountain was unlikely to create a wave big enough to affect Guadeloupe. But they took the British governor aside. *'Mais, Monsieur le Gouverneur, attention!* Your little mountain is perfectly capable of wrapping a tidal wave around your own island. Be prepared.'

It was the last thing Frank Savage wanted or expected to hear, but he could not afford to ignore it. In an effort to cheer up refugee youngsters, he and Frank Hooper had planned a Christmas beach party. Father Christmas was supposed to come in on board the police patrol boat MV *Shamrock*, step ashore by Danny Sweeney's spot on Old Road Bay and hand out presents. Given the new tsunami threat, Savage felt he had better call the beach party off. Suddenly, he was Governor Scrooge. 'We're stuck in shelters, they won't give us housing. Now the British government won't even give our kids a Christmas party,' went the street talk. But Christmas Day passed and The Mountain made no waves. Not this Christmas.

No tidal waves, but several new domes, new mountains-within-mountains, kept growing. Under a rotation system, experienced seismologist Willy Aspinall replaced his fellow Englishman Simon Young as the MVO's chief scientist. Aspinall was known as coolness itself, but the high rate of dome growth worried him greatly. What goes up must come down. His colleagues shared his concern but, over a few drinks, teasingly gave him the obligatory nickname – Doctor Panic. It was meant as a joke, but it stuck. It was to prove highly inappropriate.

13

Ninety seconds

In late March 1997, the 'cold' rock falls over Galways Wall gave way to the first pyroclastic flows on the more heavily populated western side of The Mountain, the Plymouth and St Patrick's side. They were small at first, reaching only the upper reaches of the White River above St Patrick's, but they were enough to remind villagers of Angus Miller's warning in the Anglican church the previous November: 'There's no way you will survive a pyroclastic flow.' Many now left for the safe zone. But not all.

Then, on March 30 and 31, blocks from the new dome on the south-western side collapsed, bursting over the ancient Galways Wall that towered over St Patrick's. Pyroclastic flows rushed down the White River valley, over the famous tourist picnic site of Galways Soufrière, and reached the site of the islanders' beloved Great Alps waterfall. Few people saw the searing flows. Most folks were in the 'safe' north, but they knew this was a big one from the 10,000-foot ash cloud they could see from Salem. As Rose Willock came on Radio Montserrat ZJB to tell them of the latest development, the islanders feared the worst.

The flow had travelled more than two and a half miles down the White River, incinerating or flattening trees and shrubbery in its path. Such was the damage to the land-scape that the foreign scientists had needed to bring along a local resident to try to recognise what was what. Bennette Roach, feisty editor of the *Montserrat Reporter* and a native of St Patrick's, went up for a helicopter overflight with Jim McMahon and MVO scientists. Shooting video was the MVO's local technician and cameraman Dave Williams.

Flying in from the coast, over the big rocks and white cliffs where he had swum, run and fished as a child, Roach was at first relieved. St Patrick's was untouched, green as ever and dotted with red galvanised roofs. But as the Canadian pilot eased the Jet Ranger up to the White River valley, Roach realised the upper half of the valley was barely recognisable. It had been filled in and was now a grey, twisting ribbon down the mountainside that extended beyond the valley and covered a large area of formerly lush land. Galways Soufrière, where tourists used to bring picnics and watch the local guides boil eggs in the little sulphur ponds, where singer Jimmy Buffett had scribbled his song, had been buried. It was now an expanse of pure grey.

Williams asked McMahon to ease in closer to a small cliff. The chopper threw up dust clouds from the ground and it took the two Montserratians a few minutes to register, but then Roach and Williams realised they were looking at the spot where the famous Great Alps waterfall used to be. Williams kept filming, panning, zooming, as though hoping he would find the glistening 80-foot waterfall he had filmed only a week earlier with the sun shimmering through it. But it was no more. There was no water. The former cliff, surrounded by thick green jungle, was now a rounded 20-foot step in an expanse of grey. No water. No trees. No green. Just grey.

Sections of the dome, 'like a cracked boiled egg' in

Roach's words, were emitting steam and ash. If there were a major explosion now, the ash cloud would envelop the chopper before Jim McMahon could pull away. But he and Williams wanted to get this on film. Looking at the site of the famous waterfall, they could hardly believe their eyes. The islanders might never get a chance to see this. They would only believe it if they saw it on video. McMahon hovered, then eased the goldfish-bowl nose of the chopper forward. Williams felt he could almost reach out and touch The Mountain.

'Ease away, Jim, give me a fade away,' he asked the pilot. The two men had developed what Williams called 'a pretty choreographed movement of filming', a kind of air ballet. Using the zoom lens on board the chopper gave too much shake to the images, so McMahon used his machine, and his experience, to move back and forth according to the cameraman's needs.

'Okay, Jim, can you take me back in close?' Williams had opened the zoom wide to reduce the shake and was relying on McMahon's skill to give him his close-up. The little white and black helicopter – McMahon called it 'Fluffy' because of its woolly seat covers – was hovering 20 yards from the steep rock face like a hummingbird checking out a hibiscus. Then McMahon's voice, loud but calm, broke the silence.

'Hold tight, Dave. We're out of here.' He didn't take the time to explain what he'd seen, a churning grey cloud thundering down from Galways Wall like an avalanche. It was on its usual path down the White River valley, but only seconds from reaching the cliff face that used to be the Great Alps Falls. McMahon seemed to take the little turbine chopper to the left and backwards in a single manoeuvre, buzzing away over the still lush area beyond the river's banks. Williams had seen the pyroclastic flow himself. He could already feel its heat. Still harnessed but leaning out of the open door with one foot on the skid, he kept filming as the churning grey mass surged down the valley directly below them. It was some of the closest footage of a pyroclastic flow ever shot.

Word of the waterfall's destruction spread like a verbal version of a pyroclastic flow throughout the island. 'Dem say waterfall all mashed up, man.' 'Mashed up': the local way to say 'destroyed'. There was hardly an islander who hadn't romped in the pool below its powerful, refreshing cascade. The Great Alps Falls had been Rose Willock's favourite spot for relaxing on her rare days off, to feel the narrow waterfall like a shower of tiny pebbles on her back. It was where Danny Sweeney took Sting, Dire Straits and a host of other rock stars and where his little daughter Sarah loved to plaster herself with mud. It was where the surefooted local boy Winston 'Kafu' Cabey, now presenter of the 'Drivetime' programme on ZJB, used to earn pocket money by carrying tourists across the rocks behind the waterfall.

When he heard the news that the famous waterfall was 'all mashed up', Police Constable Kelvin White recalled his last trip up there. He'd picked wild raspberries with his parents and his younger brother André just before his father passed away in January 1997. Now, two months later, the waterfall was gone. For Kelvin White, as for most islanders, losing their greatest tourist attraction was like losing a close relative.

Until now, they had kept the faith and remained optimistic. They had assumed they'd be going home. Now, it occurred to them that this mountain might be getting the upper hand.

Frank Savage was getting weary. He had been due to leave the previous autumn, 1996, after a posting of more than three years, but he had stayed on in the hope of finishing what The Mountain had started, of ensuring the islanders' safety and providing the refugees with housing. The trouble was, almost two years after it first awoke, the volcano was still very much alive and kicking and it showed no sign of going to sleep soon. Savage couldn't stay on forever. He was going to have to hand the baton to someone else. Since 18 July 1995, when the friendly mountain turned into a monster, he had worked round the clock with barely a day off. It was with some relief that he heard the news, on 18 April 1997, that a successor had been appointed. Savage would hand over the job, along with the pith helmet and swan feathers, in September. He would not be going far. He had been appointed Governor of the British Virgin Islands, based on Tortola. It would be his last posting before his scheduled retirement in a couple more years.

By now, envoys from the London-based World Society for the Protection of Animals (WSPA, usually pronounced 'Wispa'), had arrived on the island. Frank Savage had been increasingly concerned about the number of animals left behind in the exclusion zone – mostly dogs, cats, cattle, donkeys and goats – not to mention wildlife such as the mountain chicken, the unique bats, the rare black-and-gold oriole. But he felt his hands were tied. 'We were getting a lot of flak from animal lovers in Britain about animals being abandoned to the volcano,' he said, 'but we simply didn't have the wherewithal. We didn't have enough people to cover all sides of the crisis. We were struggling to house and feed human beings.'

There were hundreds of dogs. Most were strays, but there were also many pets left behind by their owners because they were barred from shelters, or else to guard property against looters. Most of them were locked up or tied up, since evacuees had been expecting to return to their homes soon, so the animals had no access to food. Some owners got special permission or slipped through police roadblocks to feed them but that became increasingly difficult. Others set their animals loose to find food for themselves. The stray dogs were becoming increasingly wild. Police and the MVO scientists had already seen evidence of dogs killing and eating goats, sheep and cows. Farmers had also been shooting feral dogs. There were many hundred head of cattle, perhaps a few thousand, previously tended by farmers but now abandoned and roaming ash-covered areas. Again, it was now getting too difficult and too dangerous for farmers to return to tend them.

The first WSPA envoys began rounding up dogs in and around Plymouth. With the help of dog-loving locals, including expatriates such as Bev Kleeb, makeshift kennels were built close to the airport. Dogs and cats were shipped out to find adoptive homes in Florida. After watching TV footage, Floridians were queueing up to get a 'volcano dog'. But the 'canine mercy flights' gave rise to complaints from refugees suffering in the shelters. 'If you're a dog, you get fed properly and taken to Florida,' went the complaint. 'But we're human beings, and we're black. No visas for us.'

Late on the night of 1 May 1997, Britons were following the results of that day's general election. At his home in

Tonbridge, semi-retired civil servant Peter Burton took a call from his former boss at the Overseas Development Administration, Andy Bearpark, still in fifth-floor office V527. Burton had formally retired from the Civil Service at the end of 1996, but he couldn't stay away from aid work. In the New Year he had started as a consultant for the ODA and was now with their contracted, semi-private Emergency Logistics Team in Sutton, Surrey. 'Peter, we no longer work for the Foreign Office,' Bearpark said on the phone. 'But not to worry, mate, we're not fired. Apparently, we now work for DFID.'

The new prime minister, Tony Blair, had elevated overseas aid to the level of a department, or ministry, instead of part of the Foreign Office. He had scrapped the ODA title and christened his new baby the Department for International Development (DFID). Bearpark would still be in charge of emergency aid, including to Montserrat, but he and Burton would have a new boss, Labour's Clare Short. ODA chief Lynda Chalker had already packed her bags in her office along the corridor from Bearpark and come by to thank her staff.

Burton preferred to stay out of politics. He voted according to party policies of the time. He took the *Daily Telegraph* at home, but his passion was helping those around the world who were suffering. So he found himself rather pleased that Labour had won. It meant overseas aid had been upgraded to cabinet level. That could only be good for those who needed it, especially Africa, he thought. As for little Montserrat, it might now be easier to squeeze out some more funds for housing. Lynda Chalker had cared for the islanders. But cutting through the red tape? That had been a different matter entirely. He hoped Clare Short at least knew where Montserrat was.

The change of government in London meant little to Montserratians. All they could hope for was a more sympathetic ear. Few had heard of Tony Blair, fewer still of Clare Short. Soon after the British election, Danny Sweeney, Margaret and six-year-old Sarah were driving across the 'Central Corridor', the twisting two-lane road that cut through the centre of the island along the northern foothills of The Mountain, linking Plymouth to the east coast and the airport. The road, around five miles long, was in the exclusion zone. But Danny knew all the local policemen. Everybody bought his freshly-caught tuna fish or wahoo. Everyone swam on Old Road Bay beach, where Danny was a legend. So he and Margaret had no problem getting through the police checkpoint to drive to the airport and lime at its Cockpit bar. On an island as small as this, the airport bar, where you knew almost everyone who was flying out or flying in, was one of the most popular spots for a drink. And bar manager Catherine Daley made bacon-and-egg sandwiches to die for.

Danny and Margaret had passed Streatham village, about half way to the airport, when they saw the usual bunch of cars and pick-up trucks parked beneath the fertile, terraced fields of Farrell's Yard on The Mountain's northern slopes. Danny could see groups of men and women working on their crops. Harry Lewis was there, with his wife Isolyn and her sister Felina, 2Pac Matthew's mother. Young Keithly Ponde, better known as Joe, was up there too. Danny knew most of them by name, or, in most cases, by nickname. These were the folks who sold their fruit and vegetables in the bustling Plymouth Public Market, close to the clockstand and the old red phone booth. Joe Ponde was known for the delicious corn-on-the-cob he sold outside Arrow's Man Shop.

Further along the road, there were more people, despite the ban, in the villages of Harris and Farm, on the banks of the deep Paradise Ghaut and Pea Ghaut. Danny drove on towards the coast, over the tiny bridge at Trant's and on to the airport. The area was deserted, but for a car driving up towards Spanish Point. It was the American couple, the Chloupeks from Nebraska. Danny had heard they were were still living there in the exclusion zone with their little girl, Mary, right in the shadow of The Mountain.

Danny and Margaret had a drink in the Cockpit bar, exchanging first-name greetings with everyone, including 2Pac the young fireman, Simon Tuitt the baggage handler and Horrance Boatswain the airport gardener. Margaret turned to look at The Mountain. It somehow seemed awfully close today. She suggested Danny drive home the long way round, north away from The Mountain, instead of back along the Central Corridor. That took them up the grandly named but narrow and twisting Great North Road on the east coast, round the northern tip of the island and back down the west coast to their home. It took 40 minutes instead of 20, but Margaret felt more comfortable. The Mountain was beginning to make her jittery.

The following day, Margaret wondered if she had had a premonition. She was listening to Radio Montserrat when Rose Willock introduced two of the MVO scientists. 'The first rock fall has occurred from the northern slopes of the volcano,' one said. It had spilt on to the upper slopes, above Farrell's Yard where they had seen people tending their crops the day before. 'It could be the precursor of pyroclastic flows in the same area,' the scientist said. 'Any pyroclastic flow down that flank would endanger the Central Corridor and the villages alongside it.' If a flow were to surge down the deepest and steepest ravines, Paradise Ghaut and Pea Ghaut, it could continue down towards the airport.

After an emergency meeting, Frank Hooper ordered the Central Corridor to be closed. The local government insisted the airport remain open, although it was arguably in the danger zone. It was the island's only human link with the world, of tremendous psychological importance. Emergency workers had been helping get fuel in and rice out through Plymouth port, but that zone was becoming increasingly dangerous to them and to visiting seamen. Goods were unloaded hurriedly by dockers with one eye on The Mountain. So the airport was even more vital. But from now, only airport staff and bona fide passengers would be allowed through and they would have to come and go on the Great North road along the east coast. The Cockpit bar would be out of bounds to all but staff and passengers. No more limin'.

Rumours of an off-island evacuation grew. Governor Savage and the local authorities denied it was on the cards, but the governor had always said it would be imprudent not to have a contingency plan. A three-man team from England – a Scotland Yard police inspector and two Army officers – had arrived discreetly on the island on 10 May to fine-tune contingency plans for 'Operation Exodus'.

By mid-May 1997, Barry Voight had become particularly concerned about the possibility of a violent eruption which could send pyroclastic flows over The Mountain's northern rim. He made his feelings clear at meetings of the crisis group. People were still being allowed on to the Central

Corridor and the surrounding villages and fields, and it was simply not safe, he said. Lloyd Lynch of the SRU agreed. 'Think of the volcano as a creature,' he told officials. 'An octopus whose tentacles are the major ghauts around it. The magma could grow and grow into one big mountain and could overflow on all sides.' It was vital to get on to The Mountain and install some tiltmeters, electronic versions of a spirit level, which show whether the volcano is 'inflating' or 'deflating' according to underground pressure.

On 18 May, the weather was bad. Chance's Peak was fogged in, but Jim McMahon said he would give it a go. It occurred to Voight that this was the anniversary of the 1980 Mount St Helens blast he had been so involved in. Good omen or bad? Anyway, lives were at stake. The job had to be done. McMahon eased 'Alpha Hotel', the Jet Ranger's callsign, through the fog and dropped off Voight and Lynch on Chance's summit. They managed to install the vital equipment, but the Canadian pilot couldn't get back through the thickening fog and the two men had to hike down The Mountain to meet him. When they got 'home', their tiltmeter signals were loud and clear. Job well done.

Around that time, Jim McMahon was in the habit of landing on the roof of an unfinished and apparently abandoned house in Harris Lookout, in the evacuated zone. It was about the only flat spot big enough to land on, though he had to watch out for the protruding steel rods. Waiting for him to land one day, Barry Voight found himself alongside a local man, Robert Parsons, who had obviously slipped into the exclusion zone.

When McMahon stepped from the chopper, the man yelled: 'Hey, man, that's me house you landin' on. Me woman is in there scared to come out. I know there's a crisis an' all but I think you should recompense me for any damage, you know.'

McMahon and Voight exchanged smiles. They took Parsons up for an impromptu tourist ride right close to the dome and everybody was happy.

By the end of May 1997, the volcano's new dome could be seen to be growing by the day, when cloud cover cleared enough. It was now at its greatest volume so far, 60 million cubic metres, and was growing by no less than four cubic metres a second. As the scientists liked to put it, that was the equivalent of four household washing machines per second. That meant 240 washing machines a minute, nearly 15,000 an hour: a stunning 350,000 washing machines every day. The scientists believed the islanders could relate more to hundreds of thousands of red-hot washing machines falling on them than to cold cubic metres. They were right.

The dome now towered 200 feet higher than Chance's Peak, once the highest point in the island at 3,000 feet. When Paul Cole of Luton University flew in at the end of May for a new six-week stint at the MVO, he couldn't believe how much it had grown since his last posting just over a month earlier. He said he was 'surprised and alarmed' at the height and steepness of the northern side of the dome, which looked down directly over the Central Corridor and, further east, to the airport.

When Amanda Clarke, one of Voight's graduate volcanology students from Penn State, came down for a spell at the MVO, Voight told her: 'Stay on your toes. Be careful. That mountain hasn't killed anyone yet, but it easily could.'

American missionary-cum-filmmaker David Lea knew

from his recently acquired expertise that the dome was bound to crumble, sooner rather than later. Like everyone else, he hoped it wouldn't. But he knew it would. So he hoped to be on hand to film it as part of his video chronicle. David and Clover Lea had continued their religious radio programme, 'Friends', broadcast throughout the Caribbean, but since the start of the crisis, Lea had been smitten, like the career volcanologists, by 'volcano fever'. He had become fascinated with The Mountain and decided to record as many of its moods as possible on video in a documentary series, *The Price of Paradise*. Since the first venting, he had done so at considerable risk. He believed he was in God's hands. 'We're up here by the crater,' he used to say to his own camera in the early days, when it was still possible to climb to the rim. 'Oh, and when I say "we", I mean the Lord and I. Hey, I sure wouldn't venture up here all on my own.'

Jesus Christ apart, one of David Lea's biggest heroes had been Maurice Krafft, the French volcanologist engulfed by a pyroclastic flow along with his wife Katia and American volcanologist Harry Glicken while filming the eruption at Mount Unzen in Japan in 1991. Krafft's films of eruptions, often taken at extreme risk, were widely considered the best of all time. David Lea could not match that. He had only one little mountain to cover. But he was determined to do it to the best of his ability so that future generations might see what this mountain was capable of. After all, it could go back to sleep for thousands, even millions of years. 'What you do is you try to continue the work Maurice and Katia Krafft did,' Lea said. 'These guys were aware of the significance of their images. If they were alive today, they'd be in Long Ground, right beneath The

Mountain, that's where they'd be. Maurice would be like a kid in a candy store.'

Since moving to Montserrat, the Leas had always lived in the village of St Peter's, towards the north of the island, close to the famous Providence plantation house where Paul McCartney, Eric Clapton and other stars used to stay, and now well inside the safe zone. It was only five miles north of Plymouth, but that was close to half an hour on the twisting, climbing and plunging main road. Before the volcano, it was considered somewhat out in the sticks. But there were two sides to the coin of living beyond the volcano's apparent reach. David Lea felt that Clover and his sons Sunny, Jesse and Noah were safe, but he could not see The Mountain from anywhere near his home. Not so handy for a filmmaker. So he discreetly rented a house inside the exclusion zone, on the hill known as Harris Lookout, outside the supposedly evacuated village of Harris.

The missionary had a special 'enter at your own risk' police pass. He could get in and out past the checkpoints, even if the police officers thought he was crazy. So he planned to commute to and from his rented house with his camera to record The Mountain's activities. He gathered a supply of water and food, as well as a radio, a walkie-talkie, a beeper, a bright red volcanologist's hot suit and lots of batteries and candles. Harris Lookout was only 3,500 yards from the new dome, in direct line of sight to The Mountain. David Lea would be, as the volcanologists liked to put it, 'looking up the gun barrel'. He hoped his elevated position would keep him safe.

Lea was a devout Christian, but he liked to tell his friends he was 'prepared *not* to die'. He had chosen to rent the little house because it had a ten-foot steel water tank alongside, which was empty and covered by a metal plate. The missionary gathered cement blocks and built a stairway from the rim to the bottom of the tank. He couldn't be sure whether he would survive a pyroclastic flow in there but at least he was giving himself a fighting chance. He would, of course, need to breathe. Once, working as a fireman in Ohio, he had seen his lieutenant die because he didn't have adequate breathing equipment. That's why he had asked his friend, German scuba diver and tourist guide Wolf Krebs, for an aqualung set. If The Mountain blew and a flow came down, the plucky preacher planned to don the scuba gear, slip into the tank, slide the lid closed and pray to his maker. He knew he might have little more than a minute to do so.

Lea found he was not alone in the zone. He spotted at least a dozen people around Harris Lookout. In the house right next to his water tank was 90-year-old Ellen Thomas, who had refused to leave. Wearing a scarlet shirt and red woollen hat, she told him on camera: 'Me get down on me knees and me say, "Father, if it time to go, put it in me that I leave." He no tell me to go, so me still awaiting God.'

In early June, the scientists' predictions proved accurate. The rock falls that had spilt from the northern rim of the crater the previous month had been 'cold', that is, old rock, destabilised and pushed aside by the growing lava dome. But the first two weeks of June saw pyroclastic flows come over the same rim, red-hot rock from the growing dome itself. The flows were small at first, but this time they did not spill north-eastwards down the Tar River valley towards Long Ground. Instead they spilt due north, into the upper reaches of the ravines known as Tuitt's Ghaut and Mosquito Ghaut. They burnt out within the ravines but covered a greater distance each time, eventually passing within yards of houses in the village of Harris, in the valley below the house rented by David Lea. The scientists were concerned that a big one would just keep on going. Both ravines led directly to the Central Corridor and the villages straddling it – Streatham, Windy Hill, Farrell's, Harris – and on to those on the eastern coastal plain, Farm, Trant's and Spanish Point. Ultimately, they led all the way to W.H. Bramble airport and the coast.

Lea drove along the Central Corridor to film the sites of the latest flows. Parked on the main road, below the terraced farmland at Farrell's Yard, was a group of cars and pick-up trucks. Farmers were tending their crops. Lea knew he himself was taking a risk, but it was a calculated one. He wore a yellow hard hat, kept the engine of his little van running while he was filming and always knew which way he would head if he had to drive for his life. But these farmers were digging and hoeing, preoccupied with their work, only a couple of hundred yards from Mosquito Ghaut. The American zoomed in on two farmers, digging a field on the fertile slopes directly below the crater's northern rim. 'These people here are in about the worst place you could possibly be,' he said in his audio commentary. 'Because any surge, any big one came down there and didn't make the corner, it would come over the top of that ridge there and straight on to these guys before they could even get in their cars. It's hard to believe, but this is how people get killed in volcanoes.' Panning his camera from the farmers up to the ghaut, which was still smoking from the heat of the previous day's flow, he went on: 'Here's people working in the field, and there's where the pyroclastic flow came from. And lo and behold, they're right there in front of it.'

The trouble was, the farmers needed to live. And they felt they were doing Montserrat a service by providing fresh food to a largely isolated island. Harry Lewis was supplying fresh fruit and vegetables to the island's only hospital, to government officials and to a leading supermarket. He was also donating fresh food to the refugee shelters. 'These folks can't live on just rice and macaroni,' he insisted. All of that made it worth taking the risk, he and other farmers said.

Englishman Willy Aspinall, the current chief scientist at the MVO, knew only too well that there were many people still living under the volcano. He saw them himself on his field trips and always urged them to leave. He had occasionally been insulted for doing so. Some of his colleagues had been threatened with personal violence: unusual on this island, but nerves were on edge.

'You've got to remember that their animals are like part of the family to these people,' an island official told him. 'Their crops and animals are their bank accounts. Some even put down the names of their farm animals on forms asking them to list family members.' As Aspinall's friend and compatriot Frank Hooper said: 'It would take the equivalent of a Berlin Wall to keep these folks out of their homes.' It also worried Aspinall that the airport was still open despite the fact that gravity and the island's topography made the airport the most likely target for any major flow to the coast. It did, after all, sit on a flat coastal delta that must itself have been created by a pyroclastic flow thousands or millions of years earlier.

Aspinall and his team were under heavy local political

pressure. Plymouth port was out of bounds for all but emergency workers and was becoming increasingly dangerous. A new jetty, being funded by Britain at Little Bay in the safe north, was not yet ready. The airport remained the island's only real link with the rest of the world. But pilots of the Caribbean airline Liat, the regular carrier to and from W.H. Bramble airport, were getting nervous about the volcanic activity. Liat issued a disclaimer to its passengers warning them of the risks. It insisted that the MVO should station a scientist at the airport, so that planes could be warned off in advance.

On 9 June 1997, Aspinall called a meeting of the entire MVO team at their villa headquarters in Old Towne, with The Mountain for a backdrop. After an exchange of opinions, he hammered out a memorandum to Governor Savage and the local government. It was to prove a prophetic document, and a crucial one, although it was kept under wraps from the islanders. To a certain extent, the English scientist was covering himself and his colleagues by putting it in writing. He felt the new Labour government in Britain was distracted by other matters, both at home and elsewhere in the world. It was harder to keep them interested in the problems of one of their tiny colonies in the Caribbean. Aspinall wanted it on the record that the scientists could predict the volcano's activities as best they could, but could give no guarantees.

'The possibility of a rapidly growing pyroclastic flow being initiated without obvious precursor activity, big enough to reach the sea in the vicinity of Bramble airport, cannot be precluded,' Aspinall wrote. An MVO scientist could be stationed at the airport to alert officials. 'But it must be recognised that this notice may be as short as ONE AND A HALF MINUTES before the flow or accompanying surges reach the line of the coast, and that absolutely no assurance can be given that even this short warning time will be possible in all circumstances.'

One and a half minutes' warning. Ninety seconds from the start of a flow until it incinerated the airport and everyone in it. Governor Savage, Chief Minister Osborne and everyone else who saw the memo got the message. Not to mention a few shivers down the spine. Savage called an urgent meeting of the crisis group. The career diplomat in the grey suit was unusually animated and unusually blunt. He looked his disaster expert, the Antiguan Franklyn Michael, in the eye. 'Frankie, I want an airport evacuation plan and I want it now. Within hours, not days. Get a plan going, get up to the airport to make sure everyone understands it and is prepared to follow it. And have a copy of it on my desk in the morning.' The group agreed that an MVO scientist, in touch with his base by walkie-talkie, should be stationed at the airport to warn airport officials of any pyroclastic activity and increase the 'lead time' – the period of warning.

The following day, Michael and MVO scientist Paul Cole went to the airport to brief its staff on the dangers and on the emergency evacuation plan. Everyone gathered round Cole in the small but grandly titled VIP lounge under the portraits of the Queen and Prince Philip. There were no flights coming in, so 2Pac left his fire post beneath the Control Tower to hear what was going on. He was interested for himself, but he also knew that his mother, Felina, worked regularly with her sister and Harry Lewis in the family's plot at Farrell's Yard, below the crater and close to Mosquito Ghaut. The airport gardener, Horrance

Boatswain, and the baggage handler, Simon 'Muta' Tuitt, listened intently. Both lived in Farm village, between The Mountain and the airport, and came and went, tending crops and livestock, even though it was in the evacuated danger zone.

Paul Cole did not reveal Aspinall's memo, but he told the airport workers that if a big pyroclastic flow came down they might have less than two minutes to evacuate. Some began to laugh. They thought Cole was joking. When he swore he was not, the mood changed. Their final response, though, reminded Frankie Michael of the Alamo, when Texans refused to bow to the Mexican army and crossed a line in the sand to volunteer to fight. 'Not a single person said he or she would not go on working,' Michael said later.

If the duty scientist knew – either by sight or by radio contact with base – that a pyroclastic flow had started, he would tell the airport manager and sound a siren. Cars and taxis were to be parked in pre-planned, orderly fashion, facing away from the terminal. Staff would have designated drivers. Keys would be left in the ignition (already more the norm than the exception on the island). An old dirt road round the Arawak Indian ruins at Trant's Yard would be resurfaced to allow vehicles to head immediately north, away from The Mountain. The existing road first ran west from the terminal, straight towards the volcano, before turning north.

Cole had done his duty, but he was not comfortable. For one thing, he felt the scientists, some of whom were students, were being unfairly burdened with the responsibility of evacuating the airport. That simply wasn't their job. For another, the vantage point at the airport was far from perfect. The summit was often clouded over, particularly now that the storm and hurricane season had started. Even if the weather were clear, any pyroclastic flow which might be seen leaving the dome would disappear from sight behind intervening hills. You would not know it was major unless it helter-skeltered round Harris Lookout towards you. By then, you'd only have about 20 seconds to make peace with your creator.

Willy Aspinall had nothing but sympathy for Cole's view. In his spine-chilling 9 June memo to the governor, the chief scientist had expressed 'a very substantial concern among the [MVO] team that, in an emergency situation with a pyroclastic flow approaching the airport area, one of their colleagues on station may delay extricating himself or herself from the area with suitable speed because of the predicaments of others nearby, thus becoming exposed to an unacceptable risk of personal danger.'

Although Willy Aspinall had jokingly been nicknamed Doctor Panic by his colleagues for his constant safety warnings, he was, like most experienced volcanologists, extemely cool under pressure. These men knew the risks, took all possible precautions, then 'got the hell out of Dodge' whenever they got warning. Civilians were different. 'If you try to organise them and wait for them, they'll say, "Oh, let me just get my suitcase and finish my beer,"' Aspinall said. He was sincerely worried that his own men and women of the MVO would be the last out of the airport. Instinctively, he'd rather they be first. When civilians saw a volcanologist 'run like the clappers', they tended to follow suit. He'd experienced that first-hand on another volcanic island, St Vincent, some years earlier. 'Nothing was happening with the volcano but I was late for a flight and running for it. By the time I got to the plane, islanders who had recognised me as "the scientist" were queuing up behind me to get out. Our job is to advise evacuation, then retreat. A dead scientist is no use to anybody.'

The new Labour government may, as Willy Aspinall felt, have been distracted by other matters. The new minister for international development, Clare Short, was known to be preoccupied with the starving children of Africa, but her inherited troubleshooter down the fifth-floor corridor from her office on Victoria Street, emergency aid chief Andy Bearpark, knew that when Willy Aspinall spoke, you listened. Bearpark flew out to the island on 12 June 1997 to show solidarity, make an up-to-date assessment and, specifically, to speed the building of 500 small homes for refugees and the opening of the new British-funded jetty at Little Bay. If the airport had to close, the jetty would be essential for ferrying passengers to and from Antigua and shipping in vital fuel. Bearpark, the former rugby player from Rochdale, did some blunt, northern English 'get-your-finger-out' talking to representatives of the island's government. Work speeded up noticeably.

On 17 June, Bearpark had barely got back from Montserrat to his DFID office overlooking McDonald's on Victoria Street when he got a copy of a telegram addressed to the Foreign Office. Dispatched by Governor Savage, it had crossed the Atlantic as fast as the airwaves could carry it but, as always, had taken many times longer to wind its way through the Foreign Office bureaucracy in Whitehall. 'First pyroclastic flow over Gage's,' was the gist of the message, originating from Willy Aspinall. Bearpark knew that Gage's Mountain towered over Plymouth.

Gage's Wall formed the western rim of The Mountain's

ancient crater. So far in the two-year-old crisis, pyroclastic flows had burst through the horseshoe-shaped gap on the north-eastern rim down the Tar River Valley past the village of Long Ground. Then they had burst over Galways Wall on the south-western flank, down the White River valley close to St Patrick's. Latterly, flows had come over the northern rim into the ghauts that ultimately ran down by the airport. But Gage's Mountain, jungle-clad until the ash falls of the past two years, was directly above the capital. The big ravine that split Plymouth and ran to the sea, Fort Ghaut, emanated from Gage's. Even a child could tell you anything heavy enough that fell from Gage's would follow the path of Fort Ghaut and end up in Plymouth port.

It was preoccupation over Gage's Wall that had induced the British-led MVO to call in American landslide expert Barry Voight in the first place. The new dome, or mini-mountain, within the ancient crater had previously collapsed in other directions, but Voight had been in no doubt that if the dome kept growing, pyroclastic flows could burst over Gage's Wall. And in that scenario, Plymouth was not a place you'd want to be. From the first time he saw it, Voight had been struck by the resemblance between the Plymouth area and the old photographs he'd seen of Montagne Pelée and the town of St Pierre on Martinique. That was the mountain that erupted with little warning in 1902, devastating the town and its 28,000 residents with a hurricane of lethal, scorching ash. At least *we* have had some warning, he thought.

When the scientists broke the news of a pyroclastic flow over Gage's, the Second World War-vintage sirens wailed in Plymouth and Rose Willock, as always, came on the radio. 'All workers in Plymouth are advised to leave immediately.'

They did. The broadcaster barely had time to think of her own abandoned home at Upper Amersham, above Plymouth and below Gage's Wall. She had managed to get back into the exclusion zone during the past year to remove some personal effects, even some furniture, but it was still her home. Like everyone else, she hoped to return, *planned* to return. Plymouth was her town. Montserrat was her island. Rose kept her mind off her own problems by broadcasting, telling her fellow islanders to stay calm, that everything would be all right in the end. This thing would blow over sooner or later. She wanted badly to believe it.

On Sunday 22 June 1997, Governor Frank Savage, taking Veronica with him for a break from the ash in the air, flew to Barbados to try to squeeze some more aid money from his regional Foreign Office administrators at the Dependent Territories Regional Secretariat (DTRS). Frank Savage was nothing if not persistent. He was due to leave his post in September, but he wanted to get as much assistance to the islanders as he could before he bade them farewell. When Savage and his wife drove up to W.H. Bramble airport, the baggage handler Simon Tuitt greeted them as always with a smile and 'Good marnin',' and carried their bags to the VIP lounge. The airport was quiet and even more laid-back than usual. It had a reduced staff because of the volcano threat. On the governor's return, three days later, things would not be quite so laid-back.

Arriving at the little airport just as the governor left was Keith Rowley, a Trinidadian volcanologist who knew the island well and was starting a new six-week stint at the MVO under the current chief scientist Willy Aspinall.

Rowley noticed the old dirt road running due north from the airport terminal had been bulldozed and tarred as a hasty escape route. The main road, which went west towards the volcano before turning right, was deserted.

Two days later, on Tuesday 24 June, local farmer Devon Sutton, from the village of Farm near the airport, flew in from Antigua after visiting his in-laws with his 23-year-old Antiguan wife Alicia and their baby boy Allister. He greeted his two fellow villagers who worked at the airport, Simon Tuitt and Horrance Boatswain, then walked the 300 yards west to the T-junction. He noticed the usual police checkpoint had gone and walked left, across the bridge over Pea Ghaut, past Constable Kelvin White's home, and a couple of hundred more yards to his house in Farm village. The area was in the exclusion zone. It was almost empty, but not quite. Devon's grandparents, Anthony and Virginia Sutton, had grown weary of their northern shelter and come back for some privacy. Builder Bobby Harris and his wife Mary were at home in the village too, and the two airport workers came and went daily, to tend their animals or crops, from shelters in the north.

When he passed Kelvin White's home at Trant's, Devon noticed that it looked unoccupied, but that Kelvin's cows, sheep and goats were grazing in the area. He knew Kelvin's father had passed away in January and his mother, the special needs teacher, was living in the safe zone. Kelvin must be on duty, he thought. I suppose he'll be down to tend the animals after his police shift.

Kelvin White *was* on duty, at the current police headquarters in Salem, but he wasn't a happy camper. He had just been told the force was short of drivers and that he'd have to deliver lunches to the men at the checkpoints and the airport. A CID officer having to deliver the lunches. Kelvin was irked. He had refused to drive six months earlier after being given a broken-down jeep whose door would only close if you tied it up with rope. You're under a volcano, he thought, and you've got to get into or out of your vehicle quickly, and you've got to untie a rope? But today the senior officer was adamant. We need drivers, Constable. If you want to keep your job, you'll drive.

With his widowed mother not in the best of health, 400 head of livestock to look after and a home in the shadow of an angry volcano, Kelvin White didn't have a lot of choice. He'd drive. He was not in the best of moods as he went back to Trant's that evening to tend his animals. But his change of job was to prove a twist of fate. Driving the following day would be a matter of life or death.

On that same evening, Tuesday 24 June, scientists Willy Aspinall and newly-arrived Keith Rowley dined at the Vue Pointe hotel. Neither felt comfortable. The Mountain had been 'breathing heavily' for several days. There had been what the scientists called 'hybrid earthquake swarms' at regular intervals as well as small pyroclastic flows on the upper slopes. Although the two men expected to be on duty at dawn, they decided to 'walk the course' that very night before they turned in. That's what Aspinall called going out into the field to observe the dome, the way a professional golfer walks a course to gauge its yardage, fairways and pin placements. Aspinall wasn't worried about which way his golf ball would run. Lives depended on which way the next pyroclastic flow would go – and how far, and how fast.

The two scientists drove through the deserted streets at midnight, into the exclusion zone, along the Central

Corridor. They stopped half way to the airport and turned left up a side road to a high vantage point at Windy Hill. From there they could look over the fertile slopes of Farrell's Yard and up the deep contour that worried them most – the ravine known as Mosquito Ghaut. Their concern was justified. Against the blackness of The Mountain there were broken lines of luminous red, as though someone was shooting tracer bullets in slow motion down from the dome. Red-hot rock falls. This thing was not just breathing; it was panting. Felina Celestine had been reaping vegetables in those fields at Farrell's Yard with her sister and other farmers earlier that day, and Aspinall knew there were many other people living in semi-secrecy in the villages along this, the main road to the airport. He and Rowley decided to grab some shut-eye and return at first light.

Aspinall did not get much chance to sleep. While he was at Windy Hill, American missionary David Lea was wrapping up a voluntary four-hour shift at the MVO villa in Old Towne, monitoring the seismographs. His teenage son Sunny was with him. 'Suddenly the patterns went from nothing to fully spiky,' Lea said in a call to Aspinall, describing the way the seismograph needles began inking the entire drum. 'There are regular hybrids, every minute. They're intense. We're having to keep changing the paper. It's as though The Mountain is having labour pains, Willy. It looks like this thing's going to have a baby.' It was a graphic analogy. But it was not life that The Mountain was labouring to create. Quite the opposite.

Also at midnight, Felina Celestine telephoned her 25-year-old son Theo, better known as 2Pac. She had to get up at dawn to help Isolyn and Harry, her sister and brother-in-law, plant vegetables in Harry's plot at Farrell's Yard. She knew Theo would be getting up early to do the 6 a.m. fireman's shift at Salem police station. Would he give her a wake-up call at five?

'No problem, mum, sleep well.'

14

A swift, silent death

The Mountain was 'breathing' more heavily than ever. Each of the volcanologists who watched it like a father-to-be at his wife's hospital bedside had a feeling that 25 June 1997 was going to be a busy day.

Englishman Richard Herd, a volcano deformation expert, started his shift at Eiffel House – the MVO villa in Old Towne – at 3 a.m. on the 25th. Two hours later, still before dawn, Paul Cole popped in on his way to the 6–11 a.m. 'redeye' shift as observer at the airport. 'Trickster' Herd told him of the late-night hybrid swarms and showed him the seismograph copies on the wall. 'Okay, Ricky, keep me informed when the tiltmeter turns so that I can watch out for PFs [pyroclastic flows],' Cole asked his colleague. Then he set out for the airport, at 5.30 a.m.

By six, Cole was at the barely-awake airport. Horrance Boatswain and Simon Tuitt arrived soon afterwards, walking down the road from their homes in the village of Farm. Within minutes, just after dawn, Cole could see pyroclastic flows spilling from the dome into Mosquito Ghaut. They looked relatively small, but his earlier concerns proved justified. Viewed from the airport terminal, the flows disappeared from sight behind the hill at Harris Lookout. That meant that a powerful flow wouldn't reappear in his line of sight until it was almost on the coastal plain. If a big one came down, he and everyone else in the airport could be dead within seconds of seeing it come over that hill.

Paul Cole knew his volcanoes. He knew enough to realise that he was, in his own words, 'powerless and ill-informed' in this location. He decided there and then that the observation role at the airport was 'futile'. After this shift, he was going to tell Willy Aspinall, respectfully, that he would not do another. That decision would prove to be irrelevant.

At 7 a.m., Willy Aspinall and Keith Rowley were back on Windy Hill, watching the same flows as Cole. Although the two men were closer to the volcano than he was, they were on higher ground and had an uninterrupted view of the dome. More time to run. They kept the keys in the ignition of their jeep. If they got a tip from the MVO on their radios or scanners, they were out of there. But if a flow were big enough, it could reach the Central Corridor and cut them off. It might even climb Windy Hill, where they were standing. They could already see clusters of farmers in the fields of Farrell's Yard. The foreign scientists didn't know their names. Any islander would have.

James Ponde was there as usual, along with his son Keithly, nicknamed Joe, and other members of their family. On a nearby plot, Harry Lewis was digging up carrots with Isolyn, Felina and their friend and farmhand Melville Cuffy. 2Pac had called his mother at 5 a.m. sharp to wake her before he headed off for the early fire-service shift at Salem police station. He was surprised to find that she was already wide awake. 'Hi, mum, you still going up The Mountain?'

'Yes, I'm off up to Farrell's now. Harry's picking me up. Love you, Theo. See you later.'

It occurred to the young fireman that his mum had been saying 'I love you' an awful lot lately. And telling friends to look after him when she was gone. She lived part of the time in New York, so that remark did not strike him as strange at the time. It did later.

At 8 a.m., Police Constable Number 7 of the Royal Montserrat Police Force, Kelvin White, arrived at Salem police station for the morning briefing at the start of his shift. He had left his mother Linda at home in Trant's, a stone's throw from the airport, still in the exclusion zone. But she assured him she'd be going up to the safe zone in the north for the day, to the village of St John's. She had to prepare for a workshop on how to teach reading to special-needs pupils. Kelvin was aware of the dangers of living in Trant's, but he had to tend his animals. At least today he knew his mother would be in the safe zone. He didn't have to worry about her.

At the station, his sergeant confirmed the bad news straight off. 'Driving duty today – PC 7 – White.' Kelvin would have to drive fellow constables to and from check-points and deliver their hot lunches. He felt demeaned. But the hard reality was that, as his boss Police Commissioner Hooper regularly bemoaned, many of the 95 policemen on the island did not have a driving licence.

White walked to his designated police jeep, registration plate G2400. 2Pac Matthew was loading gear on to a fire brigade pick-up truck in the station yard. They greeted each other with the usual 'Ahl-right?' 'Ahl-right now.' In addition to the fact that they worked together – the fire brigade came under Frank Hooper's command – the two had a lot in common. They were almost the same age, both enjoyed running and both were particularly close to their mothers. But neither could have any idea that the next few hours were going to change their lives, that at exactly the same time later that day, fate was to deal them contrasting hands.

From early in the morning, ZJB Radio listeners heard Rose Willock repeat the latest scientific reports. No one should be in the exclusion zone and anyone close to it should carry a transistor radio tuned in to ZJB for updates. She warned people not to enter the danger zone and asked anyone already inside to leave for their own safety. The scientists were well aware that many people were still living in the village of Harris. Abraham White, better known as Brother Hammy, the doomsaying street preacher, was one of them. Every time the scientists passed through Harris, they would see people drinking outside Scott Greer's bar. Governor Frank Savage's policy remained the same: Leave. It's crazy to be here. But the British government is not going to force you.

Rose Willock had been stepping up her warnings for several days as the volcanic activity increased. She did not merely suggest people leave. She pleaded with her fellow islanders to come out of the danger zone. Recently, in the safe zone, she had bumped into Beryl Grant, the cheery 73-year-old fruit farmer who used to sell bananas and other fruit outside Ram's supermarket in Plymouth. Everyone in the capital knew Beryl. She told Rose she was coming and going to Harris to check her plot and orchard and to pick ripe fruit. Willock warned her not to go into the exclusion zone, that it was truly dangerous, but the old lady just laughed. 'Everybody got to make a living, Rose.'

On 25 June 1997, despite Rose Willock's warnings, Beryl Grant was doing just that. She was making a living. She shared a fruit and vegetable yard in Farm village with Simon Tuitt, the airport baggage handler and part-time farmer. Today, colourfully dressed as always, this time in white and purple, she first helped her 53-year-old neighbour Elvira Harris press cassava to make some traditional fruit bread. Then she set off on foot along the banks of Pea Ghaut towards Harris, more than a mile away, to chop bananas. Pea Ghaut was a lowland continuation of Mosquito and Tuitt's Ghauts. It came directly from The Mountain's northern slopes, and it hit the ocean only a penalty kick away from the southern end of the airport runway.

Around the same time, Beryl's young neighbour Devon Sutton, who had flown in from Antigua the previous day, set off from Farm to deal with some bureaucracy at the relocated Ministry of Agriculture in the north of the island. He left his girlfriend Alicia and baby Allister at home, close to his grandparents' house. It occurred to him that little Allister was 16 weeks old today.

By mid-morning, the seismographs at the MVO had quietened down. Willy Aspinall knew the lull would be temporary. The Mountain had been breathing in and out in regular cycles, every few hours. But the lull was an opportunity to send someone into the field to take some on-the-ground measurements. These might prove crucial to anyone in the danger zone. Two scientists, Rob Watts of Bristol University's Department of Earth Sciences and Amanda Clarke, the young researcher who had been working with Barry Voight at Penn State University, donned their gear and set out along the Central Corridor at around 9 a.m. They would do a GPS survey that would help the MVO detect any 'ground deformation', any movement of The Mountain.

Before joining the Central Corridor to the airport, Watts and Clarke checked in with the MVO by radio. The road was now considered dangerous. It was barred to the public. It ran along the northern foothills, and you didn't want to be there if The Mountain was about to burp. But the seismographs were quiet. The MVO gave the all-clear and the two scientists drove on. Dangerous or no, as they passed Farrell's Yard they saw a cluster of parked pick-up trucks and a handful of farmers in the fields below Mosquito Ghaut. The scientists did not know them, but they were Harry and Isolyn Lewis, Felina Celestine and Melville Cuffy. In a nearby terrace of fruit and vegetable plots were James Ponde, his wife, their son Joe and their daughter.

Back at Salem police station, 2Pac Matthew was setting out to upgrade the fire appliances at the island's Public Works Department. At the station door, he saw Constable Kelvin White chatting with his younger brother André. André had got a message from the local cable company saying his TV would be cut off if he didn't pay the bill that day. Their offices were just below the police station, so he'd popped in to see his brother. 'Oh, by the way, Kelvin, mum didn't go to St John's after all. Apparently it's too cramped for space to get much work done up there. She decided to stay at home in Trant's and work there.'

Kelvin White waved his brother goodbye. He had barely registered André's remark.

With their needles, ink and drums, the MVO's seismographs are reminiscent of the lie-detectors you see in Hollywood cop movies. At 10.50 a.m. on 25 June 1997, after a quiet couple of hours, The Mountain appeared to be lying through its teeth. The needles started shaking as if they wanted to get off the drum. It was the start of a new hybrid earthquake swarm. By eleven o'clock, the field tiltmeter on Chance's Peak was revealing fractional changes of surface inclination caused by pressure from magma. To make matters worse, cloud moved in over The Mountain's peaks. The line of sight was gone, from both the MVO and from their man at the airport. Now the volcanologists had to rely on their equipment. They were like pilots flying on instruments.

The cloud cover further frustrated and worried Paul Cole as he handed over the airport shift at eleven o'clock to the Trinidadian colleague everyone called 'Polly'. Despite the name, Polly was male. His actual name was Lutchman Pollard, and he was an SRU oldtimer who had first worked with Willy Aspinall in the 1970s. Looking up at the descending cloud cover, now shrouding the top 500 feet of the 3,000-feet plus mountain, he and Cole knew that their lives and those of the airport staff and incoming and outgoing passengers could now depend on Chief Scientist Aspinall, their colleagues at the MVO and the instruments they had previously set up on The Mountain. Pollard kept his walkie-talkie and scanner close to his ear for the words 'Lima Papa' – his MVO radio traffic codename based on his initials.

After his shift ended, Paul Cole – 'Papa Charlie' – drove through pouring rain from the airport to the MVO, avoiding the Central Corridor and choosing the safer route round the north of the island and back down the west coast to Old Towne.

At the same time, Governor Frank Savage was still 'off island' but not far away. He was at Antigua airport, waiting

to board a five-seater charter plane. He was returning to
Montserrat with Veronica after chasing up further aid
money from his regional administrators in Barbados. Any
problems in Montserrat would have been communicated
to the Antigua control tower, but everything at Antigua
airport appeared normal. Their charter pilot was ready to
take off. The Savages were looking forward to seeing
Winston.

When they arrived at Montserrat airport, the governor's
driver and general handyman, Solomon Samuel, was
waiting with the official white Land Rover Discovery, a
little Union Jack on its bonnet. In line with the recent
emergency plan, the driver had parked facing outwards and
north, keys in the ignition, outside the VIP lounge. Inside
the terminal, Arrow was having a coffee in the Cockpit bar
with his cousin Norman Cassell, the duty airport manager.
He was headed out on the Liat flight to Antigua, then on
to New York for a concert. Neither he nor his cousin had
any idea that it would be the last commercial flight out
of W.H. Bramble airport for a long, long time. Only one
plane would leave after the Liat flight. It would be a small,
private one and it would be in a hurry.

'You know, Norman, I had a strange sense, an eerie
feeling this morning. I drove here the long way round,
round the north,' Arrow told his cousin. He would
normally have taken the direct route across the Central
Corridor. What policeman would stop Montserrat's
best-known citizen?

Simon Tuitt was nearing the end of his shift but came
up to take Arrow's bags to the Liat check-in.

'Simon, man, you been working here a long time,' the
singer said.

'Oh, yes, man, let me come tell you now, me been here too long. Me goin' to leave soon.'

Arrow recalled the remark later and wondered whether the baggage handler too had had some kind of premonition.

Soon after the singer and the rest of the Liat passengers had taken off for Antigua, Simon Tuitt and his friend and neighbour Horrance Boatswain ended their shifts and walked up the road, as always, up the side of Pea Ghaut to their homes in Farm.

Lewis Chloupek saw the Liat flight take off and wheel towards Antigua. The former farmer from the hamlet of Surprise, Nebraska, was working on the roof of his home at Spanish Point, less than a mile south of the airport. Inside the house were his wife Sandy and four-year-old daughter Mary. They were the only people still living in the coastal settlement once crowded with American, Canadian and British expats. All others had taken the scientists' advice and gone north. Lewis Chloupek was a Baptist. He believed God would protect the house, himself and his family.

While he was on his roof, a four-wheel-drive vehicle drove past the Bethel Methodist church above his house, coming down from the abandoned Long Ground village. In it were Rob Watts and Amanda Clarke of the MVO, on their way back from taking measurements in the deserted Long Ground area, only 1,500 yards below the north-eastern rim of the crater. Routinely, Clarke got on the walkie-talkie to Willy Aspinall at the MVO for permission to move on to their next planned site, a place called White's Yard. Aspinall told them of the new earthquake swarm. 'What are you up to?' he asked.

'We're just going down to pick up some kit we left off at

White's Yard. It'll only take three minutes,' said Amanda Clarke.

Aspinall knew White's Yard was on their way home. He also knew it would take them three minutes to dismantle their equipment and pack it into their jeep, but he didn't want them hanging around taking photographs. 'Make it a short three minutes,' he replied. As he spoke, one of his colleagues was with Rose Willock in the ZJB Radio studio, giving the islanders the lunchtime scientific report on the latest activity. Rose repeated her calls for people to leave the exclusion zone.

Just before 12.45 p.m., Watts and Clarke were about to return to the Central Corridor. They wanted to do a few more measurements at Windy Hill on their way back to the MVO. As always, they called their chief and asked permission by radio. At the MVO, things were heating up. The pulse of the tiltmeters on The Mountain had peaked, showing clear ground deformation. On the seismographs, the signals had blended into a continuous tremor.

Police Commissioner Frank Hooper had called off a special lunch with his wife and their visiting son, Simon, at Providence House, the mansion where Paul McCartney used to stay. Hooper was at the MVO, peering at the seismographs. Paul Cole, back from the airport, had 'a palpable sense that The Mountain must be shaking'. He too gave up on lunch and stayed on base, watching The Mountain from beside the MVO villa's pool and reporting what he saw to Aspinall, inside in the seismic room. There had previously been a window in the seismic room looking directly out and up to The Mountain: an obvious advantage. But an earlier scientist had had the window filled in because the light was too distracting. That was something that had never ceased to amaze Willy Aspinall. Now you had to run in and out from the seismographs to see The Mountain itself.

Aspinall listened to the radio message from Watts and Clarke. He had not realised they were planning to go back over the Central Corridor. 'Alpha Charlie, Alpha Charlie,' he said calmly but briskly into his walkie-talkie, using the radio code for Amanda Clarke's initials. 'Do not continue on your route. Go directly to the airport. Remain there until further notice. Over.' It was exactly 12.45 and Aspinall's call was to prove vital to the two young scientists. Watts and Clarke joined 'Polly' Pollard at the little airport terminal at 12.55.

There were only a couple of dozen people still at the airport, including two notable new arrivals. Governor Savage and his wife had touched down at 12.50 in their little Carib Aviation charter plane and were sitting in the VIP lounge while their driver, Solomon, loaded their bags into the Discovery. Clarke and Pollard were outside, watching the cloud-veiled Mountain. They'd already been told by the MVO to be on high alert.

At 12.57, in the MVO, Aspinall saw the seismograph needles go berserk. It was the first pulse of seismic activity that usually precedes an eruption. And it was a big pulse. At 12.58 p.m., he called his colleague Pollard at the airport and told him to start a phased evacuation.

The people at the airport heard an eerie silence descend on the coastal plain. The only sound was of the waves lapping gently on the shore beyond the runway. Then it seemed as though every stray dog within miles began to bark or howl. Frank Savage recalled Winston's pre-eruption antics, his sixth sense. Something was about to happen.

Paul Cole, looking through binoculars beside the MVO villa pool, saw it first. It spilt from the base of the normal white cloud cover like a river of dirty, boiling milk. A pyroclastic flow. A big one, hurtling down Mosquito Ghaut, close to Farrell's Yard where the scientists had seen farmers working earlier, down towards the Central Corridor, the island's main east–west road. That would bring it close to the villages that lined the road and, ultimately, the ghaut's estuary a few yards from the airport runway. Cole ran inside and told Aspinall. At the same moment, the seismographs showed another massive pulse of seismic activity. The Mountain was panting. The chief scientist grabbed his walkie-talkie and squeezed the talk button. It was precisely 1 p.m.

At the airport, Aspinall's voice on Pollard's walkie-talkie, turned up full volume, echoed through the terminal building. 'Observatory calling Lima Papa, Observatory calling Lima Papa. Evacuate airport immediately. Repeat. Get everyone out of there. And get yourselves out. Get out now. Over.'

Pollard sounded the airport siren. From the MVO, Frank Hooper ordered the sounding of all the sirens in the exclusion zone and radioed the sites where a few dozen 'essential workers' were still operating in Plymouth – the port, the rice mill and the power station. (As it turned out, most of the sirens did not go off. The system was new. Someone at the control panel in the Salem police station did not find the main activating switch.)

Seconds later, Paul Cole was back outside by the pool to see a dark grey ash plume rise rapidly from above The Mountain, the second element of a pyroclastic eruption. The thick, heavy ash would eventually fall. Things were going to get dark. Cole and Aspinall knew the third type of pyroclastic event was also likely to follow, the dreaded surge, a fast-moving hurricane of red-hot ash mixed with gas and air, lighter and more dilute than the dense basal avalanche of a pyroclastic flow, almost soundless, travelling in a straight line, obeying gravity but not following the contours of the land the way pyroclastic flows do. The kind of surge that had killed the residents of Pompeii, and those below Montagne Pelée on Martinique. A swift, silent wave of death.

2Pac saw the rising ash column, too. He was installing equipment at the Public Works Department in the safe zone. 'Everything was nice and dandy, then I heard a big boom, man, a big, big boom,' he told friends. He'd heard that sound before. He knew it was the volcano. What witnesses through the ages had described as the 'terrifying majesty' of the ash cloud mesmerised him. 'The ash start goin' up in the sky, man, goin' up, goin' up, goin' up high. And it's just risin', risin', risin' like a mushroom, and it's openin' out. I'm excited, you know what I'm sayin'. It was nice. It was the biggest one I'd ever seen. So I'm lookin' at it and lookin' at it, and I'm saying "wow". I was lookin' at it for about ten minutes when something clicked me, and I said to myself, shit, my mum is up there working. I jumped into my little fire tender and drove at full speed to the police station.' His boss, Frank Hooper, had left the MVO and was headed there, too.

The black ash cloud blew westwards with the trade winds. All around the island people came out to watch. Over the past two years, they had come to know their volcano, and they could tell this was a big one. Calls began pouring into the radio station. Rose Willock repeated the scientists' latest bulletin, told everyone to stay calm and urged anyone in the danger zone to get out immediately. From the Providence plantation house in the north, where she and her son had been awaiting Frank for lunch, Sheila Hooper saw the plume and feared the worst. Cars were pouring up the main road to get away from the cloud before it descended.

Carol Osborne was at Providence House too. She knew her beloved Vue Pointe was likely to get 'ashed out'. She was right. From the hotel, her husband Cedric and son Michael had had time to see a big pyroclastic flow rush down from below the cloudline in Mosquito Ghaut. Its path was way east of them, but a big, drifting ash plume came their way and turned day to night at the hotel.

Just before it did, Jim McMahon was able to get airborne from the hotel's helipad in the little Jet Ranger, carrying Paul Cole and MVO technician and cameraman Dave Williams for a first look at the damage. David Lea had been lunching at the hotel with two journalists from the German magazine *Der Spiegel*. He filmed the pyroclastic flow from a healthy distance and the German photographer got some good shots. Lea thanked God, literally, that he had not taken them to his rented house at Harris Lookout, as they had wanted. He had somehow sensed today was not a good day to be there.

Down below the Vue Pointe at Old Road Bay, Danny Sweeney and Margaret Wilson watched the black cloud rise and descend. They were used to being 'ashed out' by now. But two tourist couples who had anchored their yachts in the bay and were having a drink ashore were not quite so cool. 'Don't worry. Look, put your t-shirt over your face and breathe through it. You'll be okay,' Margaret assured them. 'Unless of course there's a pyroclastic flow behind it.' They hoped she was joking. So did she.

After Aspinall's evacuation message and the sounding of the airport siren, the air traffic controller in the little tower radioed the pilot of the only aircraft on the runway, the little Carib Aviation charter plane that had brought in the governor and his wife, to take off immediately. The pilot was already taxiing. He could see the big churning grey cloud thundering downhill in his direction. It was only a few hundred yards away when he got airborne and wheeled to the east.

The scientists Rob Watts and Amanda Clarke went round the terminal ensuring everyone was leaving. In the Cockpit bar, two ladies were preparing bacon and egg rolls. Watts told them to leave everything as it was and go to their designated minibus. The wail of the Second World War siren echoed around the terminal.

Frank Savage had been born during the war. The sound made him shiver as he tried to ensure everyone was evacuating without panic. Then he hurried from the terminal with Veronica and shot a glance up at The Mountain. There it was, below the cloud line: a hurtling grey avalanche only a few thousand yards above them, following the path of the ravines like a bobsled, and above it an enormous ash cloud.

A few hundred yards from the airport, in the little village of Trant's on the banks of Pea Ghaut, Linda White heard the siren clearly. She was in her makeshift office in a shed outside her house, preparing notes for her remedial teaching workshop. She'd told her son Kelvin she'd be going to the north today, but she'd changed her mind because she needed a bit of space, and peace and quiet.

And it was quiet, quieter than ever, until she heard every dog barking, and then the siren. She peeked up at The Mountain. Nothing unusual. Just cloud. From her low vantage point, she could not yet see the ash column or the pyroclastic flow hurtling down the upper ghauts that ultimately ran right past her home to the sea. Of course, she thought, it's Wednesday. It's just the weekly siren test. Funny, though. They usually do it in mid-afternoon. She continued with her work.

From her shed, Linda White did not notice the governor's Land Rover or the little convoy behind him, speeding along the road from the airport that passed within 200 yards of her house. Solomon, the governor's driver, had been in such a hurry that he forgot about the dirt track that had been tarmacked for a quicker exit, due north from the airport, away from The Mountain. He took the usual road, the one that went west, directly towards the volcano, before it turned north at the T-junction near Pea Ghaut and Linda White's house. It occurred to the governor that his driver was travelling at 70 mph towards a deadly avalanche that was coming his way even faster. He prayed they would reach the T-junction, and head north, before the pyroclastic flow got there.

While everyone was fleeing the airport, Linda White's son was on his way towards it in his white police Suzuki Vitara. As police driver for the day, he had just picked up WPC Jessica Sweeney – Danny's niece – at the end of her shift, from the last checkpoint before the airport. Before taking her back to the police station in Salem, he had to deliver hot lunches to the immigration and fire officers at the airport. He reached the Flats, the coastal plain on which the airport sat, when he saw the ash plume. He'd seen those before. He kept going. His colleagues would want their lunch. He could see his house and many of his cows, sheep and goats as he approached the T-junction.

It was there that he passed the governor's car and another vehicle making the turn at unusually high speed. Not like Solomon to drive like that, he thought. He saw a white face leaning out of the passenger window and an arm waving, gesturing to him to go back. It was none other than Her Majesty's Governor himself, Frank Savage. Constable White had never seen him so animated. The policeman waved back, pointed to the airport and kept driving. He understood what the governor meant. There was an eruption. But the airport was only a few hundred yards further on. His colleagues in fire and immigration would be hungry. He'd better deliver their hot lunches.

When he got to the terminal, no one was waiting for lunch. There wasn't a soul. A string of cars was speeding north up the dirt track. It occurred to Kelvin White that he should get himself and WPC Sweeney out of there, fast. In the excitement, what his brother André had told him earlier – that their mum had changed her mind and decided to work at home today, only a few hundred yards from the airport – had not occurred to him.

The three pulses of the 25 June 1997 eruption, the three pyroclastic flows, lasted little more than 20 minutes. Gas pressure and rising underground magma destabilised the dome and sent millions of cubic metres of rock, mixed with a lethal cocktail of scorching hot ash and gas, thundering downhill in the form of pyroclastic flows.

The first flow started at 12.57 p.m, the second three minutes later and the third at 1.08 p.m. The whole thing was over by 1.20 p.m. Those 23 minutes were enough to make 25 June 1997 the deadliest day in the island's recent history, worse than the day of Hurricane Hugo. All three flows came from the northern rim of the crater as the dome collapsed on that side. All three entered the top of Mosquito Ghaut and followed the twisting, downhill path of the successive ravines, first to the north, then eastwards towards the ocean.

One flow, however, was so fast and powerful that its sandy, dusty, lighter top layer did not follow the curves of the ghauts like the usual helter-skelter. This one became a blazing hot, high-velocity sandstorm that flew over the banks of the ghauts, defied the contours of the land and just kept on going in a more or less straight line. This was the pyroclastic surge the scientists had feared. The first thing it hit was the green, fertile farmland at Farrell's, where Harry and Isolyn Lewis, her sister Felina Celestine – 2Pac's mother – and farmhand Melville Cuffy had been harvesting carrots all morning. In a nearby field, 32-year-old Joe Ponde had been bagging potatoes with his father, mother and sister.

Harry Lewis had heard the barking dogs seconds earlier and felt uneasy. 'This doesn't feel right. Stop working. Let's go,' he told the others. He'd parked his pick-up truck in the field to make loading easier. He ran to get it. The other three raced downhill towards the main road, the Central Corridor, where Lewis had said he'd pick them up. Joe Ponde's father, mother and sister had spotted the initial ash cloud, jumped in their truck and driven away from the volcano up the side road at Windy Hill. Joe himself had been higher up in their terraced fields, planting potatoes. His only transport was his donkey.

Isolyn, Felina and Melville knew about pyroclastic flows. They'd heard Rose Willock and the scientists describe them and they'd seen earlier, smaller ones. But they could not have conceived of the lighter, faster pyroclastic surge that defied the curves of the mountain's ravines. Instinctively, the three did not stop at the main road. They kept running, faster than they'd ever run before, north, away from the volcano, up the slopes of Windy Hill. They prayed the pyroclastic flow would bend east with the ghaut. It did, but the hot ash hurricane that followed it did not.

Harry Lewis drove to and fro frantically on the main road but could not see them. He drove up Windy Hill as far as the road continued, then jumped from his vehicle and ran through the bush as the ash cloud descended. He stumbled past the disused Air Studios on his way to seek help at Salem police station.

The pyroclastic surge swept across Farrell's and the Central Corridor at 80 mph, incinerating three people instantly in the village of Streatham. At Farrell's Yard, it swallowed up 32-year-old Joe Ponde and his donkey, then continued up the lower slopes of Windy Hill. It was there, where Willy Aspinall had observed The Mountain earlier that morning, that 2Pac's mother, her sister and Melville Cuffy ran behind a farmhouse. It was a desperate and instinctive attempt to protect themselves from what they thought would be a thick, grey pyroclastic flow.

But the flow itself never reached them. It careened down the consecutive ghauts, for the first time spilling over the banks alongside the Central Corridor and all the way down the side of the road that led to the airport and the ocean. Moving at close to 50 mph as though on giant rollers, it billowed along the edge of Harris, instantly torching homes in the lower part of the village and the fields where elderly fruit vendor Beryl Grant had been cutting bananas in her white and purple dress. She was never found. It poured on below Harris Lookout, below the hillside house the American missionary David Lea had rented to film The Mountain. Lea's instincts had told him it was a bad day to go there, despite the urgings of the two men from *Der Spiegel*. Had they done so, they might well have been killed on the road. Ellen Thomas, the 90-year-old who lived next door to Lea's rented house, was spared as the flow rushed by below her home.

Those still living in Harris village had a close call. Lenroy 'Slim' Daley, a lorry driver from Bramble village, had been chatting to Scott Greer at the latter's bar in Harris when they saw the flow rush down Paradise Ghaut. Their survival instincts kicked in. Greer ran for his life across a field. Daley, his bright yellow tropical shirt flapping behind him, jumped in his car, which had latterly served also as his home, but he got cut off as the flow blocked the road. He, Greer and Brother Hammy the street preacher survived but were trapped, surrounded by red-hot material.

Linda Daley, a 42-year-old from Harris, also survived – just. She was doing some washing outside her home. 'Man, I look up and see this mighty sea rush towards me. I drop my pail and I run and I hide and I say, "Lord have mercy, I'm going to die." Then I feel this surge of heat and I see this great fire all above me. It got very dark, blacker than black. I thought I never see daylight again. Then there come a great rushing wind, and let me come tell you now, God was in that wind because it blew away the heat and the darkness. And after the darkness depart, I tell you, the sun shone like pure gold. Pure gold.'

Still picking up momentum, the lighter surface of the flow failed to make the sharp left turn in the ravine and rushed up over the 100-foot banks to set fire to the evacuated village of Bramble. Slim Daley's house was destroyed along with everything else in the village. David Lea later described it as 'like Ground Zero at Hiroshima'. The lighter overspill hit the hamlet of Bethel, gutting the old stone Methodist church. Rob Watts and Amanda Clarke had passed there half an hour earlier and would now have been driving into the path of the flows had Willy Aspinall not stopped them and diverted them to the airport. The flow's lighter but no less hot or deadly overspill raced on towards Spanish Point, where the Chloupek family were still living. Its heavier main body thundered down Pea Ghaut and again overflowed to torch the entire village of Farm as if it were made of paper.

In Farm, baby Allister Joseph never lived to see the end of his hundred and twelfth day. His mother Alicia also perished, as did the baby's great-grandparents, Anthony and Virginia Sutton. The two villagers who had just ended their shifts at the airport, the 67-year-old gardener Horrance Boatswain and 45-year-old baggage handler Simon Tuitt, both lived on the edge of Pea Ghaut. Simon had just shifted some of his goats and had been planning to go to the safe zone. They may have seen the swift tan-grey monster rush round the bend from Harris, but only for a matter of seconds. They were engulfed and died instantly.

Villager Elvira Harris, who had earlier baked cassava bread with her friend Beryl Grant, saw the flow come down and spill over the ghaut. She also saw Simon Tuitt directly in its path. Elvira survived as it rushed past her home, incinerating everything it touched. The sturdy home of builder Kenneth 'Bobby' Harris, where he had left his wife Mary earlier to go to work in the safe zone, also survived, but Mary was not in it. She may have fled to what she thought was a safer area. It wasn't. She was never found. In all, nine people died in Farm village, including 43-year-old Alvin Allen and his 41-year-old brother Winston, who had returned from a northern refugee shelter during daylight hours to tend their animals. The remains of the dead were never traced. They became part of the flattened, grey landscape.

Below Farm lay the village of Trant's and the airport. So silently did the cloud of death come down The Mountain that Linda White, in her Trant's home, noticed nothing. She had taken a break from her research to cook some porridge for lunch. Down at the airport, realising there was no one there to deliver lunches to, her son Kelvin was about to flee for the north with his passenger, WPC Sweeney. Then it dawned on him what his brother Andre had told him earlier. 'Oh my God, my mum stayed home today. Hold tight.' He put his foot down, screeched up to his house in little more than a minute and yelled: 'Mum, mum, come on, let's go. There's a pyroclastic flow on its way!' Linda White had learnt a lot about volcanoes. She knew exactly what a pyroclastic flow could do. She ran out in her slippers, carrying only her handbag.

The little police jeep sped off northwards to get away from Pea Ghaut. The deadly flow was rushing down the ghaut at 50 mph and now had Trant's, the Whites' house and the airport in its sights. Kelvin saw it in his rear-view mirror as he pushed the little Suzuki to its limit.

A few hundred yards south of Trant's, in the township of Spanish Point that was once full of expatriates, the

American Chloupek family were the only ones who had refused to leave. They had been heavily criticised by Frank Hooper and their own neighbours for keeping their four-year-old daughter, Mary, in the danger zone. Lewis Chloupek had seen the initial flow start while he was working on his roof. He rushed downstairs to tell his wife Sandy and little Mary to get into a windowless inner room, but even as he did so he saw the churning grey monster billowing down the valley only 500 yards away, headed for Trant's and the airport. It appeared to have passed them by and was so beautiful in its majesty that Sandy actually rushed out to get a few photographs. What she was photographing was the main body of the flow. The lighter overspill broke off and surged towards their house.

Through a window Lewis saw it coming, an opaque avalanche of billowing grey, 'just a streak of material zipping towards us at maybe 100 mph, right across the ground, singeing things as it came'. It was like the dust cloud behind a rally car in the desert. But this cloud was gas-borne and hundreds of degrees hot. 'Everybody, run to the bedroom. Mary, run fast!' he yelled. They'd been sleeping in the windowless inner room as a precaution. Little Mary was the slowest. And it dawned on the little man from Nebraska that he had left the outside door open.

'It was just like a . . . whooooof, it hit, like a flame shot through the door,' he said. 'I saw red flame. It was just a fraction of a second and then it was so pitch black from the ash that you couldn't see anything any more, you couldn't see your hand in front of your face. I couldn't see Mary, but I could hear her crying. Then she came past me and she wasn't running any more. I think she was in shock. The thing came in through the door and drew a fine line, kind of in a semi-circle inside the door. Mary had been running, so her right foot was back just a little bit behind the left foot, the right hand was behind the left hand. It singed the hair on the back of her head, singed her right foot and burnt her right arm worse than her left.'

The dense pyroclastic flow ploughed through Trant's, swallowing up hundreds of mesmerised cows, sending goats and sheep and stray dogs scrambling in terror. They died running. Many of the cows and goats belonged to Kelvin White and his mother. Lewis Chloupek saw it demolish the bridge over the ghaut at Trant's and bury the only road to safety in a bed of steaming grey. The flow slewed in the coastal plain, slithered on to the end of the airport runway and stopped just short of the abandoned terminal. Lewis knew there could easily be another flow, and it could well be bigger. He grabbed his daughter up into his arms and he and his wife ran down towards the ocean and the airport. It looked like the only possible way out, but the flow had left red-hot debris right up to the shoreline. They'd have to paddle round it, in the ocean, hoping the sea was not itself a furnace.

As they walked, Lewis looked back. Spanish Point and Trant's looked like a front-line European town after a World War Two battle. Houses were ablaze. Incinerated cows lay with their legs in the air. The flow had passed, miraculously, on both sides of the Chloupeks' house, diverted by a slight incline. The old Bethel Methodist church next door, now also ablaze, appeared to have helped protect them. 'It was just like if God put his hand there and stopped it from overflowing our house,' Lewis said.

The family were now at the edge of the ocean, at the mouth of Pea Ghaut, only yards from where the flow had stopped, leaving the ravine filled with burning grey ash. Lewis put Mary down just by the edge of the steaming mass and paddled into the surf to test the temperature. Hot, but bearable. The three waded across the estuary, only 20 feet beyond the pyroclastic material, to the airport perimeter fence. Now what? They could walk up the side of the ghaut, next to the red-hot layer, towards the main road, or they could climb the airport fence and walk up the runway.

Lewis decided it would be better to scramble over the fence. As they did so, another pyroclastic flow appeared down the same ravine, spilling over the northern bank they had considered walking up. Had they chosen that option, they would have been cremated instantly. They hurried up the runway, rested at the abandoned terminal and realised the seriousness of little Mary's burns. They walked on north up the deserted coastal plain to find help.

Constable Kelvin White, his mother and WPC Sweeney did not see the Chloupeks, but they were not far away. Kelvin and his passengers raced over the Flats and up the steep Jack Boy Hill, from where they could see The Mountain, the airport and much of the south-eastern coast. Near the top of the hill was a police checkpoint, at the edge of the new exclusion zone. Kelvin and his mother got out of the car. Scores of people had gathered to see what was going on. Soon it would be hundreds, and later almost the whole island showed up. Governor Frank Savage and Veronica had stopped there. Rob Watts and Amanda Clarke were there too, grateful that Willy Aspinall had stopped them from crossing the Central Corridor a short time earlier. Had they been on that road, no trace of them would ever have been found.

David Lea had raced to Jack Boy Hill from his interrupted lunch at the Vue Pointe and was filming the scene.
Like everyone else, he felt uneasy. He knew there were
people down in those villages. He thought about 90-year-
old Ellen Thomas, who lived next door to his rented house
in Harris Lookout and had refused to leave. He did not yet
know that the pyroclastic flow had narrowly missed her
home, or that she was trapped on the hilltop by the debris
that had settled on the slopes below her.

Kelvin and Linda White stood and gazed back down in
silence, across the plain, to Trant's and the home and farm
where they had spent most of their lives. They were just in
time to see the big rolling tan cloud, the final pyroclastic
flow, demolish Farm village and continue relentlessly
towards the big final right-hand bend in Pea Ghaut. Part of
it followed the deep ravine, but not all. It veered left over
the ravine's banks and torched the houses in the village one
by one in rapid succession, explosions of cooking-gas
canisters splitting the silence. The Whites saw their home,
with their beloved clamacherry trees in the garden, disappear into the jaws of the rolling monster. Kelvin thought
of the times he'd used the super-adhesive juice of the
clamacherry tree to construct kites when he was a child.
And he remembered the day his late father had used a
brake cable from Kelvin's bike to tie down their loosening
roof during Hurricane Hugo. When the flow had passed,
steamed to a halt by the ocean and settled into a sizzling
grey delta, they could not pick out their house. They could
not pick out any house. The village had been wiped out.

It occurred to Kelvin White that he had no material
possession left in the world but the police uniform he was
standing in, and his mother had only a dress, a pair of

slippers and a handbag. He felt numb. He led his mother towards his police jeep. Realising what had happened, people called out to them. Kelvin White did not say a word. He just kept walking. At least his mother was safe, and that was nothing short of a miracle. He'd been virtually forced to drive that day. And his brother had happened by the police station because he had to pay a cable TV bill nearby. Had André not told him their mother was in Trant's, he would have left the airport and fled to the north without stopping by his home. 'God just put him in place. Perfect timing,' Linda White told David Lea later. 'That morning, I specifically ask, "Father, you are in charge, you are right in the middle of that volcano, you are in control, now my life is in your hands. I'm asking you to protect me from pyroclastic flows and surges." And he sent my son right on time to get me out.'

The crowd at Jack Boy Hill pointed southwards as one at Jim McMahon's helicopter when it buzzed into view over the airport and the devastated zones of Farm village and Trant's. Main roads had been blocked, and the pyroclastic material beneath the surface would stay burning hot for days, weeks, even months. Walking into the stricken zone would be out of the question for a while. 'Fluffy', McMahon's little five-seat helicopter, could be the only hope of getting survivors out.

With the Canadian on the chopper were the Englishman Paul Cole and the MVO's local cameraman and technician Dave Williams. The pyroclastic flow had slowed but was still creeping forward, spreading across Spanish Point. Houses were burning. 'Oh, my God, oh, my God,' Williams repeated over and over again. They did not see the Chloupeks, but while hovering low over the end of the flow, so much so that the three men could feel the heat through their boots, McMahon caught sight of another man and child waving from a strip of green field in the midst of the steaming grey mass. They had fled from their car as the pyroclastic flow powered towards the main road. They had run over fields to get away and were now surrounded by the deadly, red-hot tide covering the landscape. The flow had run out of momentum but its edge was still oozing towards them, packing hundreds of degrees centigrade, eating up the remaining strip of green on its way to the shoreline. If a further flow followed they would be sitting ducks.

McMahon did not hesitate. He hovered above the last strip of green, little more than 100 yards from the front of the flow. He was looking the beast straight in the eye through the glass-fronted Jet Ranger. Cole was a little concerned, to say the least. If a faster flow came now, they'd see it only seconds before it came round the ghaut. But McMahon wasn't going to leave anyone down there. He set the little chopper down, Cole and Williams hauled the man and child on board and they were up and away within seconds.

The pilot then saw 40 people stranded on a hill at Harris Lookout. The Canadian could only get one skid on the ground, so he kept the chopper hovering to fly them out in twos, though some of the older ones were not too keen on getting on board this little contraption. Among those rescued was 90-year-old Ellen Thomas, David Lea's erstwhile neighbour. Lea filmed and interviewed them as McMahon dropped them off in front of the assembled onlookers on Jack Boy Hill. 'That thing came down like a bullet and it was big, really big,' said Lenroy 'Slim' Daley, his bright yellow shirt open to the waist. 'This thing passed so ferociously, it was like 200 miles an hour, man. There was too much heat.' The scientists pointed out that it would not have moved quite that fast, but seeing such a lethal monster come towards you understandably affects your judgement.

Jim McMahon dropped Paul Cole off to allow Governor Savage to get on board for a first-hand look. On the ground, Cole radioed Willy Aspinall at the MVO. 'I think some of Bramble, most of Bethel, most of Spanish Point, most of Farm and most of Trant's has gone. And the lower half of Harris. There are many buildings on fire.'

Flying back over Spanish Point, McMahon spotted another stranded survivor, a farmer now surrounded by a grey sizzling wasteland. The Canadian landed, but couldn't risk taking his eye off the still-seeping pyroclastic material, or The Mountain in case another flow appeared. Frank Savage's was the only pair of hands. His Excellency the Governor of the British Dependent Territory of Montserrat, West Indies, the man from Whitehall in the grey suit, jumped from the open chopper door, grabbed the farmer, still in a state of shock, by the scruff of the neck and manhandled him on board. If the folks at the Foreign Office could just see me now, he thought. It was then that it occurred to him that 'this is not where the governor should be'. He had McMahon drop him off to allow the police and fire brigade search-and-rescue team to take over.

Police Constable Julian Wade, a forensics expert with the island CID, was among those who flew with McMahon to look for survivors. The young officer, originally from the island of Dominica, had come to Montserrat to help with reconstruction after Hurricane Hugo. Hugo was bad, but this was worse. 'It was like flying into hell,' he said. 'There was a church on fire, gas cylinders exploding like bombs, big balls of fire rolling across the land.' When McMahon set the chopper down at a steep angle on a sweet potato bed, PC Wade was supposed to go out and look for survivors. He froze, suddenly in shock. 'If we're going to find anybody, they're going to be dead,' he said. 'If that's what hell is going to be like, I don't want to go there.'

Back at Salem police station, Frank Hooper had arrived from the MVO and fireman 2Pac Matthew had driven down from his installation job. 2Pac was also part of the island's search-and-rescue team. Knowing his mum had been working on The Mountain, he'd rushed off in a pick-up truck with a colleague but got only a few hundred yards, to the golf course in the Belham valley, when the ash cloud came down and blacked them out. The two could not even see each other in the vehicle. Working from local knowledge and memory, 2Pac eased the truck back to base at a snail's pace.

When the ash cleared, Hooper went with 2Pac and other search-and-rescue officers in two Land Rovers. They tried to get up the Central Corridor to Farrell's Yard, where the fireman's mother, aunt and uncle and their friend had been working. They reached his aunt's home in the village of Lee's. She wasn't there. 2Pac noticed the tyre tracks in the ash. Looks like uncle Harry came to pick up mum, he thought. But there were no tyre tracks coming back. The young fireman never said another word during the entire trip.

They moved on to the village of Dyer's, about a mile from Farrell's Yard, but could go no further. The road was covered in ash, its surface hotter as they progressed. 2Pac tried to step from the vehicle but felt the heat through his boots. He threw down a piece of straw and it immediately caught fire. It was impossible to walk here, and if they drove on their tyres would burn. They had to turn back.

Hooper had another concern. There was steaming grey debris in the riverbed at the top of the Belham valley, close to the still-populated area of Cork Hill. If the flow had reached the Belham River, the safety of several populated areas was in question. That included Cork Hill, Salem, which had become the de facto capital, Old Road Bay, where Danny Sweeney was still operating, Old Towne and its focal point, the Vue Pointe hotel.

Hooper and his men turned back, and spotted a cluster of goats whining by the side of the road. They had been badly burnt all over. For the first time it occurred to Frank Hooper that people must have died around here and that he shouldn't even be this close to The Mountain. He was just on the fringe. It had to be much hotter further up the road where the pyroclastic flow passed through. Hooper and his men did not carry guns. He turned to PC Wade and asked him to pull out his hunting knife. 'Constable, we have to put these animals out of their misery.' Hooper and Wade slit the goats' throats and the team returned to base. The ground had begun to burn through their boots.

For now, the little helicopter was all the rescuers had. The irony was not lost on the islanders. A British island, a colony, a 'dependent territory' stricken by disaster, and all they had to cope with it was a tiny helicopter from St Lucia flown by a Canadian. The West Indies Guardship was currently HMS *Liverpool*, but instead of guarding the West Indies, the WIGS was now off the Central American

mainland, off Belize, which was no longer even a British
territory. That meant the ship was at least a couple of days
away at full steam, just when needed most. Hooper was
informed that the *Liverpool* would be on its way immediately, complete with a sturdy Lynx helicopter. A Dutch
navy vessel, also carrying a British-built Lynx, was closer
and would assist in the morning. The French were sending
a chopper or two from Guadeloupe. Another private
helicopter was being sent from Barbados. There would be
more chance of rescue tomorrow, Hooper hoped.

Still desperate to find his mother, 2Pac and some of his
colleagues ventured back towards The Mountain off the
main road, 'through the bush'. Then he got a radio message
from the police station: 2Pac, your aunt's husband, Harry
Lewis, is here. He's safe. 'Thank God,' the young fireman
thought. 'That means mum and auntie must be safe, too.'
He got 'a bright, bright feeling', and hurried back to the
station. But when he got there, Harry Lewis told him what
had happened: that he had gone for the truck while the
other three fled on foot, and that he had not been able to
find them before he, too, had to run for his life in pitch
blackness. 2Pac's heart sank. It was dark already. Rescue
had been called off for the night. He and the rest of his
team were told to report for duty at the helipad, on the
plateau known as Gerald's Bottom, at seven the following
morning, 26 June 1997.

2Pac prayed his mother would be found alive and well.
But he did not sleep.

254

15

A tropical Pompeii

Just after dawn on Thursday 26 June, Jim McMahon flew Police Commissioner Frank Hooper over the devastated zone. The ash cloud had cleared. The Englishman couldn't believe his eyes. A sea of grey where it used to be green. Nothing moving. It was the first time McMahon and Hooper had been able to see the devastation clearly. The police chief then went to a meeting of the crisis group, including the governor, Chief Minister Bertrand Osborne and his predecessor Reuben Meade. Hooper knew that none of them could yet have any idea of the extent of the devastation. He stood to address them.

'Gentlemen, I'm sorry to have to tell you this, but the centre of Montserrat has ceased to exist. The villages of Streatham, Riley's, Farm and half of Harris have just been obliterated off this Earth. And I think people have been lost. I don't know how many.' The room fell silent. Hooper left to get on with the rescue operation.

At 7 a.m., 2Pac Matthew and his fellow police and fire officers fell in at the little heliport, formerly a cricket field, at Gerald's Bottom. The ground in the stricken zone would still be too hot to go in on foot. By air remained the only option. Now at least Jim McMahon, exhausted but refusing to rest, had some reinforcements. The helicopter from Guadeloupe had arrived, bringing a serious burns team.

They immediately flew casualties, including little Mary Chloupek, to the French island for treatment. Mary's mother Sandy flew with her but there was no room on the helicopter for Lewis. Carrying all his worldly possessions in a plastic bag, he wandered around the island looking for a place to sleep.

Some of the search-and-rescue men went up with McMahon; others boarded the Lynx helicopter that had just arrived with the Dutch frigate from the island of St Maarten. 2Pac wanted to help, but he was feeling shaky. There had been no word overnight of his mother, his aunt or Melville Cuffy. 'Sir, I don't think it makes much sense for me to go,' the fireman told his superior officer. 'If I see my mum dead, it'll kill me.' He was allowed to stay behind, and waited and watched as the helicopters took off and returned with survivors. He was still praying his mother would be rescued safely and wanted to be right here to greet her when she arrived.

Once he saw a woman that looked like his aunt Isolyn get off one of the helicopters. Overjoyed, he ran to embrace her, but at the last moment realised it was somebody else. Then he noticed that the helicopters were beginning to land farther up the hill, outside St John's hospital. They were offloading body bags and putting them into a big shipping container. 2Pac's heart sank. Then he spotted a shock of white hair above the little crowd. Father Larry Finnegan, the big Irish Catholic priest, was up there, comforting the relatives who had come to seek news of their loved ones.

The young fireman ran up the hill and saw a figure in an open body bag, burnt beyond recognition. 'It's all right, 2Pac, this is a man,' one of his colleagues assured him.

But until that moment, he had been unable to imagine what this mountain could do. The sight of an incinerated corpse pushed him over the edge. He began to wail. His colleagues were close to losing it, too. They all knew the victims personally. They all knew the missing. They took 2Pac away from the scene before they all fell apart.

At 10.45 a.m., the Dutch Lynx dropped off a group of police and firemen at Streatham village at the foot of Windy Hill, where 2Pac's mother and aunt had last been seen running for their lives. The ash on the ground was still hot but bearable. Police Sergeant Desmond Barzey, leading the rescue team, and three other men walked around areas they knew well, careful not to step where the ash might be deep and red-hot.

Barzey walked to the home of a friend, Joseph Greenaway, better known by his nickname, 'Carkoo'. The sergeant had seen the 62-year-old the previous day, a couple of hours before the pyroclastic flow, and advised him to leave the danger zone. 'Don't worry, man. I'm just going home to change my clothes and rest for a while,' Carkoo had told the sergeant. He held up a bottle of clear Castillo rum. 'So long as I got this, I'll be all right, man.'

Now, a day later, Sergeant Barzey found the old man's house completely burnt out. He walked into the yard and saw what he had been hoping and praying not to see. A body, totally burnt as though roasted, barely recognisable. The sergeant looked closely. There were pieces of wire round a finger and a fork bent around the left wrist, a handy way of carrying a vital utensil. Carkoo's home-made jewellery. It was him all right.

The rescuers walked on down an ashy path and turned the corner of another burnt-out house. There they were.

Three incinerated corpses, on their backs, their limbs oddly twisted, like the victims of Vesuvius in Pompeii two millennia earlier. One appeared to be male, close to the door of the house as though he had tried to shelter. His hands were held up as if to protect his face. His right leg had been burnt off below the knee. His clothes had been destroyed completely, but for his left boot. The boot later allowed his wife to identify the body as that of farmhand Melville Cuffy.

Further from the house, the two other corpses appeared to be women. Their clothes, too, had been burnt off except, oddly, their underwear. So badly was she burnt that Harry Lewis later identified his wife only from the underwear he had seen her put on the previous morning. Next to her was a corpse recognisable only by its braided hair. Most of it had been burnt off, but one single braid was stuck to the forehead. 2Pac had been taken away, but his uncle recognised that braid. It was Felina Celestine, 2Pac's mother.

Sergeant Barzey and the rescue team photographed the bodies as they lay, packed them in body bags and flew them back to St John's hospital. Several other bodies were found during the day. Some were so rigid that their burnt limbs had to be broken to get them into body bags. When no more bodies were found, PC Julian Wade, who used to have Sunday lunch with 2Pac and his mother, went home and washed over and over again with detergent. 'You smelt burnt meat, you know, burnt meat,' he said. 'For a long time, I could feel some rotten smell, but it seemed to be coming from my head.'

The young men of Montserrat's search-and-rescue squads had been more used to dancing, calypso, reggae, soca and 'jumpin' up'. After 25 June 1997, many had nightmares about seeing the burnt corpses. The local government hired a counsellor to talk them through it and help them cope with post-traumatic stress.

The island's Director of Health, Dr Franklin Perkins, found that 2Pac's mother and the other victims had died from 'neurogenic shock, as a result of total body burns'. Those engulfed by pyroclastic flow would have seen the tan-grey avalanche coming, albeit briefly. Those, including Felina Celestine and her sister, who were hit by the accompanying surge may have had a few moments of horror as it followed them up Windy Hill, like a high-velocity sandstorm hundreds of yards thick.

'It was just an intense heat wave,' said Dr Perkins. 'One can imagine that individuals exposed to the intense heat would have had all body functions frozen in time, especially the vital organs such as the brain and heart. So there was no doubt in my mind that death was immediate. The deceased would have felt pain, but only for a very brief period. I am talking about milliseconds.' (Some of the volcanologists questioned the local doctor's assessment. They say the surge was more than just a heat wave, in fact a current of hot sand and dust dispersed in heated air. The victims may have gone through at least a few seconds of suffering before they died.)

Dr Perkins had known 2Pac's mother. He had seen her in his consulting room the weekend before she died. Knowing that she was still farming beneath The Mountain, he had warned her it was dangerous. 'The volcano do its thing, doctor, an' me have to do my thing,' she had replied. In any case, 2Pac felt a little better hearing Dr Perkins' assessment, hoping his mother had had no time to feel pain. 'She died of shock. She was frightened,' he told friends.

But most victims of 25 June 1997 were never found. All in all, it was thought that 19 people perished that day. Every one of the victims was known by virtually everyone else on the island. Montserrat's population at the time, after more than half had left for Britain or elsewhere, was around 5,000.

The deaths, not to mention the narrow escape by none other than Her Majesty's Governor himself, finally shook off some cobwebs in Whitehall. 'The 25th of June 1997 signals the day the British government took this island and its problem seriously,' said a sombre Police Commissioner Hooper. 'Previously, they hoped it would be something that would go away. Then they suddenly realised they had a disaster going on and not just an awkward little nuisance four thousand miles away.'

As soon as Frank Savage broke the news of the deaths to his bosses at the Foreign Office, the Whitehall bureaucracy creaked belatedly into second gear. This time, it was the turn of new Labour foreign secretary Robin Cook to dust off his *Times* atlas. The Foreign Office called the Ministry of Defence. The MOD called the Royal Navy. Captain Keith Winstanley, who had lived through the early days of the Montserrat crisis as commander of HMS *Southampton*, took the call at the FOO, the Fleet Operations Office in Northwood. These days Winstanley was a landlubber, the man who moved the Royal Navy's ships around the world from his command post 'down the hole' – three floors underground in a secure bunker at the FOO.

'Where's the bloody WIGS?' asked an MOD staffer.

'The *Liverpool*? She's in Belize,' replied Winstanley.

'Bloody hell, how far's that from Montserrat?' said the MOD man.

Winstanley gave the bureaucrat a swift geography lesson. Then he called his friend David Snelson, captain of HMS *Liverpool*, first on a secure phone, then, in line with procedure, through a radio signal: 'Proceed with all dispatch to Montserrat.'

Snelson did so, at full steam. HMS *Liverpool* anchored off Little Bay in the north of the island on 28 June, three days after the disaster. As always since the start of the crisis, the arrival of a British warship fuelled rumours of an off-island evacuation. 'Schoolchildren say they gonna make us all leave,' islanders began saying, 'schoolchildren say' being the local equivalent of 'rumour has it'. The *Liverpool*'s captain said the destroyer was prepared to ship islanders out in an emergency but that was still a worst-case scenario. If there *was* another major eruption, the ship would probably weigh anchor and 'loiter a mile or two away', Captain Snelson said. In the unlikely event that islanders fled to the shorelines in panic, the *Liverpool* could send its RIBS (rigid inflatable boats) to pick them up, but these could only take four or five people at a time. Just in case, the warship lowered its 'scrambling net' – a rope webbing for emergency boarding.

The big pyroclastic flow of 25 June had stopped just yards short of Montserrat's little airport terminal. That meant the airfield had to be closed until further notice, probably for a long time, possibly forever. Plymouth port, used until the disaster by emergency workers for vital import and export loading, now also had to be closed. The island was cut off from the outside world, except by helicopter. And the choppers were for emergency and official use only. Montserratians were stranded on their island with their volcano.

From his fifth-floor office at the Department for International Development in London, emergency aid chief Andy Bearpark called his old friend and colleague Peter Burton at home in Kent. The two men agreed that getting a ferry service running was the priority. At least that would provide a link with Antigua and its airport. Bearpark found it hard to divert the attention of his new boss, Clare Short, from what he called 'her pet' – Africa – but it was agreed he would fly to Montserrat, along with what Whitehall staffers called the PUSS, the Permanent Under-Secretary of State at the Foreign Office, Baroness Symons.

The two did so, on 28 June. A small, bumpy inter-island ferry, the *Early Bird II*, was hired and financed by DFID. It gave the islanders a connection to Antigua, albeit one involving a rough 90-minute ride over 27 miles of Atlantic swell. An eight-seater helicopter was hired to take commercial passengers to and from Antigua, a 15-minute hop. The little heliport on Gerald's Bottom cricket pitch was now a hive of activity. 'It was just like something out of *M*A*S*H*,' Sheila Hooper wrote in her diary. 'Police, firemen and others buzzing around, talking of bodies, body bags, the danger, who they knew who had died, who they knew who was missing. It was all very tense.' A few yards from the heliport, Catherine Daley, who used to run the Cockpit bar at the airport, threw up some planks of wood and a tin roof and a new Cockpit was born.

It was not only the deaths that had upped the ante. The MVO scientists now feared that the 25 June 'event' was by no means the endgame. On the contrary, they feared it might have opened the way for an eruption of even greater magnitude. From the end of June and throughout July, the seismographs at the MVO were increasingly twitchy. The dome continued to grow. There were small but steadily growing pyroclastic flows, at first down the same northern slopes, along Mosquito Ghaut, the same path taken by the flow of 25 June. This time, there were no humans in their path, but cows, sheep, goats, pigs, hens, donkeys, stray dogs and even abandoned pets were incinerated or buried by pyroclastic debris, not to mention the inestimable number of wild agoutis, 'mountain chickens' and magnificent black and gold orioles, the increasingly endangered national bird.

When animal-loving pilot Jim McMahon spotted a badly-burnt donkey on the edge of a pyroclastic flow, envoys from WSPA risked their lives to reach it and hook it into a harness. McMahon airlifted the creature, its red-raw legs dangling, to safety and care. Somebody named the donkey Chopper, after the vehicle that had saved it, and the animal later had the rare distinction of having its picture appear in *People* magazine.

Through late June and early July 1997, The Mountain continued to explode. Pyroclastic flows began seeping over Gage's Wall, the ancient cliff-face on the western rim of the crater, towering over Plymouth. The lie of the land meant that these flows entered the upper reaches of Fort Ghaut, the wide ravine that became a fast-flowing river in the rainy season. In early July, a pyroclastic flow ran all the way down the ghaut to Plymouth, reaching a point alongside George Street only a few yards from Father Larry Finnegan's church. The flow stayed within the big ravine, but it was all getting a bit too close for comfort.

The capital, still picturesque but with its pastel-painted buildings dimmed by layers of grey ash, was now completely evacuated, at least officially. People were still slipping in to check their homes or business premises, their crops or their animals, and the scientists and policemen were still going through the town to do their jobs. When Frank Hooper went in, he often saw fresh footprints in the ash. It was as though the place were haunted. He recalled the tales about jumbies, the local version of ghosts, and had a little laugh to himself. No sweat. They're only supposed to come out at night. No, there was a far more logical explanation for the footprints. It was an open secret that some people, including the friendly white-haired vagrant known as Never Me, who used to sleep on the waterfront, were still coming and going into the capital through the bush.

Gage's Wall had always been of great concern to the scientists. It was the reason Barry Voight had originally been called in and it still fascinated and worried him. Even with Plymouth evacuated, a major pyroclastic flow from that side could reach farther north, possibly to the Belham River valley, the western edge of the current 'safe zone'. That would mean a threat to Salem, now home to most of the remaining few thousand islanders, to Olveston and Old Road Bay, site of the Vue Pointe hotel and the Nest beach bar run by Danny Sweeney and Margaret Wilson.

Still, up in the safe zone, Montserratians continued to get on with their lives. Sunday 3 August 1997 started off just like the good old days. It was a long August bank holiday weekend. Families came down to Old Road Bay beach to romp in the waves. Father Larry brought down the refugee children from St Martin de Porres church for a swim, to give their parents a break. Danny and Margaret were doing good business in the Nest. Little Sarah Sweeney splashed around with Father Larry and the shelter children. John Watts, whose Harbour Court restaurant and ice-cream parlour used to be one of the most popular spots in Plymouth, sold mango ice-cream from his little dark-blue Nissan while the van's loudspeaker played Scott Joplin's theme music from *The Sting*. Up the slope in the Vue Pointe, Carol Osborne laid on the weekly Sunday barbecue buffet.

But unlike in the good old days, the volcano was very much on everybody's mind. Even the children now glanced up at it every few minutes in awe. It had become a reflex action. And everyone knew, from the scientists' bulletins on ZJB Radio, that it had been playing up for days, the way it did in the run-up to the 25 June disaster. The tiltmeters Barry Voight and his colleagues had placed on The Mountain were showing pressure from underground. In the MVO villa the seismographs were showing hybrid earthquake swarms every ten hours or so, like clockwork. Voight had done some observation work in the morning, taken a break for a dip in the ocean at Little Bay in the afternoon, then returned to the MVO villa. At 6 p.m. he was on the pool deck, facing The Mountain, to observe and photograph it at the top of its latest earthquake cycle.

In Salem, Arrow, the King of Soca Music, was in his more prosaic role on this Sunday. He was in his makeshift store in Salem, Arrow's Man Shop, doing a bit of stocktaking and chatting to local photographer Kevin West. West was the man who in quieter times had photographed weddings, funerals and car accidents and sold tranquil pictures of The Mountain as postcards to cruise ship tourists from his little shop in George Street, Plymouth, along the seafront from

Arrow's original store. Now he had thrown up a wooden shack in Salem, close to Arrow's, to sell his photos of The Mountain's more recent, angrier moods.

No one had captured the eruptions and the pyroclastic flows better than Kevin West, a burly young man with a booming bass voice. He liked to get up close, often too close according to the MVO scientists who bought many of his pictures. To avoid police checkpoints, West would get to The Mountain the hard way, on a mountain motor-bike. 'Sometime, the Babylon Beast [the police] stop me but I just tell them to kiss my black nigger ass.'

At 6.10 p.m. that August Sunday, as West and Arrow chatted, there was a distant rumble, getting steadily louder, like a drum roll, climaxing in one great boom. The two men knew that noise only too well, but this one sounded big. They ran uphill to the crossroads outside the bakery and the Desert Storm rum shop bar, the best spot in Salem for a view of The Mountain.

Down at Old Road Bay and the Vue Pointe, all eyes turned to The Mountain, where a huge column of churning grey was mushrooming into the sky. At the same time, a rolling cloud appeared over Gage's Wall and spilt over and down, down The Mountain's western slopes. A pyroclastic flow, a massive one, and it was headed straight for Plymouth. Within minutes Old Road Bay beach was empty. Hundreds of people had rushed to the lookout point at Salem, or to a ridge beyond in the hamlet of Fleming's, where they could see the upper part of Plymouth. As always, David Lea was filming the action. Over the intervening hillocks they could see only the upper part of the capital, but they could also see that the flow was thundering towards the centre of town. And it looked as though it was far too big to remain within the confines of Fort Ghaut.

Plymouth was where most of their homes were, most of their businesses. It may have been evacuated, as a precaution, but it was the heart of the island and it remained their future. Or so they thought. As dusk fell, and the islanders continued to watch, their worst fears were realised. Flames began to flicker in the upper part of the capital, and a hazy orange glow over the hillocks suggested there were fires in the centre of town. The area of Upper Amersham, site of Rose Willock's villa, also appeared to have been hit.

Those with four-wheel-drive vehicles, including former chief minister Reuben Meade and his wife Joan, risked driving across the Belham valley into the exclusion zone, past the home of the stubborn Americans Bob and Bev Kleeb, to the top of Garibaldi Hill. From there they could look directly down on the parts of the capital. The pyroclastic flow had reached the ocean. Winston 'Kafu' Cabey went over Garibaldi Hill, too, to see as much of Plymouth as possible. He was concerned about his Auto Parts shop in the Wapping district, below Government House and near the Yacht Club at the Fort Ghaut estuary. Kafu still presented 'Drivetime', and his ambition was to be a full-time broadcaster, but the seaside Auto Parts shop was still his bread and butter. He had been looking forward to getting back to Town. Going over the hill as far as he could, he could see the gabled Government House but not his shop below. It appeared to be part of the same brownish-grey mass as the area around the estuary. It looked as if it had been buried.

'Plymout' gawn fuh true,' one old man on Garibaldi Hill muttered: Plymouth is gone for sure. David Lea filmed the flames against the growing darkness. It was too hot and too dangerous to go any closer. Jim McMahon managed to get Barry Voight and other scientists up for an observation flight before darkness fell. Sure enough, a pyroclastic flow had come down Fort Ghaut all the way to the sea. It had stayed mostly within the ravine but fanned out at the estuary and set fire to buildings along its banks. 'It was like a candelabra of flame,' Voight reported.

Subsequent pyroclastic flows in the same direction also followed gravity and topography. They started off down the deep ravine that was Fort Ghaut, but they got bigger, faster and more powerful. The flows eventually failed to make a bend in the ghaut in upper Plymouth and thundered over its banks into Lovers' Lane, burying parts of M.S. Osborne's timber yard, the old family business owned by Cedric Osborne of the Vue Pointe hotel. They hit the new Glendon Hospital head on, burying much of it and all of its modern equipment. These scorching clouds, *nuées ardentes*, contained massive chunks of the volcano's dome, boulders the size of houses. Thundering downhill at speeds of perhaps 60 mph, they crushed buildings in their path as if they were made of eggshell.

Pyroclastic avalanches spilt over into George Street and eventually ploughed through Father Larry Finnegan's St Patrick's church and the presbytery next door. They demolished Blake's Empire Shop, exploding the fine wines and liquors stocked by Raymond Blake and his German wife Hilde. The hot cocktails of ash, gas, rock and mud hit Kevin West's little Paradise photo studio, and engulfed the Plymouth Public Market, once thronged with colourfully-dressed women selling delicious tropical fruits and vegetables. The Green Flash bar alongside Fort Ghaut took hit after hit.

As if following the traffic rules, parts of the flows branched off from George Street down Evergreen Road. The super-heated rubble eventually buried the Evergreen roundabout, but the famous Evergreen Tree still protruded in the wake of the burning ash, gas and boulder rubble.

On the seafront, the semi-solid grey avalanche powered into the spindly white War Memorial clockstand, burying the memorial but leaving the four-legged tower and clock standing. No one is sure on what day it happened, but even 60 feet above the ground, the intense heat, ash and dust stopped the clock at 3.35. The landmark red phone booth, where stray dogs used to lounge in the sun, became buried deeper with each flow, but for a while its roof could still be seen sticking out from an expanse of ashy grey.

In the ensuing days and weeks, hundreds of animals were buried or burnt to death as the deadly avalanches careened down The Mountain's western slopes. Even some of those that took refuge in the ocean died as super-heated pyroclastic material continued flowing into the shallow waters. A few animals survived by chance, huddled in solid concrete buildings. Everyone watching from the hills during those days prayed that no human was down there. A few mentally disturbed people had been seen slipping back though the bush, away from the police roadblocks. The pyroclastic avalanches were travelling at around 60 mph at temperatures of 600 degrees centigrade or more. If anyone had been down there where the flows hit, they would now be ashes, or buried in mud. The watching crowd in Salem were always relieved to see among them Never Me, the friendly white-haired homeless man who had been known to slip past police checkpoints to get back into Town.

Plymouth became ever more deeply buried. Downtown buildings disappeared under hardened pyroclastic deposits up to the height of two or three-storey buildings. The old red phone booth gradually disappeared below the rising surface of the lunar landscape. Only the clock at the top of the 60-foot War Memorial tower still protruded from the rocky expanse of tan, beige and grey, a stark contrast to the still lapping, turquoise waters of the Caribbean ocean.

What had been a picturesque pastel town, named after the English port from which the pilgrims had set out for New England, now resembled Pompeii. Human bones found in the ruins later added to the image. No one was reported missing in Plymouth itself, but those bones were found, and some policemen believed two people had died, perhaps vagrants. Others say the bones might have been unearthed when ash and mudflows surged through the old cemetery.

The islanders had been enduring the hardship, enduring the shelters, waiting optimistically to go home. But looking down at Plymouth from the helicopter now was like looking at two photographs side by side. The town and surrounding landscape was an old-fashioned sepia print, the ocean a brilliant sapphire hemmed by fringes of white surf. It was immediately obvious to the scientists and others who overflew the little capital that no one was going to live in this town for a while.

With The Mountain a little quieter in mid-August, Reuben Meade took his ageing father into deserted Plymouth to see if his home was still there in the Parson's district, just south of Fort Ghaut. 'I call it the burying of the dead,' said Meade. 'It was just like mourning.' Listening to the MVO by walkie-talkie for safety, the two men walked through Town. Meade smiled when he saw that the Evergreen Tree was still there, though the wall and concrete tables below it were buried under a grey mass. It was ashy, it was grotesquely twisted from Hurricane Hugo, but it was still defiantly there. But Meade's father found himself totally lost, unable to recognise the district, or the town, let alone his house. 'I've seen enough, son, let's go back,' he said. 'I could see the loss in his eyes, the hidden tears,' the former government leader told his wife afterwards.

On ZJB Radio, Rose Willock continued to describe the damage and brought in the scientists for daily bulletins to explain what the volcano was doing and what it might do next. In between, she'd play her favourite soothing music, Lou Rawls singing 'Time Will Take Care of Everything' or 'What's the Matter with the World?' When The Mountain was rumbling or spewing ash, she'd try to calm nerves. 'I know this can make you nervous, but don't take it out on your siblings, don't take it out on your pets. But most of all, don't take it out on yourself. Take a few breaths and blow out slowly.'

Rose never mentioned it on the air but she now knew she had lost her own home, the hillside villa where she used to gaze up in awe at the lush green Mountain, then down over the trees towards St Patrick's, then on up the coast to Plymouth, watching the cruise boats and tall sailing ships come and go. The paradise island home where she had hoped to pass her later years was gone.

'I felt sadder over the destruction of Plymouth than I did over my own home, because I knew my home had to go at some point. I'd said goodbye to my home in my heart and in my head,' the broadcaster told a friend. 'But when

Plymouth went, I couldn't eat for days, you know? The grief was as strong as if a close relative had died. My heart was heavy for days. My heart was heavy. And I'm sure that's how it was for most Montserratians, on or off the island. Plymouth *is* the capital,' she said, emphasising the present tense. 'It's the link between every Montserratian. Not having access to it is like losing a part of yourself.'

It was as though Rose Willock were in her beloved little town right then, limin' with her friends under the Evergreen Tree, as she went on: 'Plymouth is not just the shops and stores. Plymouth is not just sitting on the bayfront and looking out to sea and dreaming and seeing the boats going one way and the other, or seeing the fishermen joke with each other or selling fish or buying fish. Plymouth is not just going to the Post Office and asking for your mail or going to your message box and taking out your mail, or buying stamps and sending letters from one part of the world to the next. Plymouth is not just seeing bands and bands of colourful, costumed troupes on Christmas Day or Boxing Day or New Year's Day, going up and down various streets, dancing, revelling, different colours, different moods, all gaiety and flamboyance and music and camaraderie and good fun and laughter and hey and hi and Merry Christmas and Happy New Year.

'It's not just all of those things. Plymouth is not just seeing some of the perpetual drinkers either begging for a drink or begging for a cigarette or cursing somebody who did not give them what they wanted, you know, it's a combination of things. Plymouth is the marketplace and all the women and men, the butchers' stalls and the various vendors selling the different fruits and vegetables and laughing and joking and shouting at each other, and not selling to you, or selling to you, or admiring their goods. Plymouth is a combination of experiences, good, bad, indifferent, significant, not so significant. That is Plymouth. That *is* Plymouth, you know? It's a whole culture, the heart of a country that's no longer there, that is now lifeless, you know? And all of those elements of the culture are in your heart and in your head, and in your books when you write about them, and in the stories you tell like I'm doing now. You see, that's Plymouth, you know? And that is what remains in our memories, and in our minds, and in our hearts.'

16

Golden elephants

'This volcano's acting like a Swiss watch,' said Barry Voight in a video interview with David Lea. Lea put it to Voight that The Mountain was behaving more like a pregnant woman in labour. 'We've passed the labour,' the volcanologist replied. 'The baby's out. The question is whether it will turn into a juvenile delinquent.'

What worried Voight most was that the latest pyroclastic flows did not consist of old magma, collapsing from the dome through gravity. This was fresh, new magma, enriched by water, exploding from beneath the surface, from way down in the inner plumbing. 'Until the 25th of June, the problem was the dome building,' Willy Aspinall agreed. 'Now, the collapsed dome has left a void. We're in a gas-thrust phase. The gas-rich magma is being blown out directly into the air, as if out of a gun barrel. It's like an ornate fountain. The material flowers outwards and falls to the ground under its own weight. The topography will determine where it goes when it hits the ground. We no longer have dome collapse pyroclastic flows. We have *column* collapse pyroclastic flows. And the higher they go up, the further they can reach when they come down.'

Until now, the flows had been in individual sectors. Soon, Voight and Aspinall suspected, these 'column collapses' could affect all sides of The Mountain at once.

Some of the scientists believed the collapses could affect areas up to ten miles of the crater, perhaps even more. That put the entire island within range. The good news was that pyroclastic material would have difficulty scaling the peaks of the island's Centre Hills, so the north, and the refugees in shelters there, should be relatively safe, though not guaranteed. The bad news was that, as the oriole flies, Salem, Olveston and Old Towne were only four miles from the crater, all downhill. Was the Belham River valley safe? Was the busy Vue Pointe hotel safe? Danny Sweeney's place on the beach below? The Montserrat Volcano Observatory just up the road?

No one had an accurate count under the circumstances, but there were probably fewer than 5,000 people left on the island out of the original population of 11,000. Of those remaining, perhaps half were in the general Salem area, including Olveston and Old Towne. That was more than 2,000 people, only four miles from the crater of an angry volcano.

By mid-August 1997, The Mountain seemed to be having a nap. But it continued to snore, and the scientists were not fooled. The MVO seismographs showed regular earthquake swarms. The dome, the latest sculpture of fresh magma, was growing rapidly. Islanders were leaving on the new ferry or helicopter service, but in dribs and drabs, not droves. Then the scientists announced, out of the blue, that an eruption ten times as powerful as the biggest seen so far was possible within the coming months. Ten times as powerful as the one that destroyed Plymouth! Would anywhere on the island be safe? In case the islanders didn't get the message, a senior but less-than-subtle British politician spelt it out. George Foulkes, deputy to Clare Short at DFID, was quoted as referring to a possible 'cataclysmic' eruption. On the island, that put the cat among the mountain chickens.

Panic is not a word you will find in Caribbean dictionaries. But Montserrat was now in the hands of outsiders. Some folks called them 'the Initials'. There was 'H.E.' (His Excellency the Governor), the MVO (Montserrat Volcano Observatory), HMG (Her Majesty's Government), the FCO (Foreign and Commonwealth Office) and DFID (Department for International Development). Together the Initials decided that the centre of the island, currently in the 'safe zone', was at risk. The exclusion zone would have to be extended.

First, Old Towne was billed as dangerous. Carol and Cedric Osborne had to shut down the Vue Pointe hotel. That meant the guests, including MVO staff, pilot Jim McMahon and Father Larry Finnegan, had to move out. Father Larry could no longer hold his Sunday Mass in the conference room. The legislature could no longer meet there, either, and the High Court had to find another venue. Down below the hotel, on Old Road Bay beach, Danny and Margaret had to abandon the Nest beach bar and batten down the watersports gear. Danny would have to go out fishing and catch tuna or wahoo to feed his family.

Old Towne was a wealthier, largely expatriate – that is, largely white – extension of the mostly black and poorer Salem, which had become the effective capital for business and leisure. Most Plymouth businesses had moved to Salem and thrown up makeshift premises in order to survive and serve their fellow islanders. The local government, currently led by Bertrand Osborne, knew that abandoning Salem would be a major blow, perhaps one blow too many, for the islanders. But the Initials called the shots. Based on the threat laid out by the MVO scientists, Governor Savage announced that the safety line would have to move north. Salem and Old Towne would have to be evacuated.

Father Larry Finnegan had to move again, this time from the St Martin de Porres church, along with the 100 men, women and children who were refugees from St Patrick's. They had to squeeze into churches, public buildings or homes further north. Arrow shut up his Salem shop and sought a new site in the north, in the township of Sweeney's. Kevin West tore down his wooden photo shop in Salem and threw it up again on a northern hill called Cudjoe Head. Rose Willock and the ZJB staff moved on again, from one private house to another, this time to a villa on a northern hilltop known as Nixon's. The survivors just kept on surviving. They were people of faith. But that did not mean they had faith in their leaders, neither in their own local government, nor in the Initials.

With Salem and the centre of the island evacuated, the rugged northern tip was even more overcrowded. There simply was not enough space, there were not enough houses. Rumours spread again of a Dunkirk-style evacuation using HMS *Liverpool* and a flotilla of ferries and small private boats. Andy Bearpark, Clare Short's emergency aid manager, had sent a team out to Antigua to set up a transit camp, but the details were vague and the islanders were suspicious. They had always feared Britain wanted to evacuate the entire island and wash its hands of this awkward little nuisance in the Caribbean.

Governor Savage and Chief Minister Osborne came under mounting criticism, notably from opposition politician David Brandt. 'The Heavy Roller' said he had uncovered details of a 'voluntary relocation' package by Britain, and that it was an insult to the islanders. Brandt himself had lost his home, Glenninnis, and his office in Plymouth as well as the popular La Cave basement discotheque he had owned next to the Evergreen Tree.

Clare Short's hand was forced. At DFID in Victoria Street, she announced details of the voluntary relocation scheme, with figures. Anyone moving to another Caribbean island would have their fare paid, plus cash assistance of £2,400 per adult and £600 per child. Those who went to Britain would get free passage, housing, a work permit and welfare for two years. The islanders agreed with Brandt. It *was* an insult. The natives became restless. The little island experienced something it had rarely experienced since the days of slavery: street protests. They were small, and they were very Caribbean, with reggae and calypso, rum and bottled Guinness and more smiles than scowls, but they were enough to force the resignation of Chief Minister Osborne. David Brandt, for his stance against the colonial power, was flavour of the day. In the third week of August 1997, he was voted in as chief minister by the island's legislature.

Spurred by Brandt's Brit-bashing, the protesters next focused on Whitehall. What was Britain's real agenda? Was it trying to get everyone off the island? More than two years after the crisis, people were still living in tents. What about some real housing? As Her Majesty's man in Montserrat, Frank Savage was the immediate target. Even the Queen, always respected by the islanders, came in for some stick.

On Wednesday 20 August, 150 protesters beating bongo drums marched on the governor's temporary office and home north of Salem, the villa Frank Savage nicknamed 'Camelot'. Most were well-dressed professionals but had lost their homes, businesses or both. One man, a farmer, came on his donkey. Led by local hardware merchants Don and Julian Romeo, they had formed a group called The Concerned People of Montserrat. 'We are not animals, we are human beings,' read their placards. 'No more lies.' 'British government guilty of murder.' Hairdresser Nadine Tuitt had written in felt-tip pen on her white t-shirt: 'They think we're mushrooms. They keep us in the dark and feed us bullshit.'

Frank Savage told Veronica to stay inside with Winston while he talked to the protesters. He stepped outside, accompanied by police chief Frank Hooper in neat khaki colonial uniform and looking suitably but unusually grave. Her Majesty's Governor, probably the only man on the island that day wearing a tie with his usual striped Harrods' shirt, walked into the driveway to face the music. It could have been a scene out of a Fifties English film, with Alec Guinness playing the governor. But the crowd were quite serious. 'Let me kill de boy,' yelled a dreadlocked Rastafarian.

With well-practised stiff upper lip, the white-haired governor pushed through the line of his own black police officers to talk directly to the crowd. A lifetime in diplomacy stood him in good stead. 'Thank you for coming to see me today,' he began, using that special brand of precise, extra-slow English diplomats dig out when talking to foreigners. Perhaps it had momentarily slipped his mind that the islanders spoke English, and at least as well as most folks in his native Lancashire. He did not get many more words out. 'Resign,' someone shouted. 'We used to salute the Queen,' yelled Julian Romeo. 'Let her respect us. Let her understand that either we are British citizens or she can let us go.' Diplomatic as ever, Frank Savage thanked Romeo for making his point and referred to him thereafter as 'the moderator'.

The group gave the governor an eleven-point proposal calling for compensation for lost property, housing and construction in the north of the island and guarantees that they could come back if temporarily evacuated. If Britain did not come up with the goods, the island would demand independence, they said. The governor said he would study their document. At that point, a local woman clambered atop a pick-up truck, grabbed a microphone and quoted from Psalm 104. 'Let the sinners be consumed out of the Earth and let the wicked be no more.' Frank Savage went inside, gave Winston a pat and suggested to Veronica that they have a nice cup of tea.

The following day, Thursday 21 August, the natives were not just restless, they were revolting. At least, some of them were, and this time their beloved bottles of Guinness played a greater role, directly as well as indirectly. It began in the late afternoon in Salem, where residents had been allowed back in during daylight hours, dependent on the MVO's up-to-date assessment of volcanic activity, to attend to their affairs. They had to evacuate again at dusk and head for their shelters. Outside the Reggae Lounge, a rum shop bar painted in red, yellow and green stripes, giant speakers were booming out Bob Marley songs, shaking the tarmac more than The Mountain's tremors did. A couple of dozen Rastafarian youths were downing bottles of Guinness out front and smoking ganja out back. Directly behind them was The Mountain, late afternoon sunbeams tinting its steaming fumaroles a pleasant pink.

Expletives split the air, mostly anti-British. 'Emancipate yourself from mental slavery, none but ourselves can free our minds . . .' sang Marley. Whether or not it was his words that did it, the atmosphere changed. Suddenly the big oil drums used as rubbish bins were overthrown and rolled on to the road. Tyres were set alight, adding a new element to the now-familiar smell of ash and sulphur. Then the Guinness bottles started flying. Salem's main crossroads was burning and littered with glass. Salem is burning! The word went round the island like a pyroclastic surge. It was a massive exaggeration. Only a few dozen people were involved and only the tarmac at the crossroads was burning. But no one had ever seen anything like it on the little island. It was a job for the riot squad.

What riot squad? They'd never had a riot. At Salem police station, only a couple of hundred yards from the action, somebody remembered a batch of helmets with visors, shields, gas masks, truncheons and tear-gas launchers that had been shipped from England but had gathered dust for years. Kelvin White and half a dozen fellow constables donned the gear, drove to the scene on the back of police pick-ups and pushed the crowd back with their truncheons.

Kelvin White felt a bit ridiculous. He knew all these people by name. But he was a policeman. Maintaining law and order was his job. Anyway, these boys might not recognise him behind the visor and gas mask. Riot squad constables chased four of the most active protesters behind the local bakery, arrested them and put them on the back of a pick-up truck behind the police lines.

That's when Frank Hooper, the bobby from Sussex,

showed up in his khaki uniform, armed only with a walkie-talkie. Guinness bottles were still smashing on to the tarmac as he waded into the jostling crowd and faced the protesters eyeball to eyeball.

'Let's just calm it down then, shall we?' he started. 'This is not the way to go about it. I will take my officers away if you all go away.'

'I don't have no place to go,' yelled Joseph Fagan, brandishing a bottle of Guinness he looked more likely to drink than throw. 'The volcano took my home.'

'If you clean up the street, I'll release the men detained,' said Hooper.

'You go and fucking clean it up,' interjected protester Stedroy Brade. He was wearing a t-shirt that read 'Tough times don't last, tough people do – Soufrière Hills volcano 1997.'

'What is the protest about?' asked the police chief.

'Equal rights and justice,' said Joseph Fagan. 'I want a house with two bedrooms, a bathroom and a kitchen. I can't go to Antigua. It's over-populated. I can't go to Guadeloupe. I don't speak French.'

'We demand to see the Queen,' shouted a voice from the crowd.

Seeing their boss jostled, Hooper's gas-masked men moved forward towards the crowd. 'Get back! Now!' the police chief yelled at his own men. Kelvin White was taken aback. He felt the Englishman was treating the protesters with more respect than he was giving to the riot squad.

'Let's stop all this messing about. Who's got a broom?' Hooper asked the demonstrators.

'I'll clean up the street if you free our brothers,' replied Stedroy Brade.

Hooper turned back to Kelvin White and his men. 'Free the prisoners! Fucking now!'

Kelvin White could hardly believe his ears. The police chief, a white man, swearing at his own men, including his deputy, a black man, in public. It seemed to Constable White that Hooper had broken the golden Caribbean rule, the watchword in the region: 'Maximum respect.'

But the incident had been defused. The detainees were freed. A Rastafarian youth with full dreadlocks got on his knees on the tarmac in front of the police chief and looked up at him. 'You're a good man. You rule over me,' he said, whether with irony or too much Guinness. Another black youth took Hooper's hand and walked him back to his little white jeep as protesters and bystanders applauded. It was a happy ending to a very Caribbean riot. All Frank Hooper had to do now was get an animated lady called Agnes Cassell off the bonnet of his Suzuki. She was dancing wildly to the reggae music that had never stopped throughout.

Towards the end of August, The Mountain was relatively quiet, at least on the outside, but times were getting tougher for the remaining 4,000 or so islanders. The Montserrat Building Society suspended operations on the advice of its auditors and said it could only pay out 35 per cent of people's savings. Barclays Bank, one of only three on the island, closed down. The big insurance companies cancelled all cover and said those who lost their homes in Plymouth would be lucky to get half their value and might get nothing at all. The feeling grew that Britain would prefer everybody to leave, and the islanders soon found themselves with a new focus for their growing mistrust.

The native islanders were mostly too devoutly Christian to use expletives, but the white expatriate residents, many of whom had also lost their homes, had no qualms in nicknaming her 'The Bitch'.

Her real name was Clare Short.

First, the DFID secretary of state gave an interview to Rose Willock in a link-up from Victoria Street to the makeshift ZJB studios on the island. At least by Caribbean standards, it was a historic piece of journalism. Willock was her usual self, calm, respectful but probing. Her elocution was in sharp contrast to Clare Short's abrupt and angry delivery. From the voices, you would have guessed wrongly as to which of the women on the air had just lost everything and which was in a position to help. The islanders could not understand why this British cabinet minister was so grumpy, impolite, and, well, plain mean. Money didn't grow on trees, she told the Rose Willcock.

A few days later, on 24 August, just over three months in the job, the DFID secretary of state gave another interview, this time to the *Observer*. Andy Bearpark and Peter Burton, her top emergency aid managers, waited to read it with trepidation. They crossed their fingers but feared the worst. Burton was at home in Kent when he read the article over Sunday brunch. Sure enough, the boss had put her foot in it, big time, even by her standards. Asked about Montserrat, she accused the Montserratians of 'hysterical scaremongering'. Burton cringed but read on. Clare Short was accusing Montserratians of 'wanting mad money . . . it'll be golden elephants next.'

The 'golden elephants' remark hurt the islanders to the core. They might not be the poorest people on Earth, they pointed out, but they'd lost everything they owned and could even lose their island. The only spoilt people on the island, they said, were the DFID staffers, who drove around in brand new imported RAV4 four-wheel-drives, who rented, at British taxpayers' expense, the best villas with swimming pools, and who had something of a reputation for precocious rum consumption in Gary Moore's all-night Wide Awake bar in Salem. Even Prime Minister Tony Blair, known to admire Short's forthrightness, was reportedly stunned by the 'golden elephants' gaffe. 'For sheer tactlessness towards a stricken people . . . this statement must go down as one of the most brazen in the annals of diplomacy,' wrote *The Economist*.

Clare Short recognised her mistake. She apologised to the islanders, but the damage had been done. Downing Street decided Short was not the ideal spearhead for this particular crisis. In a sense reverting to the system under the previous Conservative government, a joint team was set up from both the Foreign Office and DFID to 'coordinate' handling of the Montserrat situation. Clare Short's wrists had been firmly slapped. Foreign Secretary Robin Cook raised his profile with regard to the island and would later be the first cabinet member since the crisis to show his face there. As Governor Savage put it, 'The problem was that this was not a development issue. It was an emergency. It was simply taking too long to get the wheels moving.'

'Clare had just arrived,' her troubleshooter Andy Bearpark said. 'She was focused on Africa. She found it irritating that she had to deal with Montserrat at all. She became almost totally irrational over it. She could behave totally differently, she *did* behave totally differently when it came to Montserrat.'

The 'golden elephants' affair left the islanders confused.

How much did Britain really care? Was Whitehall's real agenda a total evacuation? Suspicions grew, fuelled by the presence on shore of sailors from HMS *Liverpool* to assist anyone wanting to leave. Although hundreds of islanders had signed up for the voluntary relocation scheme, only a dozen showed up for the ferry to Antigua on the first day. They had been told to bring a maximum of two suitcases each on the voyage to a new life. Some did not even possess two suitcases. They had abandoned their homes in the south carrying only plastic bags. The sailors from the warship, in their tropical uniforms of navy shorts and knee-length socks, came ashore to enrol evacuees, but the first 'relocation' ferry to Antigua left almost empty.

One couple who did leave, with only a couple of suit-cases, were Frank and Veronica Savage, on 11 September 1997. They did not have to suffer the indignities of the rough ferry ride. It was the helicopter for them, hence the small amount of baggage. Their personal effects had already been shipped. The governor's term, which he had extended by a year because of the crisis, had finally come to an end. Frank Savage was given an emotional farewell by local politicians, his staff, including Desmond the butler, Catherine the maid, Solomon the police driver and many other islanders. Despite the recent protests, Montserratians had warmed to the soft-spoken Lancashire man. They knew he had been torn between his loyalties to Her Majesty's government and to them, but they felt he had leant firmly their way. He had lived through hardship as they had. And he had stood by them. He left with the islanders' greatest blessing, 'Maximum respect.'

Winston, the Savages' tan terrier, had been shipped out by ferry earlier to be quarantined. The governor wondered whether the little dog had cast a green-eyed glance back at The Mountain from his travelling cage as the ferry steamed east to Antigua.

No sooner had the outgoing governor returned to London for debriefings at the Foreign Office than he had a pleasant reminder of his term on Montserrat. On 15 September 1997, to show solidarity with the islanders and raise funds for their future, Sir George Martin organised a major concert, 'Music for Montserrat', at the Royal Albert Hall. Air Studios was now abandoned, ash-covered though still intact, in the shadow of Chance's Peak, as was his private home Olveston House, on the edge of Salem, the town itself showered with ash and currently out-of-bounds. Sir George had decided to support the islanders with a little help from his friends who had recorded on the island in the Eighties. Among them were Paul McCartney, Sting, Mark Knopfler, Eric Clapton, Elton John and Frank Savage's former next-door neighbour on Montserrat, Midge Ure, whose own home in Plymouth was now partly buried.

Montserrat's own King of Soca, Arrow, opened the Albert Hall show with his classic 'Feelin' hot, hot, hot' and his own musical tribute to the islanders who stayed to tough it out, 'Ah just can't run away'. American Jimmy Buffett sang the premonitory lyrics he wrote near the top of The Mountain in 1979, long before it revealed itself as an active volcano, and recorded at Martin's studio down below:

> Now I don't know, I don't know,
> I don't know where I'm a-gonna go
> When the volcano blow.

Ground she movin' under me,
Tidal waves out on the sea,
Sulphur smoke up in the sky,
Pretty soon we'll learn to fly . . .
Lava come down soft and hot,
You better lava me now or lava me not.

Frank Savage may have been a grey suit in the Sixties but he had always been a bit of a rocker at heart and a secret lover of blue suede shoes. After watching the show from the Royal Box with the Duke of York, he was invited backstage. He was as thrilled as a teenager to meet one of his idols, Carl Perkins, who had cut some of his later tracks at Air Studios.

In the coming months, the ex-governor was to get further reminders of his time on Montserrat, not always so pleasant. For a time, he feared he might even have to go to jail in connection with the deaths on 25 June. It was a shadow that lingered over him long after his departure.

Never one to miss out on a party, volcano danger or no, the Montserratians put on their own concert the same evening on the former cricket pitch at Gerald's Bottom. 'Live from Gerald's Bottom' did not have a great ring to it, so they called it 'The Many Happy Returns Concert' in the hope that islanders who had left would eventually come home. Guest stars were England's Climax Blues Band, the very first group to record at Air Studios back in 1979. Also on the bill was a newcomer, The Mighty Ash, better known as local bar owner George Howe, singing a number about the volcano that was now being played daily on ZJB Radio: 'Don't pack your bags, just run, run, run to the north'. His wife, popular local politician and sometime cabinet minister Annie Dyer-Howe, dusted the audience with talcum powder to produce a mock-ashy effect.

From Gerald's Bottom, they could not see The Mountain. The island's central range, though lower than the Soufrière Hills, blocked the view from the plateau. But The Mountain was almost tangibly present at the concert, not just in the songs, but in people's continuing fears. They could not see it but they felt as though they were always in its sights. Even the MVO scientists had 'run to the north' four days earlier, to a new observatory above Gerald's Bottom on Mongo Hill. For the first time, they could not even see the volcano directly. Now they were relying on their instruments, including real-time video cameras.

The Mountain was looking quiet but the instruments said otherwise. The seismographs, GPS devices and tiltmeters revealed continuing tremors, continuing move-ment. The new crater left by the August explosions was being rapidly filled by a new dome, a new mountain that was certain to collapse – unless the beast suddenly decided to go back to sleep again for a few centuries or millennia.

Barry Voight had long been worried about how exposed the scientists were during their field work. Even before the fatal day of 25 June 1997 he had circulated a memo warning the scientists, especially the younger members, to be 'on their toes'. He pushed for more of the fire-resistant hot suits and admitted he had been 'dumb' to climb Chance's Peak early on in the crisis in shorts instead of the real gear.

Now, in August 1997, as the expert on collapses, Voight circulated another note to his colleagues in which he analysed the latest cycles of volcanic activity based on tilt and seismic data. The Mountain seemed to be 're-energising'

almost like clockwork, every four to six weeks. He
predicted another series of 'big' eruptions through the rest
of the year, starting around mid-September. It was Voight
who had predicted the major collapse at Mount St Helens,
almost 20 years earlier, just before it happened. This time,
he was to be proved right again. The timing of his forecast
was off, but only by a matter of days: no mean feat in the
volcanology business.

Mid-September passed without a major eruption. So did
the island's equivalent of the Ides of March, 17 September,
the traditional date for disasters. But at 4 a.m. on Sunday
21 September 1997 a massive dome collapse sent a
pyroclastic flow over the northern rim of the crater, down
the same ghauts as those on 25 June. It was faster and more
powerful, with a volume of 14 million cubic metres, twice
as big as the lethal 25 June flows. It surged out of the
ravines, took dead aim at Spanish Point and totally buried
the former haven for expatriate 'snowbirds', long since
abandoned. And this time it did not stop before the airport.
The scorching, tumbling cloud thundered down the airport
approach road like an express train. That was the road on
which Governor Savage and his wife had fled three months
earlier.

The flow ran out of steam towards the ocean, but not
before its red-hot nose had engulfed the little cream and
maroon airport terminal building, gutting it with instant
fire. It crossed the southern part of the runway and hit the
sea like a massive pan of boiling oil tossed into a basin of
water. Tropical fish, lobsters and other sea creatures were
boiled alive and washed up later along the shore in a
macabre tableau. On land, hundreds of cows, goats, sheep,
donkeys, stray dogs and other animals were incinerated.

But this time, thanks to the scientists' predictions, to Rose Willock's daily radio warnings and urgings and to the lessons of 25 June, there was no one in the airport or what was left of the neighbouring villages. They would not have had a chance. This time, the Chloupeks' home was completely buried. When the pyroclastic material cooled, Spanish Point looked like a rugged beach of giant boulders. At the airport, only the control tower was left standing. Below it, the area where 2Pac Matthew and his fellow firemen used to sit was incinerated. So was the Cockpit bar, once a favourite limin' spot, although the fire left behind some oddly aesthetic sculptures – melted bottles and glasses – like a bizarre calling card.

If there had been any hope of re-opening W.H. Bramble airport, and there had, it died when the islanders awoke that Sunday, flocked to Jack Boy Hill to gaze down on the devastation across the coastal plain and saw their little seaside airport in flames, with pyroclastic debris across the runway.

Old Road Bay, the Vue Pointe hotel and its beach bar, The Nest, were still in the exclusion zone. No tourists. No watersports. No beach drinkers. Danny Sweeney tried to feed his family by fishing, his other great love, but the thick, heavy ash from the volcano was affecting the fishing too. When the airport was first closed, and before the ferry service started, the amiable fisherman had made a bit of money by transporting TV crews to and from Antigua. For a while his little topless fishing boat, *Jumping Jack Flash*, was the only way to get to and from the island other than by helicopter. After the burst of interest in the initial venting of 1995, Montserrat had got little media coverage overseas, but the destruction of Plymouth, the once idyllic capital, brought the press back in droves. They all wanted to see 'the Caribbean Pompeii', but it was out of bounds and the roads were blocked. Enter Danny Sweeney, fisherman, windsurf maestro to the stars, follower of the Baha'i faith, and now media guide.

Jumping Jack Flash took them all into Plymouth. The BBC, ITN, ABC, NBC, the Discovery Channel. You name them, Danny Sweeney took them – at their own risk. He would tie up at the deserted Plymouth port, keep his twin Yamaha engines running and watch The Mountain as if his life depended on it. It did. His passengers would get a few minutes to go ashore, get their images and get out. If Danny yelled, 'Run to the boat,' they had to run to the boat. If they didn't, Danny made it clear to them he was getting out of there anyway. He didn't plan to leave his little daughter Sarah without a father.

One day in September 1997, he was transporting a young American photographer, a two-man Swedish TV crew and local photographer Kevin West, who wanted to see how far his former photo studio on George Street had been buried. Danny was wearing a surgical-style mask beneath his customary shades to protect himself from the ash in the air.

His four passengers went ashore, into the almost uniformly grey landscape of the half-buried capital. 'Shoot quick. Watch where you walk. Stay close to Kevin,' Danny told the foreigners as they stepped ashore. At least Kevin knew the area. He would know what was solid ground and what might be loose ash. If you sank into that stuff, it could still be a few hundred degrees centigrade under the surface. Not a nice way to go.

As always, the newsmen took pictures of the Evergreen

Tree, 'ashed out' but still alive, then the white clockstand of the War Memorial and the convex top of the now almost buried red telephone cabin. From the boat, Danny saw some shadows move up behind Barclays Bank. Could there be anyone else here? No way. He must be seeing things. He and Margaret used to have a good laugh at the folks who said the deserted little capital was now haunted by jumbies.

But then Danny was sure he had seen something move, right behind the red phone booth. Yes, there it was again: a little chocolate and tan terrier, a puppy. It reminded him of a little Milky Way bar on legs. How on earth did that little thing survive the August catastrophe? He wondered if the newsmen had seen it and hoped they would pick it up, but a grumbling sound like a growing drum roll distracted his attention. The Mountain was waking.

'I could hear the volcano makin' a lot of noise,' Danny told Margaret later. 'It was like rocks breakin'. We could hear very heavy rumblin' and tumblin'. Then it starts blowin' ash. I hear this explosion and I see this ash cloud and this flow comin' down. I see Kevin runnin' like hell, then I see the two Swedes runnin' like hell, dropping some of their equipment. But I can't see the American boy. I've untied the boat and I'm going back and forward in the boat. Then I spot him and he's shoutin' "I just want to get one shot of the pyroclastic flow!"

'He started sinkin' in old, cool ash and realised he was in trouble. But he was very, very lucky, man, I tell you. The flow stopped around the hospital, on the top of George Street, a few hundred yards up from the shore. If it had kept comin', he'd have disappeared. And we might not have got far enough out of there, either. When he come down to the boat, that boy's as white as a ghost, covered in ash and mud. He got on the boat and I used a lot of expletives, man, I tell you. "Never ever fuckin' do that ever fuckin' again." And he runs to Kevin and Kevin says the same. And he runs to the Swedes and they say the same. So he runs to the bow of the boat and shuts up. That boy thought we were going to crucify him, I tell you.'

Later that night, Danny Sweeney wondered about the little Milky Way puppy. Poor thing. Must be starving. He'd look for it next time he went in.

As it happened, John Walsh, Director of Projects for the London-based World Society for the Protection of Animals, was on the island and Danny told him about the apparent miracle puppy. Was this the last surviving dog in Plymouth? Walsh, a six-foot-four, 56-year-old Irish American from Boston, was a veteran of disaster relief for animals. He was a pioneer of the Save the Whales movement of the Sixties and had rehabilitated birds and turtles soaked by oil released by Saddam Hussein during the 1991 Gulf War. On Montserrat, he and a WSPA team had already rescued hundreds of pet and stray dogs, cats, donkeys and other animals abandoned or lost in the exclusion zone. Some did not survive the ash or scalding fumes they had inhaled. Those that did were cared for by a group of local expatriates, including Bev Kleeb, one of the stubborn American couple from Garibaldi Hill. After de-lousing and paperwork, the animals were either shipped to other islands by WSPA or, in the case of the dogs, to Florida, where the 'volcano dogs' were snapped up as fast as they arrived.

Sometimes the WSPA team would go into the danger zone with Jim McMahon, sometimes by road, with special permission, and sometimes on foot. This time they hired a certain boat by the name of *Jumping Jack Flash* to drop them off at the eerily deserted Plymouth port. They needed a guide, and Danny Sweeney wanted to find the little terrier, so this time the fisherman risked going ashore, but he kept a keen eye on The Mountain as he and Walsh walked through the grey, ash-covered ghost town that was Plymouth.

They walked from the port up towards the now-buried Artillery Square, site of the War Memorial and the old phone booth, their shouts and whistles echoing through the rubble of what used to be streets. It worked. Suddenly there she was: the chocolate-and-tan terrier puppy, furless, with sad amber eyes, probably a few months old, stuck her ash-covered snout out from behind some rubble. She obviously hadn't seen a human being for some time, or been fed, but her tail was wagging wildly. The WSPA man warily laid out a lump of cheese and some sardines from a can. The puppy responded and within minutes was nuzzling up to John Walsh in Danny's boat. They had found her in the nick of time. The volcano was now exploding regularly, around twice a day, and a big ash cloud burst from The Mountain as Danny gave it full throttle away towards Old Road Bay.

It was love at first sight for John Walsh and his new pet. There was only going to be one home for this little lady. He took her to his home in Lakeville near Boston, watched her amber eyes turn from sad to bright and registered her as Lady Ashley Plymouth de Montserrat.

Everyone just called her Plymmie.

17

Evergreen no more

After the destruction of the airport on 21 September 1997, The Mountain acted as Barry Voight had predicted. There was a series of 'vulcanian' or vertical column explosions, on average ten hours apart. Ash clouds rose as high as 50,000 feet. Pieces of pumice, or lightweight porous lava, came down like hail, the size of golf balls, sometimes hammering roofs even in the northern safe zone, six miles or more from the volcano. Pilots in the vicinity were warned to stay clear as the ash clouds drifted at high altitude with the wind. Each explosion left a new hole in the crater. Each new hole was soon filled by new magma. A new dome was building. For Montserratians, that meant a bigger, more dangerous enemy. And, as Voight and Willy Aspinall had predicted, it began sending pyroclastic flows down all sides of The Mountain at once.

Some of the scientists, including Voight, still felt that a 'Big One' could surge down or over the Belham River valley and reach Salem, Olveston, Old Towne and other central areas. These had been added to the exclusion zone in August 1997 but hundreds of people were ignoring the ban and still living in or visiting the area.

Remarkably, the village of St Patrick's, though in the exclusion zone, remained untouched but for a deepening veil of thick, dark grey ash. The village, and the entire base of the 'teardrop' at the south of the island, was still a remarkably lush expanse of greenery beyond the zone of devastation. The westward pyroclastic flows into Plymouth had not spread far enough south of Fort Ghaut to affect St Patrick's. The southward flows down the White River, close to the village, had filled in much of the deep riverbed but had not overflowed its banks. Galways Wall still towered over St Patrick's, albeit now partly breached by erosion from overspilling pyroclastic flows. By the end of October, the new dome of hardened lava stood 250 feet higher than Chance's Peak.

The word on the street was that people were still coming and going to St Patrick's to check their homes or livestock. Some were even living secretly there despite the warnings from the scientists, the police and Father Larry Finnegan to stay away. Keeping people out was not the scientists' problem. That was a job for the politicians and police. Still, the scientists cared, and they became increasingly worried. As a collapse expert, Barry Voight was most concerned about the Galways Wall sector. If the volcano blew its side instead of its top, as Mount St Helens did in 1980, St Patrick's could take a direct hit.

As for the supposedly deserted capital, Plymouth, the friendly homeless man everyone knew as Never Me was still slipping into Town, determined to sleep in his old spot behind Barclays Bank. Once, he came out and told police in Salem the town was haunted. 'There's jumbies in the bank,' he said. 'I could hear them, man, I tell you.' No one, of course, believed him.

A long time later, the numbers on East Caribbean dollars being traded on the island showed that they'd come from Barclays Bank vault in Plymouth. The staff had been in such a hurry that they had not taken the money with them when they evacuated. The robbers who figured that out some time later must have thought it was their lucky day. They had the most peaceful heist in history. All they had to do was break into a full money vault in an unguarded bank in a ghost town. Nice work if you can get it. The only risk was being buried by a pyroclastic flow. They were lucky. But they *were* later caught, after the said banknotes started popping up in rum shop bars in the north of the island. Never Me, who had heard them and told the police, was thereafter treated with considerable respect.

In late October, a mudflow surged down the Belham River valley, burying the island's lush, green little golf course under a thick brown layer littered with the grotesquely twisted bodies of dead cows. It was, in fact, caused by a rainstorm washing down volcanic ash deposits, but it was scary enough in its own right, and seeing the golf course buried was symbolic for the islanders. The little course, with the white flags on its greens displaying a shamrock, had been a major tourist attraction. It bordered the shoreline at Old Road Bay, next to what had been Danny Sweeney's spot in quieter times. The sight of the Royal Montserrat Golf Course under mud and rock and now a moonscape was a major psychological blow.

From 4 November 1997, pyroclastic flows down the White River valley grew in power and velocity, passing within 500 yards of St Patrick's. Previously they had run out of gas, literally, somewhere down the riverbed, but the valley had been gradually filled by earlier deposits. The chute was getting smoother. The pyroclastic flows began reaching the ocean at O'Garra's, next to the evacuated

Radio Antilles complex. When they settled in the sea, they formed a new, beige land delta. If the White River valley, a deep, wide riverbed, became filled to the brim with solidified pyroclastic material, future pyroclastic flows would no longer be channelled down the river's course. They would burst out over the sides. As had happened on The Mountain's northern slopes, the deadly currents could eventually fly off the edge of the helter-skelter and take their own course.

Christmas 1997 arrived. Rose Willock, as always, repeated the latest scientific reports and urged people to stay away from St Patrick's. The scientists feared that some of the villagers were likely to leave their northern shelters and sneak back home to spend Christmas in the village, to be in their own homes. Everybody knew that one family had recently returned to St Patrick's to bury a villager alongside relatives in the village cemetery. A lot of people had gone back to attend the funeral, despite the risk.

On Christmas Day, Eddie Buffonge, the popular 56-year-old proprietor of Eddie's Trucking Company in the village and husband of English expatriate Cathy, *did* go back. Eddie was the proud owner of the upright piano Paul McCartney and Stevie Wonder had used to rehearse and record 'Ebony and Ivory' on the island in the Eighties. He had seen the piano at Providence House, the plantation mansion where the ex-Beatle used to stay, and decided to buy it for his daughter Ingrid. But on Christmas Day 1997, the piano was still in the Buffonges' house at Reid's Hill, just above St Patrick's.

In the run-up to Christmas, Eddie had been worried by the ominous sound of the scientific reports. He decided he'd sneak back to his village and try to get as much stuff as possible out of the three-bedroom house he had built himself in 1971. He went back at eight o'clock in the morning of Christmas Day, on the 16-foot fishing boat of his friend Carlton O'Garro. He hoped to get the piano as well as valuable material from his lorry business.

When they clambered ashore, there was not another soul in sight. 'Man, it's as though some chemical attack has wiped everybody out,' Eddie joked to his friend. For five hours, the two men manhandled lorry tyres, rims and tools down the cliff from Eddie's business and on to the boat. Eddie knew they were taking a chance. They could see rock falls continually dropping from Galways Wall at roughly 20-minute intervals. If a big pyroclastic flow or surge came down their way, they'd have no chance unless they saw it early and were close enough to the boat to flee. Even then, they might be too late to get far enough out to sea. As they loaded Eddie's gear on to the boat, the rock falls from The Mountain got bigger. 'Hey, man, let's get out of here,' Eddie said. 'We'll come back for the piano tomorrow.'

Later that Christmas Day, Kafu Cabey was wishing he could be back home in St Patrick's. The 37-year-old missed the colourful Christmas festivities in the village. Here he was, stuck in the rugged north of the island, the future uncertain, his Auto Parts business in Plymouth buried under pyroclastic deposits since August. But still he was grateful. He'd enjoyed doing the 'Drivetime' show but now he'd finally got the job he'd always wanted, production assistant at ZJB Radio with Rose Willock. Kafu knew he'd been lucky. He had no training, but so many ZJB staff had left the island that the station needed whomever it could get.

To show his gratitude, Kafu went to the Pentecostal church in the little northern hamlet of Brade's, site of a big refugee shelter, to join a packed Christmas night carol service with refugees, mostly people he knew from St Patrick's. Despite their hardship, they raised the rafters with their hymns and carols, singing their hearts and lungs out until late. So heartily did they sing that they did not hear the growing rumblings from The Mountain several miles to their south.

At their home in Olveston, just outside Salem, Danny Sweeney and Margaret Wilson were about to turn in for the night. It had been a long Christmas Day. Danny's family had been round for lunch and they'd also had a big Christmas night dinner. They'd had a sleepover guest, Jessica, a friend of their little daughter Sarah. Margaret had learnt at the last minute that Jessica's parents were off the island, so she'd invited her round, hastily changed the labels on half of Sarah's presents and made her feel at home.

Margaret had just gone to bed when she heard the rumbling. Damn. Another eruption. And right at the end of Christmas Day, too. As always, she went outside and took all the patio furniture indoors. It was a habit. There was bound to be an ash cloud, and it would mess up everything. She went out again and threw an old rug over the windscreen of Danny's car. She could still hear the rumbling but went back to bed and slept like a log.

At the MVO, now up north on Mongo Hill, the night-shift scientists were anything but asleep. The seismographs had been showing a pattern of hybrid earthquakes throughout the day, one every 20 minutes. Now, in the wee hours of Boxing Day, there was a tremor every 20 seconds. And this was at the top of Voight's predicted four-to-six-week 'big event' cycle. The Mountain was about to throw a tantrum.

At 3 a.m. on Boxing Day 1997, the seismographs went off the wall. From their Mongo Hill location, the MVO no longer had a line of sight to the volcano, and anyway it was dark. The scientists on overnight duty knew something big was happening but could see nothing. The action was on the south side, in the Galways Wall sector and the White River: the area above St Patrick's.

Some people in the north heard rumblings, got up for a look, saw nothing light up the night sky and went back to sleep. It was only when they got up in the morning that they heard Rose Willock read the latest scientific report. A major 'event' had taken place in the south, causing widespread damage. A 'debris avalanche' had triggered a series of pyroclastic flows. There had been 'a very energetic surge that may have been associated with a lateral blast'. The scientists estimated up to 60 million cubic metres of lava, the symbolic 60 million household washing machines, had exploded from the dome in a high-speed cocktail of ash and gas.

Lateral blast. The islanders had never seen one but many knew what it meant. The Mount St Helens disaster of 1980 immediately sprang to mind. Now, like Mount St Helens, Montserrat's own mountain had finally blown its side instead of its top. Galways Wall, which had towered over the south for as long as mountains exist, was not made of solid rock, the scientists explained. It was somewhere between rubble and rock, and it had collapsed under the pressure of the monster that had grown from the bowels of the Earth, the lava dome.

The fumaroles, or steam vents, on the slopes below at

Galways Soufrière, which had inspired Jimmy Buffett to write about a volcano almost 20 years earlier, had created a weak, watery layer just under the surface. That's what caused the southern flank of the volcano to collapse in a gigantic landslide. The landslide, in turn, exposed more lava which had been trapped deep inside the dome. It was this lava that exploded towards the south in a lateral blast.

In his new temporary lodgings, Father Larry Finnegan prayed that the village of St Patrick's, including the Catholic church, was safe, and that no one had been there. The refugees in the shelters did the same and remained optimistic. They were sure their homes would be safe and that they'd be able to go back soon.

At first light, the scientists went south in the helicopter to make an assessment. They were stunned by what they saw and not a little bewildered. The weather was clear but they couldn't seem to find their bearings. When they returned to the MVO to prepare an update for ZJB Radio, the scientists, all foreigners, were not quite sure how to describe to the islanders what they had seen. Better to return down south with someone from St Patrick's, someone who had known the place all his life and could assess the extent of the damage.

Bennette Roach, editor of the little weekly *Montserrat Reporter*, was invited along. He was a St Patrick's native. So was Kafu Cabey, only recently employed by ZJB. Kafu was one of the St Patrick's kids who used to carry tourists over the rocks to get behind the Great Alps waterfall. Now here he was, asked to do an eye-witness report for ZJB Radio. He was as nervous as hell. He'd never done any reporting before but they'd given him a professional tape recorder and microphone and told him to come back with a 'good eyewitness piece'. He and Roach were given bright orange volcanologists' hot suits. Then, hooked up to the chopper's headphones and microphones, they were flown south towards the lush slopes where they had grown up. The helicopter's side doors were open to allow the MVO's local technician and cameraman Dave Williams to shoot video.

The chopper flew down the east coast to the exclusion zone, over the airport and the rubble that was Spanish Point, past The Mountain's eastern slopes. As it got towards the south coast, the base of the teardrop, it wheeled round the South Soufrière Hills, the southern end of the island's volcanic mountain spine. Kafu was amazed by how lush and green the south still was. Greener than ever, he thought. 'The forest looks wonderful. The foliage, everything is okay,' he said on the air to the islanders.

The helicopter turned west, then northwards. It was now on the west coast, headed for St Patrick's. Bennette Roach and Kafu peered up the coast, looked at each other questioningly, then peered again. Was that low cloud, that light grey mass along the cliffs and out over the ocean? Roach looked down for Seaview, the place on the cliff where he had been brought up, or the landmark giant rocks off the coast, Big Matty and Small Matty, where he used to pick whelks and swim as a boy. Kafu looked for Toby Hill, the place where he was born, on the road from St Patrick's to Galways Soufrière. He knew he wouldn't see the Great Alps Falls. They'd long since been been buried by The Mountain's angry spewings. But he still couldn't pick out St Patrick's. Everything down there seemed flat and light grey.

The little chopper made three passes over the area while

Roach, Kafu and the scientists tried to pick out the village. The scientists explained that, in addition to what they called a 'debris avalanche' down the White River, a separate, scorching current had rushed due south, defied gravity and climbed the 2,500-foot South Soufrière Hills for the first time. 'That's a fairly good-sized mountain,' Kafu told his listeners. 'If it can get over the South Soufrière Hills, you know that if this had gone the other way, Salem would have been totalled.' His audience listened in stunned silence.

'We're now heading over the area that used to be O'Garra's,' Kafu, the former car parts salesman, his voice breaking with emotion, said into his microphone. 'It has been merged into one mass, everything is just one level mass. There's lots of debris in the ocean. There's lots of steaming on the edge.' He passed the mike to Bennette Roach and asked him to make a few comments. 'Okay, this is, umm, I'm just completely amazed here,' the usually eloquent newspaper editor began. His voice was almost drowned out by the chattering of the helicopter's blades. Roach was being extremely cautious. He did not want to get the islanders unduly concerned. But everyone listening could hear the distress in his voice. 'It's very difficult to know what I'm looking at . . . a completely different landscape here now. It looks as though the material was able to flow over the ridge and over into St Patrick's, but right now we can't see anything.'

Kafu *could* see. He could see the old thimble-shaped stone sugar mill at Reid's Hill, a familiar landmark to locals and tourists alike. Clear as crystal. But he couldn't see the houses that should be below it. Where was the home of Eddie and Cathy Buffonge? No sign. Where was the house of Mark and Tricia Bridge, the English couple who used to run Moles restaurant and bar in Plymouth? No sign. Just a smooth grey slope. The old sugar mill used to tower over St Patrick's. Now it stood out as a lone building on a lunar landscape of grey. Had the mill been swept away from the village? Then how come it was standing erect? No, the mill was where it had always been. So where was St Patrick's?

Kafu turned seriously pale. He glanced at Roach, took a deep breath and spoke into the ZJB microphone. 'You must try hard . . . to be positive . . . but . . . it is not easy to view at this time.' All over the island, people were listening, especially the refugees from St Patrick's. So was Rose Willock, who went to kindergarten in the village and whose family had come from nearby. They all knew Kafu. They heard his voice crack. They could almost hear his tears. 'Total devastation,' he said with difficulty. 'It is steaming very heavily at the edge of the flow . . . for now it's just hot ash, rocks, gases. There's a slick going all the way out into the ocean. That is from the pyroclastic flow which came down here in the morning. Believe me, it is just total devastation. I walked this area as a kid. It doesn't look like that today.'

It was Kafu's first reporting job. He had been delighted to get it when he set out in the morning, but he hadn't expected to have to describe this. 'Here's hoping that I did a very, or at least a reasonably good job this afternoon,' he told the islanders above the drone of the helicopter. His words came slowly. 'It was a very emotional one for me, being from the village of St Patrick's. It was not easy reporting this story. Reporting for ZJB Radio news, I'm Winston 'Kafu' Cabey.'

Looking down again to the coastline, Kafu saw something moving amid the floating debris on the still-steaming ocean. He could hardly believe it. He raised his microphone. 'There is a boat in the water. I must say those folks down there in that fishing boat have got to be crazy. It's definitely too risky to be on the sea near here. Another flow can come down here at any time. To have people around in boats just trying to see, I think it's just reckless. It is indeed reckless.'

Kafu did not know it, but the little boat down on the steaming ocean was called *Jumping Jack Flash*. The 'reckless' people on board were Kafu's friend Danny Sweeney, Margaret and a couple of friends. Danny knew he was taking a risk, but when he heard Rose Willock's radio broadcast, he had to see for himself. He loved St Patrick's. He was proud of the Irish strain that ran through his veins, mixed with the blood of African slaves. How often had he danced the night away in the little village, especially on St Patrick's Day? How often had he watched out for the Green Flash at sunset?

So he had decided he had to see St Patrick's. He had had trouble getting his boat into the water at Old Road Bay. The ocean appeared to have swamped the shoreline and sucked away trees and bushes from the coastal mangrove swamp. It looked as though the sea had come inland 80 yards further than usual overnight, then retreated. There were watermarks three feet up the palm trees that fringed the beach. Danny had never seen anything like it before. Then he saw dead fish glinting in the sunlight. They were scattered across the black sand beach where he had taught Sting and other stars to windsurf. Dead fish on the beach? It was then that Danny recalled Governor Frank Savage's fears of exactly a year before. It had taken a year for the French and English scientists' warning, and the governor's fear, to be proved right. But the latest, massive pyroclastic surge had, indeed, launched a tsunami, a tidal wave. It was estimated only at four feet above normal wave level, not the potential catastrophe the French scientists from Guadeloupe had feared, and no one was harmed because it happened in the small hours. But it had done considerable damage, not least to Danny's seafront patch at Old Road Bay, as well as to other beaches and coastal foliage. Danny just thanked God that it had occurred in the small hours. He was glad it hadn't happened during a busy day on the beach, when his little daughter Sarah liked to romp in the surf.

Danny and Margaret got the boat in the water and sailed towards St Patrick's. The first thing they noticed, sailing past the coastal village of Kinsale, was the Seaquarium, owned by their good friend Moose. The once throbbing restaurant, where you could watch the tropical fish from the rickety pier while you ate lobster or tuna, was covered in ash. Behind it, buildings were on fire.

Danny recalled how Moose had built the restaurant, adding to the pier whenever he found materials, and turned it into one of the most popular spots on the island for locals and tourists alike. He thought of the nights when Irish singer Mick Moloney shook the boardwalk when he jammed with the local, black string band musicians. Danny fell silent and sailed on.

No one else spoke. Margaret had never seen anything like this. A pyroclastic surge had clearly reached the ocean. The water along the shoreline was steaming. Around the little boat it was warm, the surface a kaleidoscope of ashy debris and dead tropical fish. There were picasso fish and parrot fish, beloved by scuba divers, now drifting like sodden leaves, grotesque in death. Among them was a single dead bird, floating on its side, one eye fixed on the sky as though in horror, its yellow breast holed as if by a bullet. A gold-breasted oriole. The island's national bird. It must have been blasted from its hilltop habitat and unceremoniously deposited in the ocean.

Danny slowed the boat right down. He was afraid it might be damaged by debris, or that the water would be too hot to get closer to shore. Margaret wondered where all this flotsam had come from. It looked as though a cruise ship had gone down, leaving parts of its cabins and furniture to float to the surface. There were tables, chairs, sheets of galvanised roofing. Margaret peered more closely. The innards of a piano, the hammers and strings, were bobbing to and fro amid the steam. She thought of their friend Eddie Buffonge and his treasured 'Ebony and Ivory' piano. No, it could be anybody's. But she knew Eddie had been up here yesterday. God, I hope he wasn't here today, she thought.

Danny was still trying to get his bearings. He knew this coastline like the back of his hand. By his calculations, he was directly off the coast below St Patrick's. The White River estuary was right there, although it was now a mass of grey where pyroclastic material had solidified into a new fan-shaped delta of land. But the same grey extended all the way up from the shore, where St Patrick's should be.

It was then that Danny Sweeney saw a single splash of colour, bright yellow, on the beach. It was a bulldozer, one of Eddie Buffonge's. God, that thing must have been swept a couple of hundred yards and over the cliff, Danny thought. Something powerful came down here, boy, let me tell you.

So where was the village? Danny gazed up. The smooth, light grey expanse was broken only by a twisting ribbon of a flat, darker charcoal colour. He recognised the curves of the ribbon better than anyone would. He'd seen them so often from the ocean. It was the main road, the one that curved uphill from the coast to St Patrick's and on to Galways Soufrière or the south. 'Look, Margaret, look, that's the road through St Patrick's. My God.' Yes, Danny thought, it's the road through the village. But where *is* the village? Where are the churches? Where's the police station? Where's the primary school, the cemetery, the houses? Where's anything?

Danny's gaze followed the road. He began imagining the village in his mind's eye. He saw a few concrete steps in front of a concrete slab. They looked like the steps to the home of his friends Mark and Tricia Bridge, the couple from Leatherhead in Surrey. But that was all there was. Steps. Amid the grey he could also see a row of brown steel rods, like the ones you see protruding from an unfinished building. But they were flat on the ground, pointing away from The Mountain and down towards the ocean and his boat. It was as though a row of bulldozers had flattened them. The police station should be right there, where those rods are, Danny thought.

He saw a few red tiles on the ground, standing out against the landscape of grey. Red tiles. The Anglican church. The place where scientist Angus Miller had previously briefed villagers on the dangers and urged them to leave. God, I hope they all did, thought Danny.

Margaret turned from the slope and saw Danny's light hazel eyes freeze as she had never seen them before. All they revealed was the reflection of the grey landscape on shore. She waited for him to speak but his gaze was fixed on the slope. Margaret knew St Patrick's well, when on land, but she hadn't come out in the boat so often. She couldn't get her bearings from this angle. She saw the road clearly enough. 'But where's St Patrick's, Danny?'

Danny had traced the road to the spot where the community centre used to be. He couldn't find it. He thought of St Patrick's Day, the costumed parade along that street, the stalls, the cups of the national dish, goatwater stew, the emerald-green shirts and dresses against the black skin of the revellers, his own little daughter Sarah in her leprechaun costume. He thought of the jump-up, of himself dancing with every woman in sight and 'sweatin' dem wives off the floor'.

Danny cut the big twin engines. The hiss of steam from the ocean was now the only sound. A confused pelican hovered over the boat and then flew north. Danny's eyes followed it and then turned back towards the smooth grey slope. There was almost total silence, but Margaret felt that Danny was listening for something. He was. And with the engines cut, he began to hear it. There were throbbing bongo drums, pounding out an African voodoo beat. There were the strains of 'Molly Malone' and 'When Irish Eyes are Smiling', there was the lilt of a calypso, the throbbing beat of a soca song. He could hear the gentle plucking of a tenor banjo and a sweet Irish voice lamenting a country left behind. And he could see people gazing at the sunset, watching for the Green Flash. He could see Irish and local dancers doing quadrilles on passing floats, Africa and Ireland, slaves, servants and masters, swaying and dancing together along the twisting streets. The black and the green.

Danny blinked and the sounds and the colours were gone, the hillside again deserted and silent and grey.

Margaret looked back up over the cliffs, up the sloping grey wasteland, then back to Danny. The hazel eyes had thawed. He swivelled his sunglasses down from his hair, turned his back on the land and gazed out across the sapphire ocean to the shimmering horizon. A sleek silver wahoo broke the surface at speed, then disappeared without a splash. Danny Sweeney hit the ignition and the two big Yamaha engines shattered the silence.

'All blown away, Margaret, St Patrick's gone. Let's go home.'

Epilogue

A few days after Boxing Day 1997, Father Larry Finnegan and villagers from St Patrick's crowded into the Pentecostal church at Brade's, where they had sung carols with gusto on Christmas night. This time, the scientists were showing video footage, taken from the helicopter, of what was left of their village. Or rather, what was not. 'There was a silence, a sadness, a sense of separation,' the big Irish priest said. 'Home was gone, St Patrick's was gone, the graveyard where loved ones were buried and where most expected to be buried alongside them some day was gone. It sank in. There is no going home. Hope is gone. It is final. The south is no more.'

The scientists estimated it took 50 seconds for the pyroclastic flow and surge to wipe St Patrick's from the face of the earth. As far as anyone knows, there were no human beings in the village on Boxing Day 1997, but there were hundreds of farm animals, stray donkeys and dogs. Had the pyroclastic flow come down a couple of hours later, after dawn, Eddie Buffonge the haulage contractor would have been there, trying to get his famous piano on to a small boat. He believes the piano is somewhere in the Atlantic Ocean.

Father Larry Finnegan moved on to a new flock on another Caribbean island, St Kitts.

313

In 1998, an inquest was held into the deaths of 25 June 1997. It was headed by British lawyer Rhys Burris as coroner appointed by the Crown, and its findings were decided by a five-person jury of islanders. After hearing more than 50 witnesses over almost two months, the jury found that no one was to blame for the deaths themselves. They were 'by natural catastrophe of volcanic eruption / pyroclastic flow'. But the jury insisted on adding to its conclusion. It was not solely the victims' fault that they were where they were that day. In the case of the victims close to the airport, the authorities' decision to keep the airport open in an otherwise evacuated zone had contributed to the cause of death. In the case of Felina Celestine, her sister and others, 'the failure of both the local and British authorities to provide alternative land for displaced farmers' had contributed. In one case, the squalor of the shelters had pushed a victim into going back to his home in the exclusion zone.

Citing the need to avoid a repetition of the deaths, the British coroner issued his own concluding statement. It was obvious that Montserrat's most pressing need was for refugees to be supplied with housing and land in the north, he said. 'The British government response has been unimaginative, grudging and tardy. It is simply inadequate to the scale of the need. I suspect that if he were here, the Prime Minister [Tony Blair] might find useful one of his favourite adjectives – pathetic – to sum it all up.'

Montserrat's volcano is still in a constant state of eruption. Most of the time it appears to be slumbering, but magma still pushes forth to create new lava domes – new mountains – at the rate of three cubic metres, the symbolic three washing machines, a second. They regularly collapse to create pyroclastic flows. At the time of writing, these have followed the same paths, down the same riverbeds and ghauts, staying within the evacuated zone in the south. In a signal to the islanders that it considered the centre and north of the island safe, the MVO built a state-of-the-art observatory closer to The Mountain on a high ridge above Salem. That put it within three miles of the crater and in direct line of sight.

Carol and Cedric Osborne re-opened the Vue Pointe hotel, just south of the Belham river, in late 2000. Room guests were few but the hotel again became a focal point, a symbol of the islanders' determination, their defiance. Down below them, the Old Road Bay beach on the Belham river estuary remained eroded through mudslides. Watersports were not an attractive option but, in what used to be the pavilion for the hotel's tennis courts, Danny Sweeney and his English partner Margaret gave life to a new bar and restaurant, Jumping Jack's. It quickly became a mandatory limin' spot for locals, scientists and visitors. Margaret cooked and served fresh wahoo caught by Danny and things were looking up.

In late 2002, however, the volcano raised the ante. It sprouted a new 'lobe' to the existing dome, this time to the north-west. That meant that if it collapsed, with its tens of millions of cubic metres of red hot rock, it could send a pyroclastic flow down the Belham River valley. On the advice of the MVO, the exclusion zone was extended to take in the river's northern banks. The Osbornes had to abandon the Vue Pointe and their nearby villa and live with friends. Danny and Margaret locked up their little blue and purple-painted restaurant but were able to stay in their home in Salem. Refusing to give in to the volcano, they opened a new Jumping Jack's restaurant by the pool in their Salem garden. Danny continued to get up at dawn, hit the twin engines on *Jumping Jack Flash* and chase wahoo, 'the fastest fish in the sea.' He, Margaret and the Osbornes were optimistic they'd be back on Old Road Bay by the time this book was published.

Sir George Martin retained his home, Olveston House, and built a modern cultural centre close to the ferry port at Little Bay to serve as community centre, concert hall and general focus for the scattered community. The centre is in the safest area of the island. But Olveston House fell within the new 'danger zone' late last year, as did the unoccupied Air Studios.

The volcanologists believe the volcano will eventually go back to sleep, perhaps in a few years. But an even bigger dome collapse is also possible. This volcano has been an unusually slow burner, unlike most which peak early in their eruptive cycles and then burn out. The MVO say this volcano is among the most closely studied ever, and has taught volcanologists vital lessons about the build-up to pyroclastic flows and surges. The observatory broadcasts twice-daily reports on volcanic activity and residents and visitors to the island are advised to stay tuned. Shipping is barred from a two-mile strip around the south but Caribbean cruise liners come close to that line to give passengers a glimpse of the fuming mountain.

There are currently estimated to be fewer than 5,000 people on Montserrat, less than half the pre-crisis figure of 11,000. They live mostly in the rugged northern third, around 13 square miles, with two thirds of the island still out of bounds. Of those who left, most are in England, many in the Hackney area of London, but some have been filtering back to help with reconstruction under the slogan 'Montserrat: Still Home, Still Nice'. The destroyed airport remains in the no-go zone. Residents and visitors, including day-trippers from Antigua who wish to see the volcano, come and go by ferry, often a rough ride of over an hour, or on an eight-seater helicopter. The Montserratians hope the volcano will attract specialist tourists and help them rebuild at least part of what used to be their main source of income. There are plans for a new airport for small planes but the north's rugged terrain makes planning difficult.

A new cricket ground has been built in Salem to replace Plymouth's Sturge Park stadium, now covered in ash and mud. In the inaugural match, between a West Indian selection and one from South Africa, players and spectators scarcely batted an eyelid as a pyroclastic flow tumbled down the northern slopes of The Mountain, only three miles away. 'Not to worry, man, that's just a small one.'

In the north, a rugged hillside was dug out and flattened to create a small but picturesque soccer stadium. With Plymouth abandoned, Montserratians, including the national team, had nowhere to play for several years. On the day Brazil beat Germany in the 2002 World Cup Final, the Montserrat team was on the other side of the world, in the foothills of the Himalayas. They were playing Bhutan in 'The Other Final', to decide who would go bottom of FIFA's rankings. Montserrat, dubbing themselves the Monster Rats, lost by four goals to nil. On paper, that made them the worst national team in the world, at least among

FIFA members, but it didn't bother them. They turned the occasion into one big soca party and soon had the Bhutanese fans singing their compatriot Arrow's most famous song, 'Olay, olay, olay, olay, feelin' hot, hot, hot . . .'

The volcano gave rise to a new wave of art on the island, from volcano-related paintings and quilts to poetry and calypso songs with titles such as 'Seismicity' and 'South Gone'. The erupting volcano adorns most t-shirts sold to tourists. There is not a schoolchild on Montserrat who cannot tell you what a pyroclastic flow is.

Concerned for the future of the unique Montserrat oriole and the rare 'mountain chicken', the island shipped a group of the birds and frogs to Jersey Zoo in the Channel Islands. In specially-designed breeding areas simulating their natural habitat, the zoo has successfully bred both species. Back on the island, efforts to preserve both species continue. Serving mountain chicken, once a favourite delicacy, is officially banned in restaurants. In private homes it may be a different matter.

Rose Willock, 'The Voice of Montserrat', was awarded an OBE, nominated by former governor Frank Savage. 'She was the Vera Lynn of the people there,' he said. Rose lives in the north of the island and still presents programmes for ZJB Radio.

Andy Bearpark and Peter Burton, the emergency aid troubleshooters first at the Overseas Development Administration and latterly at Clare Short's Department for International Development, received a CBE and an OBE respectively for aid work beyond the line of duty. At the time of writing, more than seven years after the first eruption, Ms Short had not visited the island.

Lady Ashley Plymouth de Montserrat, or Plymmie, the amber-eyed, chocolate-and-tan terrier puppy rescued in Plymouth, still lives with the man who found her, John Walsh of WSPA, in the Boston area. She has put on weight, grown some fur, likes to play tag and loves romping in the New England snow.

Former police commissioner Frank Hooper and his wife Sheila live in retirement in Hassocks, Sussex. But Frank has the perfect retirement pastime and it takes him back to the Caribbean every winter. He sails brand new yachts out there from Europe for rich folks who prefer to skip the Atlantic crossing.

Frank Savage is now retired and living with his wife Veronica in the Bexley area of north Kent. In 1998, called back to Montserrat for the inquest, he faced a hostile grilling from lawyers for the 25 June victims and suffered from stress problems for some time. As the man in overall charge of the island, he knew it was not inconceivable that he could be blamed and even jailed. He had recurring nightmares about what he went through but was relieved at the outcome of the inquest and hopes, during his retirement, to maintain links with the Caribbean as a Foreign Office consultant.

Winston, his green-eyed Montserratian terrier, is getting a bit longer in the tooth. He's a long way from volcanoes, and with luck hurricanes, in north Kent, but he still trembles and chases his tail when a storm comes in off the North Sea.

Plymouth remains a deserted ghost town, covered to varying degrees by hardened pyroclastic material – rock, mud or dried grey ash. The MVO scientists still go into Town when the seismographs say The Mountain is quiet. On the seafront, they now walk on a rocky, grey landscape, probably 30 feet above the long-buried red English phone booth. At the time of writing, only the face of the clock at the top of the War Memorial, originally 60 feet high, is above ground. The clock's hands remain at 3.35, the moment at which they stopped in early August 1997.

Above the monochromatic landscape there is one, albeit ashy, splash of colour. Greyed green leaves protrude from what was the Evergreen roundabout. The Evergreen Tree, where the villagers used to meet to lime, is still alive, its roots perhaps stimulated by fertile volcanic ash.

Montserratians are unlikely to gather round the tree for generations to come, if ever. But thanks to modern technology, those on the island and scattered around the world still manage to lime, with no less passion, beneath the branches of a new Evergreen Tree. It's called the Electronic Evergreen: a chat forum on the Internet, on which they share their hopes and dreams of paradise reborn.

Acknowledgements

Almost everyone on Montserrat assisted me in this venture, with great patience despite their losses. For most of them, all they have left of their homes and businesses is a bunch of keys.

I would like to point out that I have focused on certain characters for the sake of fluid narrative. Dozens of volcanologists not mentioned here, from the SRU in Trinidad, from Britain and from the US, have assisted the island by working at the MVO since 1995. Those I chose for the sake of my narrative may feel unfairly highlighted in what was and remains a team effort.

I am most grateful to all who contributed photographs, notably Peter Dunkley at the MVO, Barry Voight and Paul Cole. As regards the text, Barry Voight was particularly tireless in answering my endless queries over a long period. Thanks also to Sheila Hooper for providing her diaries, and to my meticulous editor at Methuen, Eleanor Rees.

Special thanks to David Lea. His dramatic and comprehensive video series *The Price of Paradise*, available through his website, www.priceofparadise.com, is indispensable viewing.

Picture credits

Leprechauns on St Patrick's Day 1995 © *Margaret Wilson*

Rose Willock, 'The Voice of Montserrat' *Courtesy Bennette Roach*

Police Commissioner Frank Hooper and Governor Frank Savage *Courtesy The Royal Montserrat Police Force*

The mountain explodes © *Paul Cole*

'The Mighty Arrow' *Courtesy Arrow Music Ltd*

Danny Sweeney chasing wahoo *Courtesy Danny Sweeney*

Cricketers ignore a pyroclastic flow *Courtesy Alex Elder*

Rick Anderson and 'Swampy' Marsh fly their Royal Navy Lynx *Courtesy The Royal Navy*

Two-pronged pyroclastic flow, 25 June 1997 © *Paul Cole*

Barry Voight ... *Courtesy Barry Voight*

... amid devastation after Boxing Day 1997 *Courtesy Barry Voight*

Father Larry Finnegan with his flock *Courtesy Beryl Chadwick*

George Street, Plymouth *Courtesy H.M. Governor's Office*

Montserrat seafront, pre-1995 *Courtesy Blake's Empire Shop*

War Memorial and phone booth, 1998 © *Christine Boyd*

War Memorial and seafront, 2002 © *Phil Davison*